SO-AJR-911

HANDBOOK ON

HAZARDOUS MATERIALS MANAGEMENT

EDITED BY

H. Tom Carson PE CHMM
Doye B. Cox PE CHMM

INSTITUTE OF HAZARDOUS MATERIALS MANAGEMENT

Copyright © 1990, 1992 (Fourth Edition) by Institute of Hazardous
Materials Management

All rights reserved. No part of the material protected by this copyright
notice may be reproduced or utilized in any form or by any means,
electronic or mechanical, including photocopying, recording or by any
informational storage or retrieval system, without written permission
from the copyright owner.

Printed in the United States of America

Library of Congress Catalog Card number: 90-81996

The Institute of Hazardous Materials Management (published) provides
the material in this publication as a service to the Hazardous Materials
Management profession, and does not warranty the accuracy of the
information presented.

INTRODUCTION

The first edition of this publication was actually an internal document developed by the Tennessee Valley Authority. When published in 1986, TVA envisioned the program as a method of protecting the Tennessee River by educating the professionals in the field on unified hazardous materials management.

Six years and over 3,000 Certified Hazardous Materials Managers (CHMM) later, this edition represents the fifth edition. As editors of this work, we want to reinforce certain items which we have stated from the project's inception:

- This publication can be utilized as a study guide by candidates for the CHMM examination. However, it has not been written to specifically teach the examination.
- Major portions of the CHMM examination include questions which require experience and maturity of judgment -- no one can teach that.
- As does the CHMM examination, this edition stresses a unified approach to hazardous materials. Specifically, we encourage learning enough about all the various areas of hazardous materials to manage the whole picture. The "one subject" expert can not be expected to understand how it all fits together.
- This revised and expanded edition can be utilized as a reference work. In indexing the book, we tried to approach it from the needs of a professional. We have not listed words or phrases every time they appear, only when the usage was significant.

Tom Carson, CHMM
Doye Cox, CHMM

For further information, please contact:
Institute of Hazardous Materials Management
11900 Parklawn Drive
Rockville, MD 20852
1-800-437-0137

Acknowledgments

The following authors did an outstanding job. We could not have developed this book without their contributions.

Belton G. Aldrich
Keith Angell, CHMM
William Beranek, Jr.
Russell Barnett
Col. William F. Brandes
Michael G. Browman, CHMM
Bruce A. Brye, CHMM
Edward E. (Gene) Burgess
Earl R. Burns
Robert L. Carlson
H.T. (Tom) Carson, CHMM
Richard T. Cartwright, CHMM
Charles J. Caudill, CHMM
Brian D. Lopez-Cepero
Doye B. Cox, CHMM
Karen Dean
Pat Eddy, CHMM
David Richard Gengozian
John H. Frick, CHMM
C. Douglas Goins, Jr., CHMM
Cliff Harper, Sr.
George J. Hyfantis, Jr., CHMM
David Koepper, CHMM

Nic E. Korte
George L. Kramer
David D. Lamm
Gary Lindgren, CHMM
Jerry M. Loftin, CHMM
Jack Don Lokey, CHMM
Regina Mahoney, CHMM
Patricia Mahoney, CHMM
Kenneth L. Manchen, CHMM
David W. Mayfield, CHMM
James T. McVey, CHMM
Paul E. Morris, Jr.
Pat Siefferman Ogle
John Peoples
Jeffrey P. Perl, CHMM
Elizabeth Phillips
Joseph W. Phillips, CHMM
Philip J. Schworer, Esq.
Brian Thomas
David M. Trayer
Charles A. Waggoner, CHMM
James M. Weaver, Esq.
Donald E. Witt

Special thanks to Brian Thomas, a senior co-op student with the University of Tennessee at Chattanooga, for his help in assembling, organizing, and collecting revised and new chapters for the book.

CONTENTS

Science

Regulations

Management

SCIENCE

CHEMISTRY OF HAZARDOUS MATERIALS

Doye B. Cox, P.E., CHMM
Signal Environmental Services, Inc.

and

Michael G. Browman, Ph.D., CHMM
Tennessee Valley Authority

INTRODUCTION

The identification of salient points and their presentation in a manner concise enough for a study guide is always a difficult task for any topic. It is all the more challenging when the topic is a broad one, such as chemistry. The presentation of the basics of chemistry would fill several study guides of this size. So rather than deal with the topic in a comprehensive manner, this section will present information in two formats.

There are a number of excellent references available that detail the physical and chemical properties of hazardous materials. They are available in hardbound, ringbound, and computerized formats and are, with a few exceptions, relatively easy to use. They provide a wide range of data for use in a variety of situations. These data are only useful if interpreted properly. This study guide will provide an explanation of typical physical, chemical, and biological properties and their significance.

Secondly, it is important to commit to memory the important properties of general classes of chemicals and of a few commonly used industrial chemicals. This guide will attempt to familiarize the reader with the "high points." This part of the study guide is not intended as anything other than a refresher for those with strong backgrounds in chemistry. It is intended to provide a brief introduction to chemistry for the environmental manager who must, as a part of his responsibilities, deal with hazardous materials issues.

CHEMICAL PROPERTIES

All chemicals, including hazardous ones, are commonly described in terms of their physical, chemical, and biological properties. To use this information fully, it is necessary to understand the meaning and importance of the various individual properties, and also to have some grasp of the significance of the various numerical values within the context of chemicals at large. These properties can then be used along with other information to predict the likely behavior of hazardous chemicals, and to recognize and avoid potentially dangerous situations. The first step is to define and comment on several of the more critical properties that are useful in the handling of hazardous materials (Table 1).

Table 1

LIST OF COMMONLY MEASURED PHYSICAL/ CHEMICAL PROPERTIES

Color

Odor

Physical state at 20°C

Molecular weight (MW)

Chemical formula

Melting point (MP)

Boiling point (BP)

Vapor pressure (VP)

Density

Vapor density

Specific gravity

Solubility (water; other solvents)

Octanol/water partition coefficent (Kow)

BOD_5

ThOD

Fire point

Auto-ignition temperature (point)

Flashpoint

Explosive limits

Heat content

Threshold limit value (TLV)

Physical State at 20°C -- The physical nature of the chemical (solid, liquid, or gas) at 20°C (i.e., room temperature). Changing the temperature may alter the physical state, depending on the magnitude and direction of the change relative to the melting and boiling points of the chemical.

Boiling Point (BP) -- The temperature at which a liquid changes to gas under standard atmospheric pressure (760 mm mercury). The BP of water is 100°C, while the BPs of ethyl alcohol and n-hexane are 78.4 and 68.7°C, respectively. Lowering the atmospheric pressure (e.g., by applying a vacuum) will lower the BP; conversely, higher pressures result in elevated boiling points.

Melting Point (MP) -- The temperature at which a solid changes to a liquid. The melting point is not particularly sensitive to atmospheric pressure, but it is responsive to dissolved salts which depress the melting point. Thus, in winter, it is usual to salt sidewalks to keep water from freezing.

Vapor Pressure (VP) -- The pressure exerted by the vapor in equilibrium with its liquid at a given temperature. Vapor pressure is a measure of the relative volatility of chemicals. Liquids with high vapor pressures generally represent a greater fire hazard than those with lower vapor pressures. For a given liquid the vapor pressure increases with increasing temperature. Consequently, drummed materials with high vapor pressures in particular should not be stored in direct sunlight, as overheating of the materials and resultant increases in vapor pressures could result in "pregnant" drums with failed or weakened seams. When used with solubility data, vapor pressure values can be used to predict the rate of evaporation of dissolved solvents from water. At 20°C, water, ethanol, and benzene exert vapor pressures of 17.5, 43.9, and 74 mm of mercury, respectively.

Vapor Density (VD) -- The mass per unit volume of a given vapor/gas relative to that of air. Thus, acetaldehyde with a vapor density of 1.5 is heavier than air and will accumulate in low spots, while acetylene with a vapor density of 0.9 is lighter than air and will rise and disperse. Heavy vapors present a particular hazard because of the way they accumulate:

if toxic they may poison workers; if nontoxic they may displace air and cause suffocation by oxygen deficiency; if flammable, once presented with an ignition source, they represent a fire or explosion hazard. Gases heavier than air include carbon dioxide, chlorine, hydrogen sulfide, and sulfur dioxide.

Density -- The mass per unit volume of any substance, including liquids. The density of a liquid determines whether a spilled material that is insoluble in or immiscible with water will sink or float on water. Knowledge of this behavior is essential in checking whether to use water to suppress a fire involving the material.

Specific Gravity (SG) -- The ratio of the density of a liquid as compared with that of water. Insoluble materials will sink or float in water depending on the SG. Materials heavier than water have SGs > 1, and materials lighter than water have SGs < 1. Thus, lead, mercury, and carbon tetrachloride with SGs of 11.3, 13.6, and 1.6, respectively, will sink, whereas gasoline with a SG of 0.66 to 0.69 will float on water.

Solubility -- The amount of a given substance (the solute) that dissolves in a unit volume of a liquid (the solvent). This property is of importance in the handling and recovery of spilled hazardous materials. Water insoluble chemicals are much easier to recover from water than spills of water-soluble chemicals. Acetone, which is miscible/soluble in water in all proportions, is not readily recoverable from water. In contrast, benzene, which is lighter than water and insoluble as well, can be readily trapped with a skimmer. For organic compounds, solubility tends to decrease with increasing molecular weight and chlorine content.

Flashpoint -- The lowest temperature of a liquid at which it gives off enough vapor to form an ignitable mixture with air near the surface of the liquid with the vessel used. Two tests are used -- Open Cup and Closed Cup. Generally, the Open Cup method results in flashpoints 5° to 10° higher than the Closed Cup method. Flashpoint < 140°F (Closed Cup) is the criterion used by EPA to decide whether a chemical is hazardous by ignitability. DOT regulates materials with flashpoints of < 100°F as flammable and between 100°F and 200°F as combustible.

Fire Point -- The temperature at which a liquid gives off enough vapor to continue to burn when ignited.

Auto-Ignition Temperature -- The temperature at which ignition occurs without an ignition source and the material continues to burn without further heat input.

Flammable or Explosive Limits -- The upper and lower vapor concentrations at which a mixture will burn or explode. The lower explosive limit of *p*-xylene is 1.1 percent by volume in air, whereas the upper explosive limit is 7.0 percent in air. A mixture of *p*-xylene vapor and air having a concentration of <1.1 percent in air is too lean in *p*-xylene vapor to burn. By subtraction (7.0 - 1.1) *p*-xylene is said to have a flammable range of 5.9.

Heat Content -- The heat released by complete combustion of a unit weight of material. Methane has a heat content of about 21,500 Btu/lb while benzene contains about 17,250 Btu/lb.

Octanol/Water Partition Coefficient (Kow) -- The equilibrium ratio of the concentrations of material partitioned between octanol and water. This coefficient is considered to be an index of the potential of a chemical to be bioaccumulated. Higher values of Kow are associated with greater bioaccumulated potential.

Biochemical Oxygen Demand at Five Days (BOD$_5$) -- The quantity of oxygen required by microbes for the oxidative breakdown of a given waste material during a 5-day test period. BOD$_5$ is usually taken as an index of the ultimate oxygen demand (i.e., oxygen required when sufficient time is allowed to achieve maximum microbial decomposition). BOD$_5$ is used to predict the impact of a spill or release of material on the oxygen content of a body of water.

Theoretical Oxygen Demand (ThOD) -- The cumulative amount of oxygen needed to completely oxidize a given material. The ThOD is the upper limit for BOD$_5$ values, although it is seldom achieved. A comparison of the BOD$_5$ and ThOD values for a given chemical provides an indication of the biodegradability of that chemical.

Threshold Limit Value (TLV) -- The exposure level under which most people can work for eight hours a day, day after day, with no harmful effects. A table of the values and accompanying precautions for most common industrial materials is published annually by the American Conference of Governmental Industrial Hygienists.

pKa -- The negative logarithm of the equilibrium constant for acids or bases. This parameter is an indicator of the strength of an acid or base. Strong acids, such as H_2SO_4 and HCl, have low pKa's (i.e., < 1.1) while strong bases such as KOH and NaOH, have pKa's close to 14.0. Weak acids and weak bases fall in the intermediate range.

A FEW KEY CONCEPTS

Concentrations -- Chemists, especially environmental chemists, seldom work with pure solutions of materials dispersed in environmental media. A knowledge of units of concentration is required. Units of concentration in common usage for aquaeous solutions include parts per million (ppm) and with increasing analytical capability and environmental awareness, parts per billion (ppb), and even parts per trillion (ppt), milligrams per liter (equivalent to ppm for dilute aquaeous solutions), moles per liter or molar solutions (a weight of substance equivalent to the gram-molecular or gram atomic weight in a liter of solution), equivalents per liter (commonly used for acids and bases, a one equivalent per liter solution is stated to be a one normal solution), and finally percent by weight or volume. For vapors and gases, mists, and particulates in air, common units of concentration are ppm, micrograms per M^3, and percent by volume.

Solubility Product -- The solubility product constant commonly referred to as the solubility product provides a convenient method of predicting the solubility of a material in water at equilibrium. Copper hydroxide, for example, dissolves according to the following equilibrium:

$$Cu(OH)_2(s) \rightarrow Cu^{2+} + 2OH^-$$

The resultant solubility product is represented in the following manner:

$$[Cu^{2+}] [OH^{1-}] = Ksp \text{ (solubility product constant)}$$

where $[Cu^{2+}]$ and $[OH^-]$ are equal to the molar concentrations of copper and hydroxyl ions, respectively. The Ksp is commonly used in determining suitable precipitation reactions for removal of ionic species from solution. In the same example, the pH for removal of copper to any specified concentration can be determined by substituting the molar concentration into the following equation:

$$[OH^-] = \frac{Ksp}{[Cu^{2+}]}$$

and then applying the derived values in turn to these other equations:

$$[OH^-]^2[H^+] = 10^{-14} \text{ and pH} = -\log [H^+]$$

Use of the Ksp for precipitation information is often complicated by a number of interfering factors including complexity of metallic ions, high ionic strength solutions, and high solids contents. This principle is applicable solely to ionic compounds, i.e., primarily inorganic compounds.

Adsorption -- Another important physico-chemical phenomenon used in treatment of hazardous wastes or in predicting the behavior of hazardous materials in natural systems is adsorption. Adsorption is the concentration or accumulation of substances at a surface or interface between media. Hazardous materials are often removed from water or air by adsorption onto activated carbon. Adsorption of organic hazardous materials onto soils or sediments is an important factor affecting their mobility in the environment. Adsorption may be predicted by use of a number of equations most commonly relating the concentration of a chemical at the surface or interface to the concentration in air or in solution, at equilibrium. These equations may be solved graphically using laboratory data to plot "isotherms." The most common application of adsorption is for the removal of organic compounds from water by activated carbon.

Volatilization -- Volatilization is a third physico-chemical phenomenon of interest to environmental managers. It is the tendency of a material to transfer from a liquid phase (either pure or dissolved as in aqueous systems) to a gaseous phase (commonly air). The volatilization, or evaporation as it is more commonly called, is controlled by a number of factors, the most important of which are the vapor pressure of the material, temperature (vapor pressure increases with temperature), air/material interfacial surface area, and the action of active mass transfer agents such as wind.

The processes of dissolution/precipitation (for inorganics), dissolution/phase separation (for organics), adsorption, and volatilization control the distribution of a spilled material in the environment. Conversely, knowledgeable manipulation of these same processes can be used to advantage in either cleaning up or mitigating the effects of spilled material. Thus, for example, groundwater contaminated with volatile organics of limited aqueous solubility can be decontaminated by air stripping of these compounds which can then be concentrated by adsorption on activated carbon for subsequent disposal.

Hazard Categories

The testing of chemicals/wastes to establish the nature of their hazard capacity/threat in accordance with regulatory requirements falls into four categories: (1) reactivity, (2) ignitability/flammability, (3) corrosivity, and (4) TCLP toxicity. Commercial chemical products, specific wastes, and wastes from specific processes may be listed as hazardous wastes because they are known to present toxic hazards in the manner of the tests above and/or are known to present serious toxic hazards to mammals/humans. In the discussion to follow, various chemical groups will be examined primarily in the context of reactivity, ignitability, and corrosivity.

Chemistry of Corrosives

The EPA defines corrosivity in terms of pH (i.e., wastes with pH <2 or >12.5) or in terms of ability to corrode steel (SAE°20) at a rate of >6.35 mm (0.250 in.) per year at a temperature of 55°C (131°F). This discussion will address corrosivity as it applies to acids and caustics. Acids are compounds that yield H^+ ions (actually H_3O^+ ions) when dissolved in water. Common industrial acids include acetic, nitric, hydrochloric, and sulfuric acids. Concentrated and dilute refer to the concentrations in solution. Mixing a concentrated acid with enough water will produce a dilute acid. For example, a bottle of concentrated HCl direct from the manufacturer is approximately 12N in HCl, while a solution of HCl used in a titration may be only 0.5N. The latter is a dilute acid solution.

Strong and weak acids are classified by how completely they ionize in solution. For example, HCl is classified as a strong acid because it is completely ionized to H^+ and Cl^- ions. Acetic acid is classified as a weak acid because it does not totally ionize in solution. As mentioned earlier, weak acids such as acetic acid have higher pKa's. The pKa for acetic acid is 4.75. The negative antilog of this value (1.76×10^{-5}) can be used to calculate the concentrations at equilibrium of the acetate and hydrogen ions. Strong acids include perchloric, hydrochloric, sulfuric, nitric, and hydriodic acids. Examples of weak acids include boric, hydrocyanic, carbonic, and acetic acids. Thus, the terminology "strong versus weak acid" may bear little relationship to the nature or extent of potential hazard, while the terms "concentrated versus dilute" most often do.

The acidic nature of a given solution is characterized by its pH, where pH is the negative logarithm of the molar H^+ concentration ($-\log [H^+]$). A solution with pH < 7 is acid, a solution with pH 7 is neutral, and a solution with pH > 7 is basic. For example, the pH of lemon juice is ≈ 2, while the pH of lye is ≈ 14.

Acids

Acids may be inorganic, such as H_2SO_4, and are then known as mineral acids, or they may be organic, like acetic acid. Mineral acids may be weak or strong, but organic acids tend to be uniformly weak. Table 2 gives a list of commonly occurring acids along with their relative strengths. It should be noted that salts of several metals (e.g., Al^{3+}, Fe^{3+}, and Zn^{3+}) dissolve in water to produce acid solutions. Acids include a variety of compounds, many of which have other significant properties that contribute to their "reactivity." Typical reactions of acids are: neutralization of bases (strong and weak) and oxidation of substances. Characteristics of common acids are presented in Table 3.

Neutralization of Bases:

$H+ + OH^- \rightarrow H_2O$

$HCl + NaOH \rightarrow H_2O + NaCl$

$$CaCO_3 + 2HCl \rightarrow CaCl_2 + H_2O + CO_2 \uparrow$$

Oxidation of Substances:

$$Zn^0 + 2HCl \rightarrow Zn^{2+} + 2Cl^- + H_2$$

$$2NaI + 2H_2SO_4 \rightarrow I_2 + SO_2 + 2H_2O + Na_2SO_4$$

Table 2

RELATIVE STRENGTHS OF ACIDS IN WATER

Increasing Strength		
	Perchloric acid	$HClO_4$
↑	Sulfuric acid	H_2SO_4
	Hydrochloric acid	HCl
	Nitric acid	HNO_3
	Phosphoric acid	H_3PO_3
	Hydroflouric acid	HF
	Acetic acid	CH_3COOH
	Carbonic acid	H_2CO_3
	Hydrocyanic acid	HCN
	Boric acid	H_3BO_3

Bases

A base is any material that produces hydroxide ions when it is dissolved in water. The words alkaline, basic, and caustic are often used synonymously. Common bases include sodium hydroxide (lye), potassium hydroxide (potash lye), and calcium hydroxide (slaked lime). The concepts of strong versus weak bases, and concentrated versus dilute bases are exactly analogous to those for acids. Strong bases such as sodium hydroxide dissociate completely while weak bases such as the amines dissociate only partially. As with acids, bases can be either inorganic or organic.   Typical reactions of bases include neutralization of acids, reaction with metals, and reaction with salts:

Reaction with metals:

$2Al^0 + 6NaOH \rightarrow 2Na_3AlO_3 + 3H_2\uparrow$
(reaction creates heat and may explode)

Reaction with salts:

$Pb(NO_3)_2 + 2NaOH \rightarrow Pb(OH)_2\downarrow + 2NaNO_3$

Characteristics to remember about some common bases are presented in Table 3.

Table 3

PROPERTIES OF SOME COMMON ACIDS AND BASES

Acids -- Sulfuric, Nitric, Hydrochloric, Acetic

a.   These acids are highly soluble in water.

b.   Concentrated solutions are highly corrosive and will attack materials and tissue.

c.   If spilled on skin, flush with lots of water.

d.   Sulfuric and nitric acids are strong oxidizers and should not be stored or mixed with any organic material.

e.   Sulfuric, nitric, and hydrochloric acids will attack metals upon contact and generate hydrogen gas, which is explosive.

f.   Acetic acid (glacial) is extremely flammable. Its vapors form explosive mixtures in the air. It is dangerous when stored with any oxidizing material, such as nitric and sulfuric acids, peroxides, sodium hypochlorite, etc.

g.   Breathing the concentrated vapors of any of these acids can be extremely harmful. Wear appropriate equipment.

h.   When mixing with water, always add acids to water, never water to acids.

Bases (Caustics) -- Sodium Hydroxide, Ammonium Hydroxide, Calcium Hydroxide (Slaked Lime), Calcium Oxide (Quick Lime)

a.   These bases are highly soluble in water.

b.   Concentrated solutions are highly corrosive. They are worse than most acids because they penetrate the skin (Saponification reactions).

c.   If spilled on skin, flush immediately with lots of water.

d.   When mixed with water, they generate a significant amount of heat -- especially sodium hydroxide and calcium oxide.

e.   Do not store or mix concentrated acids and bases, as this gives off much heat -- dilute, then mix.

f.   Do not store or mix ammonium hydroxide with other strong bases. It can release ammonia gas, which is extremely toxic.

g.   Do not store or mix ammonium hydroxide with chlorine compounds (i.e., sodium hypochlorite). It can release chlorine gas, which is extremely toxic.

General Properties and Nomenclature of Organics

Most compounds in which carbon is the key element are classified as organic. Common examples of organic compounds include degreasing solvents, lubricants, and heating and motor fuels. This section will highlight some of the more common characteristics of organics as they relate to hazards. Various relevant classes of organics will be presented in terms of chemical behavior and physical properties.

In order to facilitate the discussion to follow, a few basic definitions will be presented first.

Definitions

Covalent -- refers to a chemical bond in which there is an equal/even sharing of bonding electron pairs between atoms. This is typical of the bonding between carbon atoms and between carbon and hydrogen atoms in organic compounds.

Hydrocarbons -- chemical compounds consisting primarily of carbon and hydrogen.

Aliphatic -- organic compound with the carbon backbone arranged in branched or straight chains (e.g., propane).

Aromatic -- organic molecular structure having the benzene ring (C_6H_6) as the basic unit (e.g., toluene, xylene)

Saturated -- the condition of an organic compound in which each constituent carbon is covalently linked to four different atoms. This is generally a stable configuration (e.g., [propane $CH_3CH_2CH_3$]).

Isomers -- different structural arrangements with the same chemical formulas (e.g., *n*-butane and *t*-butane).

Unsaturated -- an organic compound containing double or triple bonds between carbons (e.g., $CH_2=CH_2$). Multiple bonds tend to be sites of reactivity.

Functional Group -- an atom or group of atoms, other than hydrogen, bonded to the chain or ring of carbon atoms (e.g., the -OH group of alcohols, the -COOH group of carboxylic acids, the -O- group of ethers). Functional groups determine the behavior of molecules. Consequently, the unique hazards of an organic compound are often determined by its functional group(s).

General Properties

Most organic compounds are flammable. They tend to melt and boil at lower temperatures than most inorganic substances. Because many organic compounds volatilize easily at room temperature and possess relatively low specific heats and ignition temperatures, they tend to burn easily. Moreover, organic vapors often have high heats of combustion which, upon ignition, facilitate the ignition of surrounding chemicals, thus compounding the severity of the hazard.

Most organic compounds are less stable than inorganics. However, the presence of one or more halogen atoms (F, Cl, Br, I) in the molecular structure of an organic compound increases its stability and inertness to combustion. Thus, partially halogenated hydrocarbons burn with less ease than their non-halogenated analogs. Fully halogenated derivatives, such as carbon tetrachloride (CCl_4) and certain polychlorinated biphenyls (PCBs) are almost noncombustible.

Most organic compounds are water-insoluble. Notable exceptions are the lower molecular weight alcohols, aldehydes, and ketones, all known to be "polar" molecules. This characteristic is of importance to firefighting because the specific gravity of the compound will then be a major determinant of the suitability of water for the suppression of fires involving the chemical.

Except for alkanes and organic acids, organic compounds tend to react easily with oxidizing agents such as hydrogen peroxide or potassium dichromate. Moreover, a mixture of an oxidizing agent and organic matter is usually susceptible to spontaneous ignition. Notably, except for flammability and oxidation, organic compounds tend to react slowly with other chemicals.

Nomenclature

This section will familiarize the reader with the naming system for some of the more common and simple organic groups, and present the salient characteristics of these groups. The basic system of aliphatic organic nomenclature is shown in Table 4. The prefix for the name is based on the number of carbons involved and remains the same for each type of compound described. The suffix is determined by the type of compound and is independent of the number of carbons in the molecule. Thus, methane, methanol, methanal (formaldehyde), and methanoic (formic) acid represent an alkane, an alcohol, an aldehyde, and a carboxylic acid, respectively, each with one carbon per molecule. In contrast, methanol, ethanol, and propanol are all alcohols, but with one, two, and three carbons per molecule, respectively. The boiling points provided in Table 4 show the systematic trends in chemical properties as the number of carbons per molecule increases with a given chemical group, and as the various chemical groups are compared for a specific number of carbons per molecule. Thus, in general, within any group, the larger molecules are less volatile. Systematic trends can also be observed for other properties, such as water solubility. It should be noted that the boiling points provided in Table 4 are for the straight-chain isomers of the molecules. If the values for branched chain molecules are included, the comparisons become complicated.

Alkenes and alkynes are similar in structure to the alkanes except the alkenes contain a carbon-to-carbon double bond ($C=C$) and the alkynes contain a carbon-to-carbon triple bond ($C\equiv C$). The name prefixes are exactly the same as for the alkanes with the same number of carbons, but the endings are -ene for compounds with double bonds and their derivatives and -yne for compounds with triple bonds and their derivatives. Ethene (ethylene) and propene (propylene) are alkenes. Ethyne (acetylene) is an alkyne.

Aromatics are molecules based on single or multiple benzene rings. Some of the more common aromatics include benzene, toluene, xylene, and phenol. As previously mentioned, benzene is a 6-carbon ring with the formula C_6H_6. The ring has alternating double and single bonds, and is quite stable. The substitution of a methyl group ($-CH_3$) for one of the hydrogens gives methyl benzene or toluene. The substitution of another methyl group gives dimethyl benzene or xylene. Substitution of a hydroxyl ($-OH$) for a hydrogen on the benzene ring gives hydroxy benzene or phenol. Aromatics can also be named more specifically based on a system of assigning names or numbers to various positions on the benzene ring. By using the numbering system for the carbons on single or multiple benzene rings in combination with the names of the relevant substituents, any aromatic compound can be assigned a unique name.

Table 4

NOMENCLATURE FOR ALIPHATICS

Number of Carbons	Alkanes Prefix	Ending	b.p.	Alcohols Ending	b.p.	Aldehydes Ending	b.p.	Acids Ending*	b.p.	Alkenes Ending	Alkynes Ending*
1	Methane		-161°C	anol	65°C	anal		anoic (formic)	100°C	---	---
2	Eth		-90°C		78°C		20°C	(acetic)	120°C	ene	yne
3	Prop		-40°C		95°C		50°C	(propionic)	140°C		
4	But		0°C		120°C		75°C	(butyric)	160°C		
5	Pent		35°C		140°C		105°C	(valeric)	185°C		
6	Hex		70°C		160°C		130°C		205°C		
7	Hept		100°C		175°C		155°C		225°C		
8	Oct		125°C		195°C		170°C		240°C		
9	Non		150°C		215°C		185°C		255°C		
10	Dec		175°C		230°C		210°C		270°C		
11	Undec		195°C								

*·Common name in parentheses
b·Commonly called acetylenes

Properties of Individual Functional Groups

Alkanes (C_nH_{2n+2}) -- These are saturated hydrocarbons. The lower molecular weight alkanes (ethane through butane) are gases at standard temperature and pressure. The remainder are water-insoluble liquids that are lighter than water and thus form films or oil slicks on the surface of water. Hence, water is not used to suppress fires involving materials, such as gasoline, that include substantial proportions of liquid alkanes. Alkanes are relatively unreactive with most acids, bases, and mild oxidizing agents. However, with addition of sufficient heat, alkanes will react and burn in air or oxygen when ignited. In fact, low molecular weight alkanes (LPG, butane, gasoline) are commonly used as fuels. Consequently, the biggest hazard from alkanes is flammability.

Organic Carboxylic Acids (RCOOH) are usually weak acids but can be very corrosive to skin. However, the substitution of Cl atoms on the carbon next to the carboxylic carbon produces a stronger acid. Thus, trichloracetic acid is a stronger acid than acetic acid.

Organic Sulfonic Acids (RSO_2H) are generally stronger acids than organic carboxylic acids.

Organic Bases (such as amines, RNH_2) are weak bases but can be corrosive to skin or other tissue.

Alcohols (ROH) are not very reactive. The lower molecular weight alcohols (methanol, ethanol, propanol) are completely miscible with water, but the heavier alcohols tend to be less soluble. Most common alcohols are flammable. Aromatic alcohols like phenol are not as flammable (flashpoint = 79°C) and are fairly water soluble (9 g/L).

Alkenes (C_nH_{2n}) -- Also known as olefins, the compounds are unsaturated hydrocarbons with a single carbon-to-carbon double bond per molecule. The alkenes are very similar to the alkanes in boiling point, specific gravity, and other physical characteristics. Like alkanes, alkenes are at most only weakly polar. Alkenes are insoluble in water but quite soluble in non-polar solvents like benzene. Because alkenes are mostly insoluble liquids that are lighter than water and flammable as well, water is not used to suppress fires involving these materials. Because of the double bond, alkenes are more reactive than alkanes.

O

Esters (RCOR) are not very reactive. Only the lowest molecular weight esters have appreciable solubility in water (ethyl acetate, 8 percent). Methyl and ethyl esters are more volatile than the corresponding unesterified acids. Most common esters are flammable. Esters are often easily recognizable due to their sweet to pungent odors.

Ethers (R-O-R) are low on the scale of chemical reactivity. Aliphatic ethers are generally volatile, flammable liquids with low boiling points and low flashpoints. Well known hazardous ethers include diethyl ether, dimethyl ether, and tetrahydrofuran. Beyond their flammability, ether present an additional hazard because they react with atmospheric oxygen in the presence of light to form organic peroxides.

Organic Peroxides (R-O-O-R) are very hazardous. Most of the compounds are so sensitive to friction, heat, and shock that they cannot be handled without dilution. As a result, organic peroxides present a serious fire and explosion hazard. Commonly encountered organic peroxides include benzyl peroxide, peracetic acid, and methyl ethyl ketone peroxide.

Aldehydes and ketones (R-CH and R-C-R) share many chemical properties because they possess the carbonyl (C=O) group as a common feature of their structure. Aldehydes and ketones have lower boiling points and higher vapor pressures than their alcohol counterparts. Aldehydes and ketones through C_4 are soluble in water and have pronounced odors. Ketones are relatively inert while aldehydes are easily oxidized to their counterpart organic acids.

Chemistry of Flammables

Flammability, the tendency of a material to burn, can only be subjectively defined. Many materials that we normally do not consider flammable will burn, given high enough temperatures. Neither can flammability be gauged by the heat content of materials. Fuel oil has a higher heat content than many materials considered more flammable because of their lower flashpoint. In fact, flashpoint has become the standard for gauging flammability.

The most common systems for designating flammability are the Department of Transportation (DOT) definitions, the National Fire Protection Association's (NFPA) system, and the Environmental Protection Agency's (EPA) Resource Conservation and Recovery Acts (RCRA) definition of ignitable wastes, all of which use flashpoint in their schemes. The NFPA diamond, which comprises the backbone of the NFPA Hazard Signal System, uses a four-quadrant diamond to display the hazards of a material. The top quadrant (red quadrant) contains flammability information in the form of numbers ranging from zero to four. Materials designated as zero will not burn. Materials designated as four rapidly or completely vaporize at atmospheric pressure and ambient temperature, and will burn readily (flashpoint < 73°F and boiling point < 100°F). The

NFPA defines a flammable liquid as one having a flashpoint of 200°F or lower, and divides these liquids into five categories:

1. Class IA: liquids with flashpoints below 73°F and boiling points below 100°F.   An example of a Class IA flammable liquid is n-pentane (NFPA Diamond: 4).

2. Class IB: liquids with flashpoints at or above 73°F and boiling points at or above 100°F.   Examples of Class IB flammable liquids are benzene, gasoline and acetone (NFPA Diamond: 3).

3. Class IC: liquids with flashpoints at or above 73°F and below 100°F. Example of Class IC flammable liquids are turpentine and n-butyl acetate (NFPA Diamond: 2).

4. Class II: liquids with flashpoints at or above 100°F but below 140°F. Examples of Class II flammable liquids are kerosene and camphor oil (NFPA Diamond: 2).

5. Class III: liquids with flashpoints at or above 140°F but below 200°F. Examples of Class III liquids are creosote oils, phenol, and naphthalene.   Liquids in this category are generally termed combustible rather than flammable (NFPA Diamond: 2).

The DOT system designates those materials with a flashpoint of 100°F or less as flammable, those between 100°F and 200°F as combustible, and those with a flashpoint of greater than 200°F as nonflammable.   EPA designates those wastes with a flashpoint of less than 140°F as ignitable hazardous wastes. To facilitate the comparison of these systems they are presented graphically in Figure 1.

These designations serve as useful guides in storage, transport, and spill response. However, they do have limitations. Since these designations are somewhat arbitrary, it is useful to understand the basic concepts of flammability.

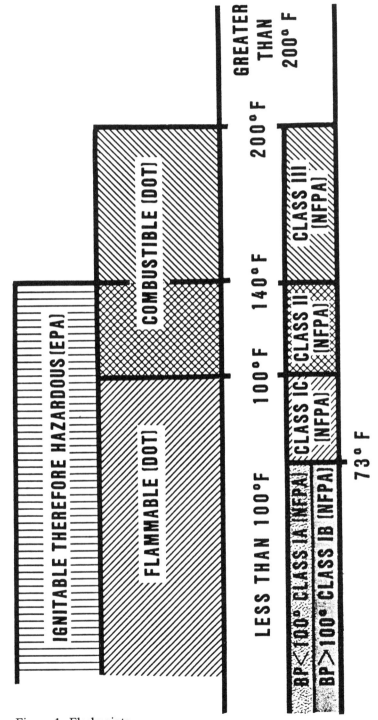

Figure 1: Flashpoints

The elements required for combustion are few -- a substrate, oxygen, and a source of ignition. The substrate, or flammable material, occurs in many classes of compounds but most often is organic. Generally, compounds within a given class exhibit increasing heat contents with increasing molecular weights (MW) (see Table 5).

Other properties specific to the substrate that are important in determining flammable hazards are the auto-ignition temperature, boiling point, vapor pressure, and vapor density. Auto-ignition temperature (the temperature at which a material will spontaneously ignite) is more important in preventing fire from spreading (e.g., knowing what fire protection is needed to keep temperatures below the ignition point) but can also be important in spill or material handling situations. For example, gasoline has been known to spontaneously ignite when spilled onto an overheated engine or manifold. The boiling point and vapor pressure of a material are important not only because vapors are more easily ignited than liquids, but also because vapors are more readily transportable than liquids (they may disperse, or when heavier than air, flow to a source of ignition). Vapors with densities greater than one do not tend to disperse but rather to settle into sumps, basements, depressions in the ground, or other low areas, thus representing active explosion hazards.

Oxygen, the second requirement for combustion, is generally not limiting. Oxygen in the air is sufficient to support combustion of most materials within certain limits. These limitations are compound specific and are called the explosive limits in air (see previous section on explosive limits). The upper and lower explosive limits (UEL and LEL) of several common materials are given in Table 6.

The source of ignition may be physical (such as a spark, electrical arc, small flame, cigarette, welding operation, or hot piece of equipment), or it may be chemical, such as an exothermic reaction. In any case, when working with or storing flammables, controlling the source of ignition is often the easiest and safest way to avoid fires or explosions.

Table 5

HEAT CONTENT/INCREASING WEIGHT RELATIONSHIPS

Compound	MW	Heat Content kg. Calories/gm.MW
methane	16	210.8
ethane	30	368.4
propane	44	526.3
methanol	32	170.9
ethanol	46	327.6
propanol	60	480.7

Once a fire has started, control of the fire can be accomplished in several ways: through water systems (by reducing the temperature), carbon dioxide or foam systems (by limiting oxygen), or through the removal of the substrate (by shutting off valves or other controls).

Chemistry of Water Reactive Materials

Characteristics of a solid waste that would categorize it as a reactive hazardous waste as defined in the Federal Register include (1) it reacts violently with water, (2) it forms potentially explosive mixtures with water, or (3) when mixed with water, it generates toxic gases, vapors or fumes in a quantity sufficient to present a danger to human health or the environment. Because water is the most common fire suppressant, the characteristic of reactivity is especially relevant since the application of water to eliminate or prevent the spread of fires may be counter-productive rather than helpful. Several categories of chemicals will be discussed from this standpoint; however, several of these same chemicals also present additional hazards.

Table 6

EXPLOSIVE LIMITS OF HAZARDOUS MATERIALS

Compound	LEL %	UEL %	Flashpoint °F	Vapor Density
Acetone	2.15	13	-4	2.0
Acetylene	2.50	100	Gas	0.9
Ammonia, anhydrous	16	25	Gas	0.6
Benzene	1.30	7.1	12	7.8
Carbon monoxide	12.4	74	Gas	1.0
Gasoline	1.4	7.6	-45	3-4
Hexane	1.1	7.5	-7	3.0
Toluene	1.2	7.1	40	3.1
Vinyl chloride	3.6	33	Gas	2.2
p-xylene	1.0	6.0	90	3.7

Substances That Produce H_2

Metals

Several metals react with water and air with the extent of reactivity being dependent upon the physical state of the metal. The highly reactive metals such as lithium, sodium, and potassium are pyrophoric (i.e., they ignite spontaneously in air without an ignition source). In contrast, the less reactive metals such as magnesium, zirconium, titanium, aluminum, and zinc, are highly pyrophoric only as dusts.

Lithium, sodium, and potassium (alkali metals) react rapidly with water to release hydrogen (H_2) gas:

$$2Na + 2H_2O \rightarrow 2Na^+ + 2OH^- + H_2\uparrow$$

Sufficient heat is generated to ignite the hydrogen gas so that it can react explosively with the oxygen in air.

Metals like magnesium, aluminum, titanium, and zirconium in pure form also react with water to release H_2, but heat must be supplied to initiate the reaction. The generalized representation is:

metal + water + heat $\rightarrow$ metal oxide or hydroxide + $H_2\uparrow$

Hydrides

True hydrides (i.e., those in which the hydrogen is in its anionic or most reduced form) are salt-like compounds in which the hydrogen is combined with alkali metals, either alone as simple hydrides or in association with other elements as complex hydrides. Hydrides react with water to release hydrogen.

Simple hydrides:

$$2LiH_2 + 2H_2O \rightarrow 3H_2\uparrow + 2LiOH$$

Complex hydrides:

$$LiAlH_4 + 4H_2O \rightarrow Al(OH)_3 + LiOH + 4H_2\uparrow$$

Peroxides

Compounds containing the O^{2-} ion are hazardous primarily as oxidizing agents but also as water reactives. An example is the liberation of oxygen from the mixture of sodium peroxide and water:

$$2Na_2O_2 + 2H_2O \rightarrow 4NaOH + O_2\uparrow$$

Substances That Produce Alkaline Aqueous Solutions

This group is exemplified by nitrides, carbides, and phosphides. Nitrides will react with water to generate ammonia (NH_3), which can be released depending on how alkaline the solution becomes. It is unlikely that sufficient NH_3 will be produced under normal circumstances to create a hazard.

$$Mg_3Na_2 + 6H_2O \rightarrow 3Mg(OH)_3 + 2NH_3\uparrow$$

Carbides, which are binary compounds containing anionic carbon, occur as covalent and as salt-like compounds. The salt-like carbides are water-reactive and, upon hydrolysis, yield flammable hydrocarbons. Typical hydrolysis reactions include:

$$CaC_2 + 2H_2O \rightarrow Ca(OH)_2 + C_2H_2\uparrow \quad \text{(acetylene)}$$

$$Al_4C_3 + 12H_2O \rightarrow 4Al(OH)_3 + 3CH_4\uparrow \quad \text{(methane)}$$

Other similar carbides are Be_2C and Mg_2C_3. Notably, each reaction is sufficiently exothermic to ignite the specific gas formed upon hydrolysis.

Phosphides are binary compounds containing anionic phosphorous (P^{3-}). Heavy metal, alkali, and alkaline earth metal phosphides exist but few of them are commercially important. Phosphides hydrolyze to the flammable and toxic gas phosphine (PH_3). The hydrolysis reaction of aluminum phosphide is given below:

$$AlP + 3H_2O \rightarrow PH_3\uparrow + Al(OH)_3$$

Substances That Produce Acidic Aqueous Solutions

Inorganic Chlorides/Halides -- These metallic salts are formed from the reaction of a weak base with the strong acid HCl. Salts such as these dissolve in water to produce a markedly acidic solution. This is exemplified by aluminum chloride, which is corrosive due to the acidity resulting from the hydrolysis that produces aluminum and chlorine ions. Anhydrous $AlCl_3$ hydrolyzes violently when contacted by water.

Several nonmetallic chlorides also react with water with varying degrees of violence to produce hydrochloric acid. Although these compounds are themselves nonflammable, the heat generated by hydrolysis is sufficient to ignite adjacent flammable materials. These nonmetallic chlorides include antimony pentachloride ($SbCl_5$), boron trichloride (BCl_3), phosphorus oxychloride ($POCl_3$), phosphorus pentachloride (PCl_5), phosphorus trichloride (PCl_3), silicon tetrachloride ($SiCl_4$), thionyl chloride ($SOCl_2$), sulfuryl chloride (SO_2Cl_2) and titanium tetrachloride ($TiCl_4$). Because of their acid-producing tendencies, many of these chlorides are considered to be corrosive.

Organic Chlorides/Halides -- Several organic compounds also are hydrolyzed (or react with water) to produce corrosive materials. Notable inclusions among these compounds are acetic anhydride [$(CH_3CO_2)_2O$], and acetyl chloride (CH_3COCl), both of which produce acetic acid upon reaction with water. Both acetic anhydride and acetyl chloride are corrosive; in addition, mixtures of the vapors of acetic anhydride and acetic acid are flammable in air, and acetyl chloride itself is flammable.

Oxidation/Reduction Phenomena

Oxidation/reduction reactions, the bane of high school chemistry students, can be similarly unkind to hazardous materials managers. The explosive potential of oxidation/reduction reactions has resulted time and time again in chemical disasters. Perhaps the largest of these was the explosion of the S.S. Grandcamp at Texas City, Texas, in 1947, where thermal decomposition (redox reactions of ammonium nitrate and subsequent oxidation reactions of the decomposition products) lead to the deaths of over 600 people and over \$33 million (1947 dollars) damage. The addition or loss of electrons involves an accompanying transfer of energy, often a violently exothermic transfer. The substance that gives up electrons (and is therefore oxidized) is the reducing agent. The substance that gains electrons (and is therefore reduced) is the oxidizing agent.

Oxidizing agents are generally recognizable by their structures or names. They tend to have oxygen in their structures and often release oxygen as a result of thermal decomposition. Oxidizing agents often have "per-" prefixes (perchlorate, peroxides, permanganate) and often end in "-ate" (chromate, nitrate, chlorate).

Strong oxidizers have more potential incompatibilities than perhaps any other chemical group (with the exception of water reactive substances). It is safe to assume that they should not be stored or mixed with any other material except under carefully controlled conditions. Common oxidizing agents listed in decreasing order of oxidizing strength include:

Flourine	Chlorine
Ozone	Sulfuric acid (concentrated)
Hydrogen peroxide	Oxygen
Hypochlorous acid	Metallic iodates
Metal chlorates	Bromine
Lead dioxide	Ferric salts
Metallic permanganates	Iodine
Metallic dichromates	Sulfur
Nitric acid (concentrated)	Stannic salts

Reducing agents present similar problems. They react with a broad spectrum of chemical classes, and the reactions can be exothermic and violent. Reducing agents are, by definition, highly oxidizable and may react with air or moisture in the air. Common reducing agents include:

Hydrogen	Sulfides
Metals (Li, Na, K, Ca, Sr, Ba)	Sulfites
Hydrazine	Iodides
Metal acetylides	Nitrides
Complex hydrides	Nitrites
Metal hydrides	Phosphites
Metal hypoborates	Metallic azides
Metal hypophosphites	

Toxics

Since toxic substances cross the broad spectrum of chemical classes, it would be beyond the scope of this study guide to do more than discuss the general characteristics of a few important classes of toxics.

Toxic Metals

The most common toxic metals in industrial use are cadmium, chromium, lead, silver, and mercury; less commonly used are arsenic, selenium, (both metalloids), and barium. Cadmium, a metal commonly used in alloys and myriads of other industrial uses, is fairly mobile in the environment and is responsible for many maladies including renal failure and a degenerative bone disease called "itai itai" disease. Chromium, most often found in plating wastes, is also environmentally mobile and is most toxic in the Cr^{+6} valence state. Lead has been historically used as a component of an antiknock compound in gasoline and, along with chromium (as lead chromate), in paint and pigments. Lead, because of its history as an air emission, has been fairly mobile and is particularly soluble in acid environments. Silver is used widely in the electronics industry. Intake of silver compounds can result in permanent discoloration of the skin and may result in damage to kidneys, lungs, mucous membranes, and other organs.

Mercury enjoys its seeming environmental ubiquity due to its use as a fungicide and as an electrode in the chlorine production process. Elemental mercury is relatively immobile, but is readily transformed to more mobile organometallic compounds through bacterial action. Mercury is the responsible agent for the infamous Minimata syndrome which is characterized by degeneration of the central nervous system. Arsenic and selenium are both commonly used to decolorize glass or to impart a desirable color. Arsenic occurs in a number of important forms, many of which have been used as contact herbicides. Important forms of arsenic include arsenic trioxide and pentoxide, and arsenic acids, arsenites and arsenates, and various organic arsenic compounds. Selenium often occurs as selenous acid. Both arsenic and selenium are fairly mobile and toxic.

In general, toxic metals can be readily removed from aqueous solution through precipitation reactions, either as the sulfide or (more commonly) as the hydroxide. Various processes are available to stabilize metals in contaminated soil, but all the processes are expensive.

Cyanides

Cyanides are dangerously toxic materials that can cause instantaneous death. They occur in a number of industrial situations but are commonly associated with plating operations, and sludges and baths from such sources. Cyanide is extremely soluble and many cyanide compounds, when mixed with acid, release deadly hydrogen cyanide gas. Cyanide is sometimes formed during the combustion of various nitrile, cyanohydrine, and methacrylate compounds. Cyanides (CN^-) are commonly treated by chlorine oxidation to the less toxic cyanate (CNO^-) form, then acid hydrolyzed to CO_2 and N_2. Obviously, care should be taken that the cyanide oxidation is complete prior to acid hydrolysis of the cyanate.

Hydrogen Sulfide

Hydrogen sulfide is a commonly occurring decomposition product of organic matter. It is relatively water soluble at higher pHs where it is predominantly dissociated as H^+ and S^{2-} ions. As the pH is decreased below 7, un-dissociated gas H_2S begins to predominate and is released. Since its vapor density is >1.0, H_2S gas tends to settle in low places and creates a toxic hazard. H_2S is readily oxidizable by a number of means to less toxic $SO_3^=$ or $SO_4^=$ forms.

Pesticides and Bioaccumulators

Pesticides include the broad categories of insecticides, fungicides, rodenticides, and herbicides. Insecticides, in common use, fall into three categories. The chloroinsecticides have chlorine in their structure.

They are less soluble than the other insecticide forms and much less biodegradable (i.e., more persistent). While they are less acutely toxic, several have been identified as potential carcinogens. Carbamates are a relatively new form of pesticide. They are less persistent and less toxic than chloroinsecticides, but some are also suspected carcinogens. Organophosphate insecticides are generally more acutely toxic than the other categories but they are not persistent.

Many formerly common herbicides now have been banned or restricted in their use, e.g., 2,4-D and 2,4,5-T. However, the number and diversity of herbicides far exceeds that of insecticides. There are both organic and inorganic herbicides. Examples of inorganic herbicides are $CuSO_4$ and $NaClO_4$. There are at least 22 chemical families of organic herbicides. Even a cursory treatment of the chemistry of these materials would be extensive. Herbicides of limited toxicity (Treflan, Atrazine) as well as extremely toxic ones (Paraquat, Dinoseb) are in use. They range from water soluble to insoluble. The detailed chemistry of each should be determined prior to handling.

Compatibility

Chemical incompatibility can manifest itself in many ways; however, we will confine our discussions to those combinations resulting in fires, explosions, extreme heat, evolution of gas (both toxic and nontoxic), and polymerization.

Because of the number of chemicals and subsequent multiple number of potential reactions, it is impractical and (perhaps impossible) to list all potential reactions. Several systems exist for determining the reactions between classes of chemicals. The most broadly distributed of these are:

The Handbook of Reactive Chemical Hazards, edited by L. Bretherick

A Method for Determining the Compatibility
of Hazardous Wastes EPA - 600/2-80-076
by H.K. Hatayaya, et al.

The volume by Bretherick is divided into two sections. The first lists general classes of compounds and gives reactivity information regarding interactions of these classes with other classes and with specific chemicals. The second and much larger section lists specific compounds and references specific adverse reactions as they have been observed or reported in the chemical literature. The work by Hatayaya provides a matrix format compatibility chart listing 40 classes of chemicals. While both of these volumes are extremely helpful, they are not and do not claim to be the definitive work on material compatibility. They serve best as useful guides in determining potential for reactions.

Because all of the potential reactions for individual chemicals are not catalogued and because there are no (or very few) pure solutions of waste materials, laboratory compatibility testing is recommended for most materials. An appropriate protocol for compatibility testing would involve the following steps:

(1) Obtain all available information about the material. If it is a surplus or off-specification product, obtain an analysis or a Material Safety Data Sheet. If it is a waste, check for previous analyses, and if none exists, obtain one. (Even if a previous analysis exists for this stream, consider running a few screening type field analyses for confirmation of important properties such as pH, redox potential or other oxidizer test, cyanide, sulfide, and flashpoint.)

(2) Once the identity of the material is known, one of the cited references can be consulted to determine potential reactions. At this point, incompatibility may be obvious. If not, then laboratory testing for compatibility is required.

Compatibility testing is almost by nature an experiment with the unknown. As such, safety must be the watchword. Procedures for compatibility testing should take into account the most severe adverse reaction possible, not just that expected. Such testing should always be performed under a vent hood while wearing, as a minimum, face shield, rubber apron, and gloves. Generally, compatibility testing entails mixing a small volume of one substance with another and observing for heat, gas generation, or polymerization. Polymerization need not be violent to cause problems. Anyone who has ever had to chisel out or replace a tank of solidified material can attest to this. Often it is advisable to heat the mixture to expected storage or process temperature and then observe for further heat, gas, or polymerization. Observation of a reaction does not necessarily preclude mixing. Moderate heat or gas generation may not present a problem. However, a number of safety precautions should be taken before mixing the material if any heat or gas generation occurs. If heat is generated, the amount should be determined and a heat balance calculated so that effects of heating on the storage tank and tank base can be calculated. Expansion of the material with heating should also be considered so as to avoid overfilling the receiving tank.

Generation of gas requires a gas analysis before mixing. If the gas is toxic or if discharge of the resultant gas violates an air quality constraint, the materials should not be mixed. If the gas is nontoxic, care should still be taken to assure that the gas generation rate does not exceed the design venting capacity of the tank. Remember that most tanks are designed to withstand a water gauge internal pressure of only about eight inches (a typical person can provide 24 inches water gauge by blowing). Secondly, even if the gas is nontoxic, it may still displace air and (for inside tanks especially) create an asphyxiation hazard.

INDUSTRIAL TOXICOLOGY

Donald E. Witt, B.S.Ch.E., M.S., P.E.
Tennessee Department of Labor

Revised by

David M. Trayer, CIH
Tennessee Valley Authority

Background

The role of toxicology has become more important to managers, workers, and health professionals in industry in the Twentieth Century, as chemicals have been used increasingly in society, and as lifetime exposures to those chemicals have been realized. Identification of toxic agents in work operations, knowledge of the potential health effects of overexposure, and the development of safe working exposure limits are some of the essential components of a practical industrial toxicology program. This chapter presents the basic language and principles of the broad and complex field of industrial toxicology.

Industrial Toxicology

Toxicology is the science that studies the harmful effects chemicals can have on the body. All chemicals may have some effect on the body, depending on the nature of the chemical, its concentration, its route of entry into the body, the length of time of exposure, and individual human susceptibly. It is the degree of exposure and the toxicity of a chemical that are of practical concern to us.

The usual means by which chemicals enter the body are by inhalation (breathing), ingestion (swallowing), and absorption through intact skin or

33

mucous tissue. Once in the system chemicals may produce such symptoms as tissue irritation, rash, dizziness, nausea, anxiety, narcosis, headache and other pain, fever, tremors, shortness of breath, birth defects, paralysis, cancer, and death, to mention a few. The amount of chemical that enters the body is called the "dose." The graphic relationship that defines the body's response to increasing doses of a chemical is called the "dose-response curve." A typical dose-response curve for the hypothetical "Chemical X" is shown in Figure 1. The lowest dose causing a detectable response is called the "threshold of effect" or the "no effect level." The threshold of effect is dependent on several factors such as the chemical's solubility in body fluids, the particle size of the chemical (if it is a dust, for example), the breathing rate and depth of breathing, the residence time of the chemical in the body, and individual human susceptibility.

To accomplish meaningful toxicological studies, the careful measurement of several variables is essential. Dose is one of these variables. In inhalation studies dose is directly proportional to the air concentration of the chemical multiplied by the length of time it is inhaled. The units of concentration are as follows:

1. Parts per million or ppm. This is a volume/volume description of concentration, that is, the number of unit volumes of air contaminant per one million unit volumes of contaminated air. Note that this permits the use of any units of volume. Parts per million is used to describe the concentration of gases and vapors.

2. Milligrams per cubic meter or mg/m^3. This is a mass/volume description of concentration, that is, the number of milligrams of contaminant per cubic meter of contaminated air. This unit may be used to describe both gaseous and vapor contaminants as well as particulates such as dusts, mists, and fumes.

Other concentration units exist, such as fibers per cubic centimeters of air (f/cc) which is used for asbestos, and "rems" for ionizing radiation. Dose for ingestion is measured in units of mass (weight) or volume. For skin applications the dose is usually expressed in units of quantity of chemical

DOSE-RESPONSE CURVE
(CHEMICAL "X")

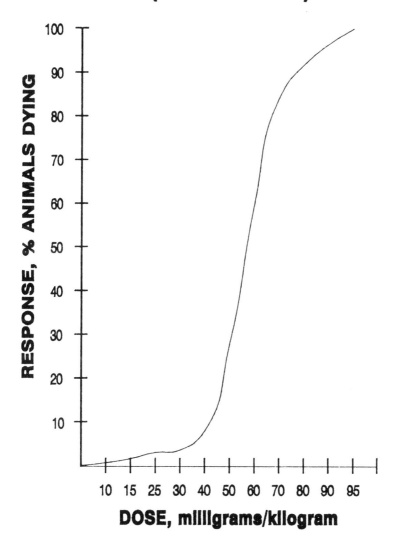

Figure 1

per unit area of skin. Regardless of the route of administration, the time over which the dose was administered must always be specified.

In order to permit comparison of relative toxicities between different animal species as well as animals of different sizes, the units of dose are usually expressed as the mass of chemical per unit mass of body weight, most often as *milligrams* (of chemical) *per kilogram* of body weight. Toxicity data are presented in the literature by such terms as the *lethal dose: 50 percent* or "LD50." In inhalation tests, the *lethal concentration: 50 percent*, or "LC50," is used. These terms refer to the dose or air concentration which is fatal to 50 percent of the animals tested. Such toxicity data as these are compiled and published in several sources including the *Registry of Toxic Effects of Chemical Substances*, published by the National Institute for Occupational Safety and Health, and *Dangerous Properties of Industrial Materials*, by N. Irving Sax (Van Nostrand Reinhold, New York). Such experimental toxicology data, along with data from health studies on persons known to have experienced industrial exposures, have been used in establishing exposure limits to protect industrial workers. A widely recognized industrial exposure limit is the Threshold Limit Values, or "TLVs," which is published and updated annually by the American Conference of Governmental Industrial Hygienists (ACGIH). The ACGIH TLVs are recommended guidelines only and do not carry weight of law. However, OSHA, using the TLVs and a few limits proposed by NIOSH and other organizations, established the Permissible Exposure Limits, or "PELs," which are mandatory. The PEL list was updated in 1989 and it covers about 600 chemical substances.

Human response to chemicals may be described as either acute or chronic. An acute effect is *generally* characterized by a single, rather high exposure with rapid onset of symptoms, followed by a quick resolution to a crisis. An example of an acute response can occur after a few minutes inhalation of carbon monoxide, which may cause symptoms ranging from headache to dizziness to death, depending on the dose (concentration multiplied by the exposure time). Chronic responses *typically* result from repeated, low-level exposures over a long period of time with slow onset of symptoms. Some examples of chronic toxic responses are the development of disabling conditions such as silicosis and asbestosis, a reduction in life span, increased susceptibility to other diseases, and the development of cancer.   Some substances, such as lead, can store in body tissues (bioaccumulation) and thereby cause continuing effects.   Many chronic occupational diseases have quite long "latency" periods.   For example, asbestosis may be detected 20 years after initial exposure to asbestos fibers.   Some chemicals, benzene for example, may be both acute and chronic exposure hazards.

Exposure to some chemicals can result in the development of cancer (carcinogens).   Others may present a hazard to developing fetuses (teratogens), which is cause for special concern in protecting the health of women.   A few industrial chemicals may induce genetic changes which could affect future generations of offspring (mutagens).   Such effects may be difficult to document due to long latency periods and lack of knowledge of the biochemical mechanisms involved.

The OSHA Hazard Communication Standard, 29 CFR 1910.1200, contains a list of certain "target organ" effects.   Also listed are some of the signs and symptoms of exposure and examples of chemicals in each target organ category.   A review of this list emphasizes the range and diversity of problems employers must be prepared to deal with in chemical protection programs.   The list is shown below.   It is representative, but is not intended to be all-inclusive.

A.   Hepatotoxins..................... Chemicals   which   produce   liver
                                         damage.
       Signs and Symptoms............ Jaundice.   Liver enlargement.
       Chemicals........................ Carbon tetrachloride.   Nitrosamines.

B.   Nephrotoxins..................... Chemicals   which   produce   kidney
                                         damage.
       Signs and Symptoms............ Edema.   Proteinuria.
       Chemicals........................ Halogenated hydrocarbons. Uranium.

C.   Neurotoxins...................... Chemicals   which   produce   their
                                         primary toxic effect on the nervous
                                         system.
       Signs and Symptoms............ Narcosis.   Behavioral   changes.
                                         Impaired motor functions.

Chemicals......................... Mercury. Carbon disulfide.

D.   Agents which act on the
blood or hematopoietic
system............................. Decreases in hemoglobin function.
Deprives the body tissues of oxygen.
Signs and Symptoms............ Cyanosis. Loss of consciousness.
Chemicals......................... Carbon monoxide. Cyanides.

E.   Agents which damage
the lung........................... Chemicals which irritate or damage
the pulmonary tissue.
Signs and Symptoms............ Cough. Tightness in chest. Shortness
of breath.
Chemicals......................... Silica. Asbestos.

F.   Reproductive toxins............. Chemicals which affect the
reproductive capabilities including
chromosomal damage (mutations) and
effects on fetuses (teratogenesis).
Signs and Symptoms............ Birth defects. Sterility.
Chemicals......................... Lead. 1,2-Dibromo-3-Chloropropane.

G.   Cutaneous hazards............... Chemicals which affect the dermal
layer of the body.
Signs and Symptoms............ Defatting of the skin.   Rashes.
Irritation.
Chemicals......................... Ketones. Chlorinated compounds.

H.   Eye hazards...................... Chemicals which affect the eyes or
visual capacity.
Signs and Symptoms............ Conjunctivitis. Corneal damage.
Chemicals......................... Organic solvents. Acids.

It should be noted that, in spite of the considerable body of knowledge that exists concerning the health effects of exposure to single, pure chemicals, there is very little toxicological data on exposure to chemical *mixtures*. Very often industrial exposures involve several chemical agents as well as physical agents such as heat, noise, and ultra-violet radiation. This may be realized most notably in the case of hazardous waste, in which exposure can occur simultaneously to a variety of mixed chemicals. It is known that the effects of some chemical combinations are *additive* - that is, the combined effect of the mixture is the same as if the effect of each chemical were added to the effect of each of the other chemicals in the mixture. This is particularly true when each of the chemicals acts in a similar manner on the same target organs. In certain instances the combined effect of two chemicals may be *synergistic* -- that is, the combined effect far exceeds an additive effect. For example, inhalation of the vapors of carbon tetrachloride together with the vapors of isopropyl alcohol can cause kidney damage far exceeding either of the vapors acting independently, and exceeds even an additive effect. A well-known synergistic effect exists between asbestos exposure and tobacco smoking. Smokers who are also exposed to asbestos fibers are at ten times the risk of developing lung cancer as asbestos workers who do not smoke and are at five times the risk as smokers who are not exposed to asbestos.

Unless current toxicological information indicates otherwise, the usual practice is to assume that the effects of mixtures of chemicals are at least additive.

RADIATION PRINCIPLES FOR HAZARDOUS MATERIALS MANAGERS

George J. Hyfantis, Jr., P.E., CHMM
University of Tennessee
International Waste Management Systems

INTRODUCTION

The field of radiation safety is probably the least understood by the professional with responsibilities for worker safety, or hazardous materials and waste management. Many of us have never had an opportunity to study the different types of radiation or their interactions and/or effects on people. Although radiation principles may be foreign to many, a review of a few of the basic principles can help us to better understand the nature of radioactive materials or radiation producing devices which we may encounter from time to time in our work. One type of machine which we have all encountered is the X-ray machine, probably in the context of a medical or dental examination. This type of equipment also has industrial applications. For example, the integrity of welds in a manufacturing process can be inspected by measuring the attentuation caused by the metal being inspected. In this case, a missed spot in a continuous weld would show up as a spot on a photographic plate or flourescent screen simply because more X-rays have passed through the defect in the weld.

One may also encounter other sources of radiation used for a variety of purposes. Manmade or naturally occurring radioactive isotopes are used every day in our society. Cobalt 60, a manmade radioactive isotope of cobalt 59, is used to treat cancer patients using radiation therapy techniques. We are all familiar with uranium 235 which is used to produce electricity in our nuclear power plants. Decaying radioactive isotopes emit radiation which, when absorbed, produce heat. The heat converts water to steam to generate electricity. Typically, the waste products fall into two categories: (1) high-level radioactive waste and (2) low-level radioactive waste. In our field we are more likely to have to deal with low-level waste.

Types of Radiation

There are three types of radiation with which we need to be familiar. For other types of radiation, consult an expert concerning appropriate safety measures.

Alpha radiation (α): Alpha particles are produced when a radioactive substance such as radium decomposes to produce radon and an alpha particle. Alpha particles are double-charged helium ions. Radioactive materials which decay by only emission of alpha particles are usually not of concern, unless the material is ingested. Alpha particles can be stopped by a piece of paper and can only travel a few tenths of a centimeter in air.

Beta radiation (β): The second type of radiation is beta radiation. The beta particle is a fast moving electron produced by radioactive decay and it requires about 1000 times more mass to stop than does an alpha particle. A one MeV electron can travel 400 cm in air but only 0.5 cm in water. Therefore, water provides a good shield against beta radiation.

Electromatic radiation (X, γ): The third and final type of radiation which we will discuss is electromagnetic radiation, in particular X-rays and gamma rays. Both X and gamma rays are similar in properties to UV light and visible light. The wave lengths are much shorter and, therefore, the energy is much greater. More energy indicates that more damage may occur in the receiving body (yours or mine) if most of the energy is deposited. X-ray production requires an electrical source. High speed electrons are accelerated in a vacuum. They then strike a target and X-rays are emitted. Gamma rays on the other hand are produced by radioactive nuclei. A one MeV gamma ray can travel over 7000 cm in air and 10 cm in water. Lead is frequently used for shielding material.

Activity

Radioactive materials emit radiation as they decay with time. Radioactivity is measured as the number of disintegrations per second (dps). The curie (3.7×10^{10} dps) is used for radionuclides which decay at large dps. European countries have already switched to a new set of units which will soon come into use in the United States. The unit for activity is now the Becquerel (Bq) which is one dps.

Half-life

One concept which we must be familiar with in working with radiation is half-life. With X-rays, when we turn off the machine the X-ray flux stops, but radioactive materials producing any of the three types of radiation discussed above decay with time. Eventually no more radiation is produced. We use the concept of half-life to describe this process. The half-life is the time required for the activity of a radioactive nuclide to decay to one half of its initial value.

Dose

The dose is the amount of energy absorbed by the receiving body. The energy which radiation imparts to the receiving body is what causes the damage, particularly in biological systems. The unit used to express the absorbed dose is the Rad. A Rad is 100 ergs absorbed in one gram of material. The Rad will soon be replaced by the Gray (Gy) which is Rads $\times$ 100.

Exposure

The unit used to measure exposure to X-rays is the roentgen. As these radiation deposit their energy in matter, the primary products are electrons. The roentgen is a measure of the charge produced as the rays pass through the air. One roentgen is the amount of radiation that will produce 2.58×10^{-4} coulombs in one kilogram of air.

Other Terms

Relative biological effectiveness (RBE) is determined experimentally and identifies the effectiveness of certain types of radiation in causing a desired change in a biological system. The reference radiation is gamma and it is assigned an RBE of 1. In comparison, the RBE of beta particles is also

1 and of alphas is 10.   Alpha particles do more damage in biological systems.

Another term which the student should be familiar with is the Roentgen Equivalent Man or rem.   It is expressed as the product of the absorbed dose in rads × the RBE.   Most radiation safety exposures are listed in terms of the absorbed dose in rems.   The International Atomic Energy Agency recommends that the maximum permissible dose be limited to 0.1 rem/week.   The total dosage should not exceed the number as determined by the following equation:

$$\text{dose (rems)} = (\text{age in years} - 18) \times 5$$

Persons under age 18 should not be exposed to radiation!

The rem will soon be replaced by the Sievert (Sv).   A Sievert is equivalent to rems × 100.

Inverse Square Law

When shielding is not available, the best protection against radiation is distance, because the intensity of the radiation decreases with distance according to the following inverse square relationship:

$$I = I_o/D^2$$

where I_o is the intensity of radiation measured at the source in rads and I is the intensity in rads measured at distance D from the source.   This concept is useful for estimating dosages as distances from a source increase or decrease.

Laws and Regulations

Many laws on atomic energy have been written, but the Atomic Energy Act of 1954 and its amendment stand as the reference.   The Atomic Energy Act created the Atomic Energy Commission, which has since been replaced by the Nuclear Regulatory Commission.   These commissions focus primarily on special nuclear materials (i.e., plutonium and uranium) but they are also charged with oversight responsibility for radiological health concerns.   The Federal government transfers responsibility for regulating to a State if the (agreement) State can develop a program that is essentially equivalent to the Federal program. Many States have entered into an agreement with the NRC under Section 274b of the Atomic Energy Act, as amended (73 Stat. 689). For example, the Tennessee counterpart of the Federal law for the health and safety aspects is the Radiological Health Services Act. The details of how to meet the requirements of this Act are contained in Tennessee's "State Regulations for Protection Against Radiation." Other States have similar statutes and regulations for radiological health protection and radioactive materials management. For more information, contact your State's Radiological Health Physicist.

The basis for radiation protection is the minimization of the exposure to radiation of persons near the source. Exposure is limited in areas where radiation is used and is detailed in the following table:

Rems per quarter

(a) Whole body; head and trunk; blood-forming organs; lens of eyes or gonads   1-1/4

(b) Hands and forearms; feet and ankles   18-3/4

(c) Skin of the whole body   7-1/2

Other provisions permit exposure to amounts in excess of the whole body dose given above. These special circumstances should be detailed in your local States's regulations or can be found in 10 CFR Part 20.

The student is referred to page 344 of *Chemistry of Hazardous Materials* by Eugene Meyer for an excellent description of transportation requirements for radioactive materials.

CONTAMINANT HYDROGEOLOGY AND REMEDIATION

Cliff Harper, Sr., PG

and

Keith Angell, P.E., CHMM
Groundwater Technology Inc.

INTRODUCTION

The degradation of groundwater by organic chemicals and other pollutants is a paramount problem of international dimensions. Literally hundreds of thousands to millions of gallons of potential groundwater contaminants (mostly organic compounds) are reported to be lost annually from underground storage tanks, pipelines, waste disposal units, landfills, and highway accidents.

The study of contaminant movement and the persistence of chemicals in soil and groundwater is a relatively new and emerging field. The past ten years have witnessed a global awareness of groundwater protection as evidenced through strict state and federal regulatory controls, an increasing number of university environmental programs, an abundance of environmental seminars and conferences, public outcry from strong media coverage, and the development of professional groundwater certification programs. Along with this increasing "user awareness," there has also been a growing public awareness of the effects of accidental spillage. The dependence of municipalities, industrial concerns, and private households on surface and groundwater supplies provides a stark contrast to the increasing frequency with which these supplies are impacted and rendered aesthetically objectionable or essentially unusable by organic contamination.

CONTAMINANT HYDROGEOLOGY

Groundwater can move through subsurface materials at a rate of several feet per day (highly fractured rock, gravel beds) or as slow as several feet per year (slightly fractured rock, clay beds). *Porosity permeability* and groundwater gradient have much to do with the velocity of groundwater. The porosity of consolidated subsurface material is that portion of total subsurface which is not occupied by solid material.   For example, porosities of gravel and certain limestone will average 20% by volume, whereas clay and sand average 50% and 25% respectively. In a saturated subsurface zone, groundwater occupies and is stored in the porous space.

The permeability of a material relates to its ability to pass water through it by means of gravity.   This term is used qualitatively to describe a "permeable sand lens" or "impermeable clay lens." A more accurate and quantitative term used today is *hydraulic conductivity.*   Hydraulic conductivity (K) is defined as the amount of groundwater that will flow through a unit cross-sectional area of a porous medium per unit time under a hydraulic gradient of 1 at a specific temperature. Hydraulic conductivity ranges over a dozen orders of magnitude. Gravels may possess hydraulic conductivity from 10^2 to 10^{-1} cm/s; limestone from 10^{-4} to 10^{-7} cm/s; and clay from 10^{-7} to 10^{-10} cm/s.

Henri Darcy (1856), an engineer, experimented with pipeflow as analogous to groundwater. His experiments lead to *Darcy's Law*, the basic equation of groundwater flow.

$$V = KI \quad \text{Where: } V = \text{Velocity of the aquifer}$$
$$K = \text{Hydraulic Conductivity}$$
$$I = \text{Hydraulic Gradient}$$

Darcy's Law demonstrates that the velocity of flow through a porous media varies directly with the hydraulic gradient. Theis (1935) introduced the term *transmissivity* (T) to represent the transmission potential of the entire thickness of an aquifer. When T is placed in the Darcy Equation, groundwater flow through any vertical selection of an aquifer can be calculated. Hydrogeologists can perform *pump tests* and/or *slug tests* within a groundwater system to determine aquifer characteristics. These aquifer characteristics tell the hydrogeologist in which direction(s) and at what velocity(s) the groundwater is flowing.

Transmissivity is the principal characteristic that shows rate of flow through an aquifer under given field conditions. The T value is expressed in gallons per day per foot width of aquifer material for a specific saturated thickness of the soil or bedrock. T values can range from less than 1,000 to more than 1 million gpd/ft.

The storage capability of an aquifer is mainly related to *porosity*, and its *specific yield*, the amount of groundwater which can be drained from a saturated medium by gravity. As an aquifer is depleted of its storage of groundwater, the hydraulic conductivity will determine how easily the groundwater is replaced. This is governed by the size and shape of the pores and their interconnectedness.

The major mechanism of contaminant transport is *advection*, which is the movement of a contaminant with the average groundwater velocity. Molecular *diffusion*, the movement of constituents under the influence of kinetic activity, will occur in a groundwater system in the direction of the concentration gradient. The spreading and mixing of contaminants through a porous medium is called *dispersion*. Dispersion is an irreversible process that causes dilution of the solute contamination.

When a release of contaminants oversaturate an unconsolidated material and move into a groundwater system under gravity conditions, a number of reactions may occur in response to the properties of the organic or inorganic contaminant. Important properties which can affect transport in a groundwater system are the contaminants' *density, viscosity*, and *surface tension* (refer to the chapter on "Chemistry of Hazardous Materials").

Its *volatilization potential* and ability to create vapor impact can be determined by *vapor pressure* and the *Henry's Law Constant* (equilibrium partitioning between water and vapor phases). Whether the contaminant will partition on soil or move with groundwater flow can be determined by *solubility* and its *Kow* (octanol-water partitioning coefficient, equilibrium partitioning between soil and water phases).

As an example, many chlorinated organics like trichloroethylene (TCE, C_2HCl_3) are denser than water and possess low solubilities in water. This is why they are referred to as a *DNAPLs* (dense, non-aqueous phase liquids). One would expect TCE to move downward under the force of gravity and by its density throughout a groundwater system. Before accepting this scenario one would have to determine the thickness and composition of the unsaturated soil or rock above the water table, the amount of TCE lost, the vertical migration potential of the subsurface material, the Kow, solubility, vapor pressure and other organic properties of TCE. Only after a complete study and field assessment could one postulate the fate of a TCE loss in a specific geologic environment. The TCE could become absorbed in the pores of unconsolidated and unsaturated subsurface material and not impact groundwater at all.

AQUIFER REMEDIATION

Case in Point: Gasoline Release

Let's look at an example of a typical organic contaminant release. A tanker truck hauling gasoline overturns and releases 10,000 gallons of gasoline into a roadside field. The soil consists of medium-to-fine-grained sand, and the water table is at a depth of 15 feet. Depending on the physiochemical soil properties, the gasoline will partition into four phases. About 60% (6,000 gallons) of the spill might adhere to the soil as *adsorbed* phase. Approximately 37% (3,700 gallons) might float atop the groundwater as *separate* phase. Another 2-3% (200-300 gallons) may become *dissolved*-phase contamination in groundwater, while less than 1% would comprise the *vapor* phase.

Seasonal or tidal fluctuations in groundwater levels tend to "smear" contamination from *separate* and *dissolved* phases through the unsaturated zone to become an *adsorbed* phase problem. Also, lighter-than-water separate-phase hydrocarbons may become trapped below the water table under an impermeable layer as the water table fluctuates.

Because the *dissolved* phase is in a solution with large volumes of migrating groundwater, its impacts are dispersed far and wide. One gallon of hazardous material, dissolved into the groundwater may contaminate millions of gallons of water at levels higher than allowable drinking water standards.

The *vapor* phase typically migrates by dispersion through unsaturated soil above the water table. Very slowly, it emanates from the *separate, dissolved,* and *adsorbed* phases. Note that these phases respect hydrogeologic boundaries, not geographic ones. Organic and inorganic contamination migrate into or from neighboring properties.

The Diagnosis

Thousands of remedial treatment programs have been developed in the United States, Canada and Western Europe in recent decades. In addition, analytical equipment and assessment methods have improved over the past decade, allowing the profiling of subsurface conditions with considerable accuracy. Experience with remedial programs and improved equipment and methodology now allow for sound methods for dealing with spills of all types. Releases of hazardous materials must prompt a phased approach to address all possible effects of the contamination.

Step #1: The first step in any project is to understand the political arena -- the applicable regulations -- that will drive the response to the release.

Step #2: Step two is to clearly define the goals of the project. Are the objectives to clean to pristine levels or background levels; meet regulations or test them?

Step #3: Performing a comprehensive site characterization and risk assessment is the most important step in limiting your liabilities and eventual cleanup costs. Experts form a history of your site by interviewing people who know how and where the spill occurred. Next, they review critical documents: your on-site hazardous materials records and local, state and federal records. This information helps the team pinpoint potential problems quickly. Primary objectives are to:

- Locate contaminated areas.
- Determine the full horizontal and vertical nature and extent of contamination.

- Identify soil and hydrogeologic conditions affecting contaminant fate and transport.
- Determine the potential hazards of the contaminants and exposure pathways in order to calculate risks inherent in the affected soil and groundwater.
- Remove imminent hazards.
- Identify the responsible parties.

Step #4: Based on the regulations, site characterization, and risk assessment, final project goals and treatment alternatives are established, and a remedial strategy is devised. Primary objectives are to:

- Determine where the project will end: how clean is clean?
- Determine which areas must be treated and in what order. Is it possible to contain rather than treat certain areas of contamination?
- Assess what treatment technologies are suitable to attack the various phases. A feasibility study of applicable remedial actions is usually performed.

Step #5: Obtain regulatory and public approval and implement the remedial strategy to closure.

Project goals specify acceptable levels of contamination in the soil and groundwater. Acceptable levels are based on current and future uses of the site and surrounding properties. These closure levels are normally either regulated, like the drinking water standards, or derived from the health-based risk assessment. The level of risk usually determines the steps that need to be taken and the associated cost.

Treatment Options for the Four Phases

The following outline presents the four phases of contamination and their possible treatment alternatives. The phases apply to both organic and inorganic releases of materials and may apply to solid, liquid or gaseous releases.

Vapor phase: In the treatment stage of any cleanup project, the first requirement is to deal immediately with imminent threats to public health and safety. These risks often are caused by an accumulation of toxic and/or potentially explosive vapors. These vapors may be vented from basements, utility trenches, and excavations and the off-gas eliminated through incineration, catalytic oxidation, biofiltration, carbon adsorption or, if permitted, direct discharge into the atmosphere. Subsurface vapors can be treated in the same fashion, through extraction techniques such as soil venting.

Separate phase: Normally, *separate-phase* contamination involves installing strategically located recovery wells. A water table depression pump within each well creates and maintains a cone of depression in the groundwater surface. *Separate-phase* material floating on the groundwater flows with the induced gradient into the recovery well. A special recovery pump removes water-free product and pumps it to storage tanks on the surface. *Separate-phase* liquids and solids can also be excavated for off-site disposal or treatment.

Dissolved phase: This material can be treated *in situ* (at the contaminant's natural or original position) or on-site (above ground). *In situ* treatment options include thermal, physical, chemical, and biological methods such as vitrification, sparging, fixation, and saturated-zone biological treatment. Above-ground treatment options include carbon adsorption, ultraviolet/oxidation, air or steam stripping of volatile organics, thermal oxidation, and biological degradation.

If aboveground treatment is feasible contaminated groundwater may be removed by a water table depression pump and pumped into a treatment unit. Dissolved hydrocarbon contaminants are removed and the clean, treated water is then discharged to surface water, local POTW, or recharged into the subsurface.

Adsorbed phase: Pumping groundwater is an effective but incomplete method for containing and removing *separate-* and *dissolved-phase* contamination. This material dissolves into groundwater when the water table rises or when rainwater percolates through the soil. Adsorbed treatment options include solidification, land farming, soil washing, *in situ* soil flushing, vacuum extraction, and bioremediation.

One of the most promising and cost-effective methods for treating contamination in all phases is bioremediation. This process utilizes naturally occurring bacteria within the subsurface to convert organic contaminants into carbon dioxide, water, and biomass. Biological treatment, which has been utilized in municipal waste plants for many years, can be used to address contaminants in the dissolved, adsorbed, and vapor phases.

Providing additional nutrients and oxygen is accomplished by using closed-loop systems to circulate oxygen and nutrient-enriched water through the saturated and unsaturated subsurface. The resulting increase in degradation rates and the corresponding decrease in contaminant concentration are dramatic. Bioremediation can be performed *in situ*, aboveground, or in specially constructed in-ground cells.

If the soils are too impermeable for *in situ* transport or nutrients and oxygen, other on-site treatment options may be used to treat soils *ex situ* or aboveground. Because aboveground treatment requires extraction or expensive excavation, *in situ* processes are generally less expensive and preferred. Other *in situ* technologies for treatment of adsorbed-phase contaminants have been developed as well. Two noteworthy processes are soil ventilation and biostabilization. Soil ventilation utilizes negative pressure in subsurface soils to evaporate contaminants and remove vapors. With biostabilization, carrier solvents or mobile organic contaminant mixtures are biodegraded in place leaving only hydrophobic, immobile organics or inorganics behind.

Planning to Limit Risks

The ultimate cost of your site cleanup project depends on many considerations, including:

- Soil type, geochemical and hydrogeologic site conditions,
- Length of time the spilled materials have been in the ground,
- Proximity of the site to populated areas or valuable natural resources,
- The degree of cleanup mandated by applicable regulations,
- The imminent danger to human health, and
- Project goals.

Despite our cautious times and the severity of cleanup costs, companies remain largely unprepared for environmental emergencies. Expenses can be minimized depending on how quickly and effectively the company reacts to such crises. Crisis prevention is the best policy, but knowing where to turn for help during a crisis is the next best step to limiting cleanup costs.

Recommended References:

Groundwater and Wells, Second Edition 1986, Fletcher G. Driscoll; Published by Johnson Division, St. Paul, Minnesota.

Principles of Groundwater, NWWA Short Course, November 12-13, 1986, Westin Galleria, Houston, Texas.

RCRA Groundwater Monitoring, Technical Enforcement, Guidance Document, September 1986; Printed by NWWA, Dublin Ohio.

REGULATIONS

FEDERAL STATUTES AND THE CONTROL OF TOXIC SUBSTANCES

Russell Barnett
Deputy Commissioner of Environmental Protection
Commonwealth of Kentucky

INTRODUCTION

Toxic substances can create pervasive environmental and public health problems. The sheer volume of toxic substances produced (chemical sales of \$125 billion in 1980 involving some 70,000 different substances) and the many avenues of exposure (occupational, consumer use, and environmental residues), greatly increase the unacceptable health and environmental risks from some of these substances. Public policy over the past century has been aimed at protecting the public from toxic substances. For example, during the latter half of the nineteenth century, Federal laws were passed to prohibit the adulteration of patent medicines, to require the contents of certain consumer products to be truthfully labeled, and to regulate the transportation of explosives. While there were some early attempts at Federal protection of the environment, it was not until the 1970s that environmental protection became a priority. A labyrinth of Federal laws has been enacted to control the public's exposure to toxic substances, minimizing potential risks to public health and the environment.

These laws roughly fall into six broad areas: (1) occupational protection statutes; (2) environmental protection statutes; (3) chemical use and assessment laws; (4) laws concerning reporting and cleanup of spills; (5) laws regulating cleanup of unintentional disposal of chemicals; and (6) pollution prevention. There are a number of Federal statutes that deal with toxic substances; however, the major laws are the:

Federal Food, Drug and Cosmetic Act (FFDCA) -- 1938

Federal Insecticide, Fungicide and Rodenticide Act (FIFRA) -- 1947

Clean Air Act (CAA) -- 1970

Clean Water Act (CWA) -- 1970

Occupational Safety and Health Act (OSH Act) -- 1970

Safe Drinking Water Act (SDWA) -- 1974

Hazardous Materials Transportation Act (HMTA) -- 1975

Toxic Substances Control Act (TSCA) -- 1976

Resource Conservation and Recovery Act (RCRA) -- 1976

Comprehensive Environmental Response, Compensation and Liability Act (CERCLA) -- 1980

Superfund Amendments and Reauthorization Act (SARA) -- 1986

Pollution Prevention Act -- 1990

These laws and the broad area or areas they cover are shown in Table 1.

Occupational Protection

The Occupational Safety and Health Act enacted in 1970 is the primary Federal law regulating toxic substances to protect workers in the workplace. The Federal law was passed as the result of increased public concern about workplace hazards and the effects of exposure to hazardous chemicals. Before passage of the law, worker safety was the responsibility of State agencies and labor groups. Federal safety requirements were confined to specific industries (e.g. mining, railroading, longshoring).

The Occupational Safety and Health Administration (OSHA) was established within the Labor Department to administer the Act.

Table 1

AREAS OF CONCERN ADDRESSED BY FEDERAL
TOXIC SUBSTANCES STATUTES

Area of Concern	Federal Statute
Occupational Protection	• Occupational Safety and Health Act
	• Superfund Amendments and Reauthorization Act
Environmental Protection	• Clean Air Act
	• Clean Water Act
	• Safe Drinking Water Act
	• Resource Conservation and Recovery Act
Chemical Manufacture and Use	• Federal Food, Drug, and Cosmetic Act
	• Federal Insecticide, Fungicide, and Rodenticide Act
	• Toxic Substances Control Act
Accidental Releases	• Emergency Planning and Community Right-to-Know Act
	• Clean Water Act
	• Hazardous Materials Transportation Act
	• Resource Conservation and Recovery Act
Cleanup Action	• Comprehensive Environmental Response, Compensation, and Liability Act (amended as SARA)
	• Clean Water Act
Pollution Prevention	• Pollution Prevention Act

The main provisions of the Act dealing with toxic substances include:

- setting standards to limit exposure to various chemical substances that could induce acute or chronic health effects

- regulating substances that may cause cancer

- informing employees of the dangers posed by toxic substances through Material Safety Data Sheets (MSDS)

- requiring employers to maintain medical and other records to track the development and incidence of occupationally induced disease

OSHA has established standards for 22 toxic or hazardous substances and 402 toxic air contaminants. In setting standards, OSHA evaluates three types of health effects: acute (immediate), chronic (long-term), and carcinogenic (able to cause cancer). Pursuant to the United States Supreme Court ruling in *Industrial Union Department, AFL-CIO* v. *American Petroleum Institute* [448 US 607, 8 OSHC 1586 (1980)], OSHA must show that a "significant risk" exists before it issues a health standard. Also under the Supreme Court's ruling in *American Textile Manufacturers Institute, Inc.* v. *Donovan* [452 US 490, 9 OSHC 1913 (1981)], a standard must be feasible, i.e. must adequately assure that no employee will suffer material impairment to their health to the extent that this is "capable of being done." OSHA standards include a Permissible Exposure Limit (PEL), labeling, protective equipment, control procedures, and monitoring requirements.

SARA sets specific training requirements, funds training programs, and delegates responsibilities to OSHA and the National Institute of Environmental Health Sciences. SARA requires 40 hours of classroom and 24 hours of site specific training for nearly all workers on hazardous waste site cleanups, at commercial hazardous waste treatment, storage, and disposal facilities, and for industrial workers who will act as hazardous materials first responders. OSHA has promulgated draft regulations to cover the SARA training and working condition requirements.

Environmental Protection

Beginning in the 1970s, Congress passed a number of environmental protection statutes beginning with the Clean Air Act in 1970 and amendments to the Federal Water Pollution Control Act (renamed the Clean Water Act in 1972). While most of these initiatives were actually amendments to existing Federal environmental statutes dating back 70 years, the changes were so extensive in both philosophy and scope that they are commonly thought of as new laws. The laws focused primarily on cleaning up "conventional" pollutants -- smoke and sulfur oxides in the air, oxygen-depleting discharges into surface waters, and solid wastes into the land. As the decade ended, these laws began to focus on toxic substances that could threaten human health at even low concentrations. These statutes were amended, or new regulations and policies to handle toxics were adopted by the administering agency.

Unlike the Occupational Safety and Health Act, environmental laws address by-product discharges of toxic and hazardous substances that are released into the environment. Standards to reduce risks to public health are established in a similar manner to OSH Act. All of the environmental laws are administered by the United States Environmental Protection Agency (EPA).

The Clean Air Act, originally passed in 1955, addressed smoky, dirty air that plagued many industrial cities. It was subsequently amended to add provisions about the effects of sources of pollution.

Amendments in 1970 and 1977 establish National Ambient Air Quality Standards (NAAQS) that applied to only a small number of the most common pollutants (sulfur dioxide, ozone, particulates, carbon monoxide, nitrogen dioxide, and lead). Emission limits were set for only seven (7) hazardous air pollutants (arsenic, asbestos, benzene, beryllium, mercury, radionuclides, vinyl chloride).

The 1990 amendments require strict control of 189 air toxics. The controls include two strategies. The first is based on technology standards for over 350 different source categories (industries). Sources emitting 10 tons per year of any one air toxic, or 25 tons per year of any combination of the 189 listed toxic pollutants, will be required to install Maximum

Achievable Control Technology (MACT). MACT standards will be promulgated by the year 2000. MACTs for the 49 source categories posing the most significant health threat will be developed by November 1992. The control technologies that will be required will be based on the best demonstrated control technology and practices of industries in the source category.

As a second phase of control, by November 1996, the U.S. Environmental Protection Agency must report on the risks posed to publish by toxic emissions remaining after the application of MACT standards. If there are any facilities in an industrial source category that pose a cancer risk greater than 1 in 1 million, additional air emission reductions may be required.

The Clean Water Act controls the discharge of toxic discharges into surface streams. The first national effort to control water pollutants was through the Rivers and Harbors Act of 1899 which prohibited discharges into navigable waterways that could interfere with transportation. Additional water pollution control acts were passed in 1948, 1956, and in 1965. The 1972 amendments incorporate two methods of approaching water pollution control. The 1899 Rivers and Harbors Act protected water bodies by imposing effluent limitations at the source of pollution, the discharge pipe. On the other hand, the 1965 amendments define pollution as those levels above which the receiving body of water would, theoretically, be incapable of handling. The discharge limit provisions (Section 301(a)) and water quality standards (Section 301(b) and 302) were included in the 1972 amendments. Discharge permits, as part of the National Pollutant Discharge Elimination System (NPDES), set enforceable limitations on the types and quantities of pollutants which may be discharged.

The 1972 Act required EPA to establish effluent standards for toxic pollutants. EPA was slow to develop these standards and environmental groups sued to force their promulgation. A consent degree in the case of *NRDC* v. *Train* (8 ERC 2120, D.D.C., 1976) imposed a schedule for EPA to develop effluent limitations. The consent decree was subsequently adopted in the 1977 amendments to the law.

EPA is required to promulgate toxic discharge requirements for 34 industrial categories covering 129 toxic pollutants. The 129 toxics include metals, volatile compounds, corrosives and pesticides. Dischargers of these pollutants are required to use Best Available Technology Economically Achievable (BAT).

Toxic and hazardous wastes are generated primarily from industries and farmlands. Industries discharging directly into surface streams are regulated by an NPDES permit. Discharges into municipal sewer plants are required to meet pretreatment requirements. Nonpoint sources, such as farmland, are controlled through the encouragement of erosion control (Section 208).

While the CWA focused on surface water quality, the Safe Drinking Water Act was passed in 1975 (amended in 1986), to protect groundwater and drinking water sources. The law requires EPA to establish recommended maximum contaminant goals (RMCG) for each contaminant which may have an adverse effect on the health of an individual. Two types of drinking water standards were established to limit the amount of contamination that may be in drinking water: primary standards with a maximum contaminant level (MCL) to protect human health; and, secondary standards that involve the color, taste, smell or other physical characteristics of drinking water source.

The Safe Drinking Water Act stipulates 83 contaminants for which regulations must be developed by 1989. These include:

- 14 volatile organic compounds
- 29 synthetic organic compounds
- 13 inorganic chemicals
- 4 microbiological contaminants
- 2 radiological contaminants

A second major provision of the Safe Drinking Water Act for the purpose of protecting groundwater is the regulation of underground injection of toxic chemicals. Injection of liquid wastes into underground wells is used as a means of disposal. Controls were needed to assure that this means of disposal did not damage the quality of aquifers. Five classes of underground injection wells were established. Class IV wells where hazardous wastes are injected into or above a formation within one-quarter mile of an underground source of drinking water were to be phased out. Under the 1986 amendments, states must adopt a program for wellhead protection. The program must include the surface and subsurface surrounding a well or well-field through which contaminants are reasonably likely to move toward a well.

The last major environmental statute passed is the Resource Conservation and Recovery Act (RCRA) of 1976, as amended in 1984. RCRA completed the circle of environmental laws enacted in the previous six years, focusing on the recycling and disposal of solid wastes. The law is divided into eight subsections. The three subsections of primary importance include provisions to regulate solid waste (Subtitle D), hazardous waste (Subtitle C), and underground storage tanks (Subtitle I). The law originally was drafted as a solid waste recycling and disposal law to eliminate open dumps; however, implementation has focused on regulating hazardous wastes.

In 1978, chemicals abandoned at Love Canal in New York and Valley-of-the-Drums in Kentucky received national attention. Studies at the time indicated that there may be an additional 50,000 similar abandoned hazardous waste dumps around the country. The State of Illinois and environmental groups sued EPA to force the Federal government to issue final hazardous waste regulations (*Illinois* v. *Costle*, 12 ERC 1597 DC 1978). Congress appropriated increased funding for regulatory programs. The regulations promulgated by EPA established a cradle-to-grave system of controlling hazardous wastes. Manifests for all hazardous wastes transported off-site are required. Hazardous wastes are defined under the law as those waste materials exhibiting certain characteristics (i.e. ignitability, corrosivity, reactivity, and TCLP toxicity) or are specially listed by EPA. Polychlorinated biphenyls are regulated by the Toxic Substances Control Act and are not defined under RCRA as hazardous wastes. Standards have been promulgated to regulate the generation, storage, transportation, treatment and disposal of hazardous wastes.

In the 1984 amendments, the owners of underground storage tanks containing petroleum products and regulated substances were required to notify the states of the existence, size, age, type, and uses of all underground tanks. EPA law also developed regulations concerning leak detection and prevention, and corrective actions that will be required in the event of a leak.

Chemical Manufacture and Use

The laws described above have focused on the effects of toxic and hazardous substances being emitted into the workplace and environment at the point of manufacture. The public and environment can also be exposed to toxic substances during the use and application of chemicals. To reduce the risk of exposure through the use of a chemical, a number of Federal laws have been passed that regulate what chemicals can be manufactured and sold in the United States.

An early Federal law regulating the manufacture of chemicals is the Federal Food, Drug, & Cosmetic Act (FFDCA). The FFDCA was passed in 1938 and evolved from Federal involvement in food and drug protection regulations dating back to 1848. The Act provides the regulatory authority for the Food and Drug Administration (FDA) to assure the safety of foods, drugs, medical devices and cosmetics. Adulteration or misbranding of any of these consumer products is prohibited. The FDA establishes standards that must be met by manufacturers before certain products may be sold. Premarketing clearances are based on scientific data submitted by manufacturers to demonstrate that the proposed product will not have an adverse effect on human health.

Major provisions of the law include the following:

- banned the intentional addition of substances known to cause cancer in animals to food products ("Delaney Clause")
- established procedures for setting safety limits for pesticide residues on raw agriculture products
- required pre-use safety assessment and approval of all food additives

The Federal Insecticide, Fungicide and Rodenticide Act (FIFRA) established a regulatory program to control the manufacture and use of pesticides intended to kill, repel or control insects, rodents, plants, trees, algae, fungi, bacteria, or other living organisms. The first Federal legislation to control chemical pesticides was passed in 1910. Like the FFDCA, the early law was aimed against adulterating or misbranding chemical pesticides to protect consumers against false advertising. Increased awareness of the health and environmental risks posed by new pesticides and by their persistent characteristics (e.g., DDD & DDT), prompted Congress in 1972 to pass FIFRA. The chief thrust of the law was to prevent unreasonably adverse effects on the environment and public health. Under FIFRA, manufacturers must register all new pesticides with the United States Environmental Protection Agency which sets tolerance levels for residues before the substance can be used on food crops. Pesticides manufactured before 1972 must be examined to assure that they meet current safety standards. EPA sets residue safety limits for *raw* (unprocessed) meat and agricultural products, while the Food and Drug Administration, under FFDCA, sets pesticide residue limits for *processed* foods. In considering registration of a pesticide, EPA must evaluate not only its environmental effects, but also its economic, social and health impacts. EPA may refuse to register pesticides judged unduly hazardous, or they may impose use restrictions. All restrictions must be printed on the label and enforcement action can be taken against pesticide users who do not comply with the printed restrictions. EPA can condition the registration for general use or restricted use, i.e., that the pesticide may only be applied by trained and certified applicators. EPA has the authority to cancel the registration of a pesticide deemed to pose an unreasonable risk. When EPA determines that an unreasonable risk exists, it issues a "rebuttable presumption against registration" (RPAR), and provides the opportunity for the registrant to provide evidence before a final decision is made. Examples of canceled registration include DDT, aldrin/dieldrin, 2,4,5-T/silvex, kepone, mirex, and ethylene dibromide.

The 1976 Toxic Substances Control Act was designed as a catch-all to close all the loopholes in the environmental protection and chemical manufacture and use laws. It gives EPA broad authority to regulate chemical substances without regard to specific use (e.g. food, drug, cosmetic) or area of application (e.g. food crops) if they present a hazard to health or the environment. The law controls the chemical at its source before it is dispersed into the environment (where environmental protection laws are employed). Excluded from coverage under TSCA are food, food additives, drugs, or cosmetics regulated under the FFDCA; pesticides regulated under FIFRA; and nuclear materials regulated by the Atomic Energy Act.

Other Federal laws controlled the release of pollutants into the environment or workplace. However, it is very difficult to monitor and set emission standards on substances that only enter the environment in very small amounts. A need was seen to control some substances before they were dispersed into the environment.

Chloroflourocarbons (CFC), used as a propellant in spray cans, amply demonstrate this need. When released, CFCs are so stable that they do not react with anything until they diffuse upward to the stratosphere. There they can be decomposed by ultraviolet radiation and enter into a chain reaction to destroy ozone molecules. Ozone depletion would allow more solar ultraviolet light through and could increase the incidence of skin cancer as well as result in climatic changes. Since chloroflourocarbons are not classified as air pollutants and pose no hazard in the workplace, there was no means of regulating their use. A need to control toxic substances at the point of manufacture was identified by Congress in passing TSCA.

The law specifically bans the manufacture of polychlorinated biphenyls (PCB). Chemical manufacturers and importers must provide EPA a Premanufacture Notice (PMN) and provide available health and environmental effects data at least 90 days prior to the manufacture and sale of any chemical. EPA can approve the chemical, request further testing, condition the manufacture and sale of the chemical, or prohibit its manufacture. The law is a risk/benefit-balancing act similar to FIFRA. EPA is required to consider the benefits of a substance to society's economic and social well being, the risks posed by alternative substances, and the possible health or economic problems that could result from regulation of a substance.

TSCA is unique in that it is designed as a gap-filling law. EPA defers to other agencies for action if those agencies having statutory authority under another law are dealing with identified problems. When EPA has sufficient authority under another law (e.g., CAA, CWA, RCRA, etc.), EPA is directed to use the other law rather than the gap-filling TSCA.

SARA Title III -- Emergency Planning and Community Right-To-Know regulates chemical storage by requiring notification of Local Emergency Planning Committees (LEPC) of storage of hazardous and extremely hazardous materials in excess of threshold planning quantities. Reportable releases, location of chemicals in plant, and safety information on the chemicals is required.

Accidental Releases

The accidental release of toxic materials pose a significant risk to public health and the environment. In December 1984, an accidental release of methyl iscyanate killed 2,800 people in Bhopal, India. There are a number of requirements for facilities to report the accidental release of toxics.

The Emergency Planning and Community Right-to-Know Act (Title III of SARA) was passed in 1986. The law requires facilities to notify their state and Local Emergency Planning Committee (LEPC) of the presence of extremely hazardous substances and to report spills or releases of these substances immediately. The chemicals that must be reported to the Local Emergency Planning Committee are those which MSDS sheets must be prepared for the Occupational Safety and Health Administration (OSHA). State Emergency Response Commissions have been established in every state. The Commissions are responsible for developing state emergency response plans to receive spill reports.

The release of any oil or hazardous substances into navigable waters of the United States must be reported in the National Response Center. The Center is operated by the U.S. Environmental Protection Agency and Coast Guard and was established under the Clean Water Act. Releases above threshold amounts (established by regulation for each type of chemical) must be reported. Threshold amounts vary by chemical but can be as little as one (1) pound. Together the Emergency Planning and Community Right-to-Know Act and Clean Water Act require reports to local, state and Federal response centers. The various centers usually work together to respond to emergencies. Exposure of toxic substances and hazardous wastes to the environment and the general public often occurs during transportation. Recent studies have indicated that the transportation of chemicals sometimes poses a higher risk of exposure than during the manufacture, storage, or disposal of these chemicals.

The Hazardous Materials Transportation Act (HMTA) of 1975 gives the Department of Transportation (DOT) authority to regulate the shipment of substances that may pose a threat to health, safety, property, or the environment when transported by air, water, rail, or highway. DOT regulations require special packaging, placarding and routing for hazardous materials. The transportation of hazardous materials was originally regulated by the Federal government in 1865 to protect railroads from poorly identified and packaged explosives and ammunition. The list of hazardous substances was expanded through the years to include additional substances (e.g., flammable liquids and gases) and transportation modes (e.g., air and highways). The HMTA consolidated a variety of agencies and laws regulating different substances and transportation modes. Enforcement of materials traveling by a single mode of transport falls to the DOT branch with jurisdiction over that type of transport, i.e., Federal Aviation Administration, Federal Highway Administration, Federal Railroad Administration or United States Coast Guard.

The Resource Conservation and Recovery Act also addresses the transportation of hazardous wastes. Transporters of hazardous waste must register with EPA and carry hazardous waste manifests required under RCRA. They must also comply with all DOT rules concerning labeling, packaging, and placarding. If bulk shipments are traveling by rail or water, DOT shipping papers rather than EPA hazardous waste manifests are required.

Cleanup Activities

Even with all of the preventive Federal laws discussed above, toxic and hazardous substances will inevitably be accidentally released. In addition there are an estimated 50,000 sites where toxic and hazardous substances have been disposed in the past that are now posing significant health and environmental risks.

It was with these problems in mind that Congress passed the Comprehensive Environmental Response, Compensation, and Liability Act (CERCLA) in 1980 (amended by SARA in 1986). Unlike the other laws, it does not regulate toxic substances. Instead it provides a system for identifying and cleaning up chemical and hazardous substances released into the air, water, groundwater and on land. It defines "hazardous substance" by incorporating into its language those substances listed in the Clean Water Act, Resource Conservation and Recovery Act, Clean Air Act, and the Toxic Substances Control Act. CERCLA established a $1.6 billion trust fund, commonly called "Superfund" ($8.5 billion in 1986), to pay for cleaning up environmental contamination where no responsible party can be found. The need for such a trust fund clearly became evident at the Love Canal when the State of New York spent in excess of $35 million for remedial measures and the relocation of 200 families. The trust fund is provided through a tax on crude oil, petroleum products, and 40 feedstock chemicals.

CERCLA also requires that spills or discharges of over 700 substances in excess of 1 to 5,000 pounds (depending on the substance) be reported immediately to the National Response Center originally established under the Clean Water Act. The Center is inspected by the United States Coast Guard who will contact EPA and other Federal agencies to initiate an emergency response.

CERCLA and the Clean Water Act authorize three types of emergency responses:

- immediate removal of material during emergency situations
- planned removal of releases where immediate response is not needed
- remedial actions to permanently remove toxic and hazardous substances

In the event of a release of a hazardous substance the procedures and methods to be followed are set forth in the National Contingency Plan. The Plan was originally prepared under the Clean Water Act and includes procedures and standards for responding to hazardous releases. These procedures include discovery, investigation, evaluation and removal activities. As part of the plan, EPA is directed to list national priorities (National Priorities List) for cleanup of known or threatened releases.

Pollution Prevention

Most of the environmental and occupational protection laws focus on standards that establish maximum allowable discharges, emissions or exposures. These often are imposed at the end-of-the-pipe, and facilities to be in compliance focus their resources on cleaning up their discharge prior to release. Many facilities are finding that the superior approach is to identify ways of not using or generating toxic chemicals. By reexamining their processes, companies have found ways to reduce their emissions or discharges and save money. These may include reformulation or redesign of their products; substitution of raw materials; improved facility housekeeping, maintenance or inventory controls; modification of process; or changes in the equipment used in the manufacturing process. This approach to protecting the environment and public health is called pollution prevention.

In 1990 the Pollution Prevention Act established as a national priority the reduction of all toxic and hazardous chemicals at their source. The U.S. Environmental Protection Agency is required to develop and implement a strategy to promote source reduction. The agency has set as a goal to reduce the amount of toxic chemicals released into the environment by 33 percent by the end of 1992 and 50 percent by 1995. These reductions are to be achieved by voluntary efforts and regulatory amendments. Since in most cases, pollution prevention activities often result in cost savings to facilities, many companies have adopted pollution prevention as a corporate policy. The Clean Air Act amendments of 1990 include pollution prevention activities as a criteria in establishing Maximum Achievable Control Technology (MACT) standards. Facilities are also encouraged to voluntarily reduce their air emissions now by allowing six (6) year extensions to facilities voluntarily reducing their toxic emissions now by 90 to 95 percent. The U.S. Environmental Protection Agency has also developed a Municipal Water Pollution Prevention program to encourage municipalities to apply elements of pollution prevention.

Within the near future, pollution prevention will be the focal point of all environmental and occupational laws.

Summary

A summary of the major Federal laws dealing with toxic substances is listed in Table 2.

Table 2

Federal Statutes and the Control of Toxic Substances

Law	Citation	State Authorization	Section	Key Provisions
Clean Air Act of 1970, amended 1977	PL 91-604 (42 USC 7401, et. seq.)	Yes	Sec. 109. Ambient Air Quality Standards	• EPA to establish primary (health based and secondary (welfare based) standards
			Sec. 111. New Source Performance Standards	• standards developed for 50 industrial processes
			Sec. 112. Hazardous Air Emissions	• 189 regulated pollutants listed • source categories identified • MACT emission standards
			Sec. 113. Enforcement	• criminal sanctions for release of toxic substances up to $250,000 per day, 15 years imprisonment
			Sec. 504. Permits	• permit requirements
Clean Water Act of 1972, as amended 1977	PL 92-500 (1972) and PL 95-217 (1977) (33 USC 1251 et. seq.)	Yes	Sec. 303. Water Quality Standards	• establish levels of specified pollutants ambient water can contain and still be suitable for certain uses (i.e., recreation, fish and wildlife, water supply, agricultural and industrial uses)
			Sec. 301. Effluent Limitations	• 65 toxic pollutants listed and effluent guidelines and pretreatment standards prepared

Table 2 (cont.)

Law	Citation	State Authorization	Section	Key Provisions
Comprehensive Environmental Responses, Compensation, and Liability Act of 1980	PL 96-510 (42 USC 960 et. seq.)	No	Sec. 307. Toxic and Pretreatment Effluent Standards	• Best Available Technology (BAT) minimum control required • standards established for aldrin, DDT, toxaphene, benzidene(1977) and PCBs (1977)
			Sec. 111. Oil and Hazardous Substance Liability	• spill cleanup provisions • establish spill quantities reportable to the National Response Center
			Sec. 102. Reportable Quantities	• spills in excess of specified size must be reported to the National Response Center
			Sec. 106. Abatement Action	• EPA authorized to issue administrative orders to require responsible parties to clean up releases
			Title II, Sec. 4661. Imposition of Tax	• tax imposed on petroleum products and 42 feedstock chemicals to create $1.6 billion cleanup fund ("Superfund")
			Sec. 104. Response Authorities	• EPA authorized to conduct immediate cleanups
Federal Food, Drug, and Cosmetic Act of 1938	PL 717 of 1938 (21 USC 301, et. seq.)	No		• food, drug, medical devices, and other regulated products can only be marketed after they are approved by the Food and Drug Administration (FDA)

Table 2 (cont.)

Law	Citation	State Authorization	Section	Key Provisions
			Sec. 409.	• adulteration and misbranding not permitted • no additive may be deemed safe if it produced cancer in animals (Delaney Clause) • pesticide residues on raw agricultural products
Federal Insecticide, Fungicide, and Rodenticide Act of 1972	PL 92-516 (7 USC 136, et. seq.)	partial (States can assume enforcement certification) responsibility	Sec. 6. Administrative Review; Suspension	• EPA may suspend, cancel, or restrict existing pesticides to prevent unreasonable risk to humans or the environment • EPA announces a "rebuttal presumption against registration" (RPAR) to allow registrants to respond to suspension
			Sec. 3. Registration of Pesticides	• all pesticides sold must be registered • pesticides classified for general use or restricted use (use by specially trained applicators)
			Sec. 12. Unlawful Acts	• Prohibits sale of unregistered pesticides
Hazardous Materials Transportation Act of 1975	PL 93-633 (49 USC 1801, et. seq.)	No	Sec. 105. Regulations Governing Transportation of Hazardous Materials	• shipments of hazardous materials must be packaged, labeled and transported in accordance with Department of Transportation (DOT) requirements • 22 hazard classes established

Table 2 (cont.)

Law	Citation	State Authorization	Section	Key Provisions
				• carriers required to report spills and emergencies concerning hazardous materials within 15 days to DOT
Occupational Safety and Health Act of 1970	PL 91-500 (29 USC 651, et. seq.)	Yes	Sec. 6. Occupational Safety and Health Standards	• establishes use and exposure limits for 22 hazardous substances • establishes exposure limits for 380 air contaminants • chemical manufacturer required to assess hazards of the chemicals they provide Material Safety Data Sheets must be provided with each chemical sold
			Sec. 22. National Institute for Occupational Safety and Health	• NIOSH established to conduct research
			Sec. 8. Inspections, Investigations, and Recordkeeping	• inspection may be conducted • employers required to keep records of any problems
Resource Conservation and Recovery Act of 1976, as amended 1984	PL 94-580 (1976) and PL 98-616 (1984)	Yes	Sec. 3001. Identification and Listing of Hazardous Waste	• EPA identifies specific wastes and processes defined as producing hazardous waste • waste may be hazardous by characteristic (ignitable, corrosive, reactive, EP toxic)

Table 2 (cont.)

Law	Citation	State Authorization	Section	Key Provisions
			Sec. 3002 and 3003. Standards Applicable to Generators and Transporters	• must register with EPA • transported waste must be manifested • exempts generators producing less than 100 kg/month.
			Sec. 3004. Standards Applicable to Hazardous Waste Treatment, Storage, and Disposal Facilities	• facilities operating in 1980 issued interim (Part A) permit • provisions on emergencies, manifest handling, record-keeping, monitoring, closure, and financial liability
			Sec. 3005. Permits for Hazardous Waste Treatment, Storage, and Disposal Facilities	• new facilities and facilities called by EPA/State must obtain final (Part B) permit
			Sec. 9003. Regulation of Underground Storage Tanks	• notification to States • requirements to owners
Safe Drinking Water Act of 1974, as amended 1986	PL 93-523 (42 USC 300f, et. seq.)	Yes	Sec. 1412. Drinking Water Regulations	• EPA establishes maximum contaminant level goals and standards for 83 contaminants by 1989 • definition of treatment technique for each contaminant regulated • filtration and disinfection to be required

Table 2 (cont.)

Law	Citation	State Authorization	Section	Key Provisions
			Sec. 1421. Protection of Underground Sources of Drinking Water	• establishes underground injection control program • five classes of wells
			Sec. 1428. Wellhead Protection Program	• states required to implement wellhead protection program by 1989
Superfund Amendments and Reauthorization Act	PL 99-499 42 USC 11013 and 11028	No	Title I: Response and Liability	• Reauthorizes and amends CERCLA
			Title II: Miscellaneous	• Catch-all
			Title III: Emergency Planning and Community Right-to-Know	• Creates a major new system of chemical storage and requires planning participation with local emergency response agency
Toxic Substances Control Act of 1976	PL 94-469 (15 USC 2601, et. seq.)	No	Sec. 5. Manufacturing and Processing Notices	• chemical manufacturers required to notify EPA 90 days prior to manufacture of new chemicals
			Sec. 6. Regulation of Hazardous Chemical Substances	• authority to prohibit or restrict manufacture of chemicals where unreasonable risk to health of environment is involved
			Sec. 4. Testing of Chemical Substances	• authority to require manufacturer to test for health and environment effects

Table 2 (cont.)

Law	Citation	State Authorization	Section	Key Provisions
Pollution Prevention Act of 1990	42 USC 13101-13109	No	Sec. 4. EPA Activities	• identify measurable goals • establish training programs • review environmental regulations to determine their effect on source reduction
			Sec. 5. Grants	• state grant program
			Sec. 6. Information	• establish national clearinghouse of information on pollution prevention

RCRA OVERVIEW

Robert L. Carlson, CSWT
Environmental Specialist
Missouri Department of Natural Resources
Division of Environmental Quality

"They become intuitively obvious after you work with them for several years."
    -- Anonymous EPA official discussing RCRA regulations

INTRODUCTION

The Resource Conservation and Recovery Act of 1976 (RCRA) is the Federal Statute that defines hazardous wastes and controls their handling and disposal. It has quickly become the largest and most intricate puzzle-piece in EPA's framework of environmental programs. RCRA may well be the most challenging part of a hazardous materials manager's job.

This chapter will review the development of the program to date, and the basics of compliance for the regulated community. The regulations, rather than the statute, are the daily bread of regulators and regulated alike, so they will be the focus of the chapter. Keep in mind that, in states with authorized hazardous waste programs, the regulations may be more stringent that those found in 40 CFR.

HISTORICAL DEVELOPMENT

One might almost call this section "A Brief History of Waste Etiquette." Until recently, we got rid of our waste via the "gravity method," dumping it down sinkholes, into rivers and oceans, off cliffs, or simply out the window. The anthropologist/sociobiologist David P. Barash has linked our present environmental crisis with the unsanitary habits of our tree-dwelling, migratory primate ancestors *(The Hare and the Tortoise*, 1986). We simply didn't think much about solid waste until our population-density reached the critical-mass point at which everywhere was somebody's backyard.

In this country, the first real piece of legislation in this area was the Solid Waste Disposal Act of 1965 (SWDA). The Resource Recovery Act was passed in 1970 as a follow-up. 1970 also saw the first Earth Day, a sort of "celebration in the trenches" which resulted in the creation of the EPA and the nation's environmental agenda.

We hastily addressed the specters of the Santa Barbara oil spill, Los Angeles smog, and dead fish in Lake Erie, by passing the Clean Air Act in 1970, and the Clean Water Act in 1972.

At this point, there was a lull. We thought that pollution had been satisfactorily addressed. However, over the next few years, the "midnight dumper" became a national archetype, and sites like the "Valley of the Drums," Love Canal, and Times Beach began raising their skeletal hands. Land-disposal became the issue of the day, especially since studies showed that 50% of us got our drinking water from groundwater supplies, and land-disposal was threatening them.

RCRA was passed in 1976 to define hazardous wastes, and to control and track their disposal through the "cradle-to-grave" manifest system. At the same time it was realized that there *were* no acceptable disposal facilities in existence, so a permitting process was created, and design standards established.

The U.S. EPA took four years to promulgate regulations implementing RCRA, which seemed a long time, especially to Congress. To be fair, it should be recalled that EPA was a young agency, and that the task was monumental. RCRA affected virtually every type of business in every SIC code, and studies had to be conducted to determine the least painful way to phase in this complex piece of legislation.

In the early years of RCRA's implementation, Congress became concerned that too many generators had been left unregulated by setting the regulated quantities of hazardous waste too high. In addition, EPA's perceived tardiness in writing regulations still rankled, and it was decided to address both issues.

The result was HSWA, the Hazardous and Solid Waste Amendments of 1984. This law was so all-encompassing that most of what we think of today as RCRA is actually HSWA. These amendments brought the small-quantity generator into the loop, and mandated several new programs, some of which are still being implemented. It also established timeframes for EPA to promulgate regulations.

RCRA is due for reauthorization, perhaps as early as 1992's legislative session. Proposed rules are always left open for public comment, and that includes the regulated community. Such commentary enables EPA to balance the environmental concerns raised by the citizenry with the economic and logistical considerations raised by the regulated community.

REGULATIONS -- RCRA Subtitle C

Hazardous waste regulations may be found in Title 40, Code of Federal Regulations (40 CFR), Chapter I, Subchapter I, Parts 260-281. I will devote space to each part in turn.

PART 260 -- Definitions; Petitions

Just what *is* a waste anyway? A simple question, with an extremely devious and elusive answer. This is the basic question every HMM must ask, because it determines whether someone is subject to RCRA. Basically, a waste is anything produced by a process or by accident, which cannot be directly used onsite as a raw material for another process without some sort of treatment. A waste is also any material which cannot be reused onsite at all, and must be sent off for disposal or processing into another product or raw material. Chemicals which are off-specification, or become so due to age, are also wastes.

Part 260 also details methods for having a particular waste stream excluded from regulation due to lack of specific hazard factors. The balance of this Part is given to the "meat-and-potatoes" definitions that clarify the language found in other parts.

PART 261 -- Identification of Hazardous Wastes

The previous part tells you if you've got a "solid waste." This one tells you whether that waste is also hazardous. There are two ways in which a waste is considered hazardous: by exhibiting one of four "characteristics," or by being found on any of four lists. (Listed wastes always take precedence in the nomenclature over characteristic wastes, so check the lists first to see if your waste is found there. A listed waste can exhibit one or more characteristics, but should only be covered under one listing. Waste mixtures are a different story. Always determine what code applies *at the point of generation*.)

The characteristics are those of ignitability, corrosivity, reactivity, and toxicity. Ignitable wastes are (1) liquids with a flashpoint less than or equal to 140°F, (2) solids able to ignite by friction or spontaneous chemical reaction, and (3) oxidizers. Corrosive wastes either have a pH of less than or equal to 2 or greater than or equal to 12.5, or corrode steel at a certain rate. Reactive wastes include certain explosives, as well as wastes which react with water or air to produce toxic vapors or explosions (examples being sodium, sulfides, and cyanides). Toxic wastes are those which, under controlled conditions, leach any of several metals, pesticides, or solvents at or above certain concentrations, or (if in liquid state) contain those materials at or above those concentrations.

The recent Toxicity Characteristic Rule added the solvents, and will add more as studies are conducted on their behavior in the environment. It also replaced the extraction procedure (EP) test with the TCLP test, which is more stringent. The characteristic or toxicity was designed to model the leaching of the various constituents from a landfill to groundwater supplies, so as to protect drinking water.

Determining whether a waste exhibits a characteristic is usually cut-and-dry, but can sometimes be almost as tricky as determining whether a material is a "solid waste." (A solid waste, by the way, can be solid, liquid, or gaseous. As long as it has mass, it's in the loop.)

The "listed wastes" fall into four categories, designated by an initial letter in the waste ID code. Thus, we have the F-list, the K-list, the P-list, and the U-list. The F-list includes solvents, plating and metal-finishing wastes, and phenolic wastes bearing dioxin (TCDD). The K-list is made up of wastes produced from specific industrial processes, and is grouped accordingly, so you can look under the headings to see if you're covered (e.g. steel-refining, ink formulation, pesticide manufacture, etc.). The P- and U-lists consist of off-spec chemical products, either the pure chemical, or a product in which the listed ingredient is the sole active ingredient. The P-list is reserved for chemicals considered acutely toxic.

A mixture of a characteristic waste with a non-hazardous waste or material is no longer a hazardous waste if it no longer exhibits the characteristic (but dilution to render a waste non-hazardous is prohibited). However, a mixture of a listed waste with something non-hazardous remains a listed waste.

Part 261 also includes several exemptions for particular waste streams; see if yours is there. Also to be found here are standards for conditionally exempt generators (of less than 100 kg per month. No paperwork requirements, as long as you're able to show that your waste either went to an authorized hazardous waste facility, or a State-approved solid waste landfill).

PART 262 -- GENERATOR REQUIREMENTS

This part sets the standards for the management of hazardous wastes by generators, of which there are two fully-regulated varieties. Small-quantity generators are those which generate between 100-1000 kilograms (about 220-2200 pounds) of hazardous wastes per month. Large-quantity generators put out 1000 kg or more per month. Both must comply with labeling and marking requirements, storage standards for tanks and drums, safety and spill-response measures, and the paperwork tracking system, including manifests, land-ban notifications, records of inspections and spills, and periodic reports to EPA on waste generation and shipments.

The basic difference between the two is that small generators may store their waste onsite for up to 180 days (or 270 if their TSD is over 200 miles away), while large generators may store only 90 days. In addition, large generators must have a formal training plan with documented training sessions, and a detailed contingency plan for emergency situations. Large generators must also comply with storage standards for tanks referenced in Part 265.

Small generators may not store over 6000 kilograms of hazardous waste at any time without a permit. This is in the regs to minimize the magnitude of potential emergencies and to discourage speculative accumulation. It also helps the inspector to determine if a large generator is masquerading as a small one, to avoid more stringent regulations.

PART 263 -- TRANSPORTER REQUIREMENTS

Hazardous waste transporters must register with EPA and obtain an ID number (as must generators and TSDs). 263 is a short Part, deferring to the DOT hazardous-materials transportation regulations in 49 CFR for the most part.

EPA requirements set forth a few basics, such as recordkeeping, spill-response actions and protocol for notification; and restrict the storage of hazardous waste in shipment to a maximum of 10 days at a transfer facility. Storage over 10 days requires a permit, and the mixing of wastes in a tanker so as to create a waste with a new set of ID codes makes the transporter the generator of the new waste stream.

PARTS 264 and 265 -- TREATMENT, STORAGE, AND DISPOSAL FACILITIES

Part 265 covers interim-status requirements for existing or newly regulated TSDs, including procedures for obtaining a Part A partial permit, and closure procedures for those not wishing to obtain a partial or full permit to continue their hazardous waste treatment, storage or disposal activities. Part 264 covers the Part B "fully-permitted" facilities.

Both 264 and 265 detail strict requirements for waste analysis, emergency preparedness and response activities, recordkeeping, personnel training, financial assurance for closure/post-closure, liability insurance, security, groundwater and other monitoring, reporting, and corrective action. There are also several subparts which lay out detailed operating requirements for specific types of facilities such as landfills, incinerators, surface impoundments, and the like. The steps for achieving closure, and, for land-disposal facilities, performing post-closure activities, are also carefully laid out. The regulations in 264 and 265 are probably the most straightforward of the lot.

(There was a limited timeframe available to either apply for a Part A interim-status permit or undergo closure. Part A's are thus not currently available. However, boilers and industrial furnaces which use hazardous wastes as supplemental fuels will soon be required to have a permit, which will revive the Part A.)

PART 266 -- RECYCLING

The requirements for the recycling of hazardous wastes are generally less stringent than for TSD processes. Covered here are the burning of hazardous wastes and used oil for energy recovery, the reclamation of lead from lead-acid batteries and of certain precious but toxic metals, and some generic standards for the recycling of hazardous wastes in a manner constituting disposal (another tricky definition). This is where boilers and industrial furnaces are currently regulated.

PART 267 -- INTERIM STANDARDS FOR NEW LDFs

This part provides standards similar to those for other land-disposal facilities as found in 264 and 265, and covers those facilities which started operations after Part A's were no longer available. These facilities must apply directly for a Part B, or cease all TSD activities.

PART 268 -- LAND-DISPOSAL RESTRICTIONS

This is possibly the most thorny part of the entire RCRA program, though its intent is simple. "Land-ban" is a HSWA provision, and is the culmination of the RCRA prime target of controlling the land disposal of hazardous wastes. Simply put, Part 268 establishes standards for the treatment of all hazardous wastes, so as to reduce the toxicity or other hazards associated with each waste, prior to land disposal.

"Land-ban" was implemented in four phases, in a rather tortuous process. Treatment standards could not always be set according to deadlines, due to the lack of data about a particular waste's behavior in the environment, or to the lack of available treatment technology necessary to achieve the desired standard. However, now that the program has been fully implemented things should go more smoothly.

Compliance is pretty basic. Generators, through testing or applied knowledge of raw materials and processes, must determine whether a waste meets or exceeds the treatment standards applicable to the waste. Then, with each manifest, a notification must be sent to the TSD documenting treatment standards, and a copy must be retained by the generator. This provides guidance to the TSD. TSDs must conduct analyses on incoming wastes and on treated wastes and residues, and keep detailed records.

Now that there are treatment standards for all hazardous wastes, the land-ban notifications must include all applicable waste ID codes, so that the receiving facility knows what treatment methods will be required. For example, if you generate spent methyl ethyl ketone (MEK), the F005, D001, and D035 codes would have to be listed on the form.

PART 270 -- THE PERMIT

This part gives instructions on how to apply for a Part A and a Part B hazardous waste TSD permit.

PART 271 -- STATE AUTHORIZATION

RCRA was always intended to be picked up by the States so it could be locally enforced, and fine-tuned for regional idiosyncracies. 271 sets up the system by which a state agency can put together an authorized RCRA program.

PART 272 -- LIST OF AUTHORIZED STATE PROGRAMS

See if your State is listed here. If so, make all haste to obtain a copy of the applicable State regulations, which are more stringent. If you were really supposed to report to the State, and only did so to EPA, you may be in trouble. Failure to report (whether it's a spill/chill/thrill or just a mundane shipment report) is the cardinal sin in environmental affairs, especially RCRA.

PART 280 -- UNDERGROUND STORAGE TANKS

This is another HSWA provision, passed because it had been estimated that 25% of all USTs nationwide were leaking. It applies to underground storage tanks (USTs) storing hazardous substances as defined in CERCLA, as well as petroleum. The definition of "petroleum" in this part has recently been expanded to include used oils, which has implications for the automotive-repair industry, among others.

Part 280 covers notification and closure requirements, upgrading procedures for existing tanks, and equipment and materials required for new tanks. Installation procedures are described, as are the requirements for monitoring, leak detection, spill and overfill prevention, and leak-response activities.

Contaminated soils from leaking UST removals (commonly known as "tank-yanks") are temporarily exempt from TCLP requirements. Use EP Toxicity as the guideline for now.

PART 281 -- STATE AUTHORIZATION

Sets the standard for authorized State programs for USTs. Check with your own State agency to see if there are more stringent regulations in effect, and to get the proper addresses and phone numbers so you'll know who to report to. Ask for copies of the State forms, if there are any. It will take a very long time for all the USTs to register; don't appear recalcitrant.

THE FUTURE

The tendency since 1976 has been toward increasing complexity and more regulations, and there is no good reason to suspect that this trend will reverse itself. The regulated community, faced with the burden of compliance and economic considerations, has never been wreathed in smiles over RCRA's acceleration. However, some facility operators are beginning to get the intended point behind it all.

RCRA, more than any other environmental program, is committed to pollution prevention through *waste minimization*. The land-disposal restrictions, or "land-ban," are especially geared toward encouraging industry to find innovative technological means to reduce the amount of hazardous waste being generated, and to reduce the toxicity of those wastes by using alternative products, or less of the ones currently used.

In many cases, innovation isn't even necessary. Many changes can be made simply by reusing materials onsite that are otherwise thrown away, such as the redistilling of spent solvents. Others have discovered products that do the same job, but are much less toxic. These may be more or less expensive up front (I'm no expert on the economics of this business) but far cheaper in terms of disposal costs. Compliance can be relatively easy if you foster creativity and avoid becoming set in your ways.

Finally, don't be afraid to call your inspector if you're not sure what a regulation means. The language can sometimes be fuzzy, and most regulators are happy to steer you toward compliance using technical assistance. Remember also that RCRA is constantly changing, and that it pays to keep up-to-date. The *Federal Register* is one way to do so; there are also several private publications available.

For an excellent analysis of RCRA's impact, its successes and failures, its economic side, and its likely future development, see *Public Policies for Environmental Protection*, Paul R. Portney, ed. (Resources for the Future, Washington, D.C., 1990).

[**NOTE:** RCRA was originally intended to regulate municipal solid waste, i.e. trash and garbage, but the hazardous waste phenomenon pushed solid waste out of the spotlight. As RCRA Subtitle C covered hazardous wastes, Subtitle D was intended to cover solid wastes. For the duration of the RCRA program, the Subtitle D "regulations," found in 40 CFR 240-259, have consisted of basic guidelines for solid waste management.

However, the full Subtitle D appeared in the *Federal Register* in the summer of 1991, and the implementing regulations will probably show up in the 1992 edition of 40 CFR. These will regulate solid waste landfills, and probably other facilities such as incinerators, transfer stations and compost operations. There will no doubt be implications for hazardous materials managers, notably those who are conditionally-exempt small-quantity generators, as this new piece of the puzzle is fitted in.]

CHEMICAL AND PHYSICAL ANALYSIS AND WASTE ANALYSIS PLANS

David Koepper, CHMM
ITT Aerospace

and

Regina J. Mahoney, CHMM
Vice-President, Environmental Compliance
Heritage Environmental Services, Inc.

GENERATOR WASTE ANALYSIS REQUIREMENTS

Generator Waste Determinations

A generator must make a hazardous waste determination on all waste generated at his facility. This determination should be performed as specified in 40 CFR 262.11. An important part of the requirement is the necessity for the generator to keep records documenting the waste determination process.

The waste determination is a three step process. The generator first determines if the waste is excluded by 40 CFR 261.4 or state equivalent. If not excluded, the generator determines if the waste is included in the lists in 40 CFR 261, Subpart D. Waste streams which are not listed or excluded must then be evaluated using the generator's knowledge of the waste or with the tests specified in 40 CFR 261, Subpart C (characteristic waste). Each state should determine if their waste determination requirements are different than those specified in the Federal Register.

93

Depending on use, especially if wastes are reclaimed, some wastes are regulated by applicable portions of 40 CFR 266. The specific wastes so regulated are listed in 40 CFR 261.6.

Table 1 in 40 CFR 261.2 lists the regulatory category in which recyclable materials fall dependant on the type of recycling conducted. Although not entirely clear in the regulations many states require that a waste determination be done on recyclable materials even if they are excluded from regulation in 40 CFR 261.2.

Waste Analysis Needs

There are three basic reasons for a generator to analyze waste. Waste may require analysis for a proper waste determination as specified in 40 CFR 262.11. Additionally, the waste material must usually be tested to properly specify whether the waste is prohibited from land disposal or whether it meets applicable treatment standards in 40 CFR 268. Some wastes may also require analysis to specify the "additional descriptions" required by DOT in 40 CFR 172.203. None of these regulations absolutely require a waste analysis by the generator. However, it is clear that the necessary certifications and waste determinations would be difficult to document without analysis.

The Waste Analysis

Once the decision is made to perform analysis, the generator must specify the type of analysis needed for a particular waste stream. Tests to determine if a waste meets a "Characteristic of Hazardous Waste" are specified in 40 CFR 261, Subpart B. Based on this knowledge of the waste certain tests (such as those for pesticides or other TC characteristics) may be excluded. The generator may also choose to use tests other than those specified in the regulation as a screening tool or because of cost considerations. Any tests other than those listed in 40 CFR 261 or 40 CFR 268 would be categorized as "generator knowledge of the waste."

Sampling

One important consideration in developing sampling requirements is waste variability. If wastes are not homogeneous or if they change over time then multiple samples may be required to properly characterize the waste.

The decision on how many samples to take, when to take them and where to take them may require the generator to seek assistance from a laboratory, a consultant or from a state agency.

Representative sampling techniques for different types of wastes are specified in 40 CFR 261 Appendix I.   Appendices II-X list other information pertinent to waste analysis such as approved test methods and hazardous constituent lists.

Record Retention

Maintenance of records of the waste determination process is necessary in order to meet the requirements of the regulations. Waste analysis records used in the determination must be maintained for at least three years after the last shipment of waste to a TSD (40 CFR 262.40). Land Ban analysis records must be maintained for five years after the last TSD shipment [40 CFR 268.7(a)(6)]. As a practical matter many generators keep these records for a much longer period of time because of concerns about future liability.

TREATMENT, STORAGE, DISPOSAL WASTE ANALYSIS PLANS

Introduction/Discussion

Accurate and definitive waste characterization in accordance with the requirements of the Resource Conservation and Recovery Act (RCRA) as outlined in 40 CFR Part 261 is paramount for understanding if subsequent waste management activities are subject to the RCRA Subtitle C Rules. Decisions on proper and compliant waste management strategies depend on accurate waste determination.   Part 261 defines and outlines this multiple-step process including determination on whether a waste is a solid and hazardous waste, identifying exclusions and exemptions including whether a generator has a "listed waste" as identified in (40 CFR 261) Subpart D. If not listed or excluded, then the waste must be evaluated using "generator knowledge" or by testing using methodologies identified in the appendices to part 261 for "characteristics" as defined at (40 CFR 261) Subpart C.

The United States Environmental Protection Agency (EPA) recently revised the test methodology for leachability or mobility of both organic and inorganic analytes present in liquids, solids and multiphase wastes. The Toxicity Characteristic Leaching Procedure (TCLP), SW846-Method 1311, replaces the Extraction Procedure Toxicity Test (E.P. Tox. Test) and added twenty-five (25) organic chemicals to the list of toxic constituents of concern on March 29, 1990.

Generators must identify and impart all hazardous constituents in the waste as legitimately acquired from the variety of options open to them, to the treatment, storage and disposal facility (TSD); thus enabling the TSD facility to accurately confirm the treatment, storage and disposal options available based on site activities and the Land Disposal Restrictions requirements if their waste is restricted. A restricted waste is that waste for which EPA has set treatment standards; these provisions apply to wastes produced by generators of greater than 1,000 kilograms as well as small quantity generators (SQG's) of 100 to 1,000 kilograms per month (or greater than 1 kilogram of acute hazardous waste per month).

Except for a few newly listed wastes and the twenty-five (25) organic "TC" wastes, the land disposal restrictions apply to all listed and characteristic RCRA hazardous wastes. And although the land disposal restrictions apply to the disposal of hazardous waste, EPA has determined that the "point of generation" must be used to determine if a waste is restricted. By evaluating the waste at the point of generation, any subsequent dilution of the waste to meet concentration-based limits is prevented. To reiterate, the generator must not only identify all hazardous constituents, but also determine if the waste is subject to land disposal restrictions at the point of generation and provide notifications and certifications (as appropriate) to TSD facilities explaining restrictions including treatment requirements applicable to their waste.

After evaluation of the information provided by the generator at the pre-acceptance stage, the TSD facility then confirms the appropriate treatment, and/or storage and/or disposal options available within the context of the land disposal restrictions if the material is restricted and determines if they can handle the material given site specific technology and capabilities; hence the need for definitive accuracy in waste determination for all constituents present in the wastestream.

TSD Facility General Permitting Requirements

By Congressional mandate, all TSD facilities must be permitted by 1992. The RCRA Part B Permit, the purpose of which is to "establish minimum national standards which define the acceptable management of hazardous waste," is generally a negotiated document with a clear administrative record. It is also the mechanism by which each state (and EPA since most states do not have HSWA authority -- hence, a dual permit) permits TSD facility activities for from five (5) to ten (10) years. The Part B Permit Application includes the Waste Analysis Plan that identifies responsibilities for the TSD facility to obtain a detailed chemical and physical analysis of the waste before they can treat, store or dispose (of a waste).

General and analytical information gathered by the generator for accurate waste characterization, while purposeful, may need to be augmented by additional information on which the TSD facility determines site specific needs. For example, evaluation of the treatability capability of a waste in order to achieve Best Demonstrated Available Treatment (BDAT) required by the land disposal restrictions prior to land disposal may be an additional consideration or, for example, storage considerations as in compatibility with a receiving tank and the need to identify specific gravity as a tank storage consideration -- all examples of Part B Permit requirements.

The TSD Facility Waste Analysis Plan

As indicated, the TSD facility has specific responsibilities relative to Waste Analysis Plans including the need to confirm that the material that has reached them is, in fact, the same material the generator has identified at the pre-acceptance stage and has contracted with the generator for treatment and/or storage and/or disposal.

These responsibilities, described in the General Facility Standards of RCRA at 40 CFR 264.13 identify, that before a TSD facility can treat, store or dispose of a waste, it must obtain a detailed chemical and physical analysis (of a representative sample) of the waste. The analysis may include data already developed under Part 261 -- Identification and Listing of Hazardous Waste, documented data or data from waste generated from similar processes.

There is a detailed comment in this section that explains if the TSD facility depends upon the generator to supply the information to meet waste analysis requirements, the treatment facility must, in turn, test their wastes, confirming treatment to the required level as defined by the land disposal restrictions (Part 268) treatment standard(s); and if the generator does not supply the information and the TSD facility accepts the waste, the TSD facility is responsible for acquiring information to comply with the need to meet waste analysis requirements.

The waste analysis as required by the TSD facility's Waste Analysis Plan must be repeated as necessary to assure that the data is current and at a minimum when the process generating the waste changes or when the results acquired by the required Quality Assurance, Quality Control (QA,QC) measures indicate that the waste does not match the waste as identified on the accompanying manifest. [Note: If QA,QC analysis identifies that the material is different from the waste as described on the accompanying manifest by the generator, as originally characterized by information provided by the generator, it is considered a discrepancy as to type and must be reconciled with the generator or transporter. If the discrepancy is not resolved within 15 days after receipt of the waste, the TSD facility must submit a letter to the Regional Administrator of USEPA (or Director of the State Environmental Protection Agency if the State has primacy in the RCRA program) describing the discrepancy, attempts at a reconciliation and a copy of the manifest at issue.]

The TSD facility's Waste Analysis Plan required to be written and maintained at the facility must contain:

(1) The parameter on which each waste will be analyzed, the rationale for the selection of the parameters and how these selected parameters will provide sufficient critical information enabling the TSD facility to treat and/or store and/or dispose of the material.

Obviously, each Plan will be designed for site specific waste management activities. For example, a TSD facility that stabilizes metal-hydroxide sludges to achieve BDAT compared to a TSD facility that conducts fuels blending would be vastly different and these site specific activities would be reflected in the TSD facility's selection of both pre-acceptance and QA,QC parameters.

(2) The test methods used to test the parameters;

Characterization of waste and pre-acceptance analytical information if used for regulatory decisions should be conducted using SW846 methods. However, as identified in the comment contained at (40 CFR) 264.71, Use of Manifest System, EPA did not intend that a full waste analysis be performed prior to acceptance of waste by the TSD facility. This requires the TSD facility to identify definitive QA,QC "fingerprint" tests for each type of waste accepted. Inherent in this concept and recently identified by EPA, is that SW846 test methods are not required for these QA,QC tests prior to acceptance. EPA realized the inordinant time delay prior to acceptance of waste at a TSD facility should SW846 test methods be required. By the nature of their very function, these fingerprint or QA,QC tests should be quick, indicative of a key parameter and scientifically valid.

(3) Sampling method to acquire a "representative sample";

The methods and equipment used for sampling waste will vary with the form and consistence of the wastes to be sampled. Appendix I to (40 CFR) 261 contains protocols for sampling waste with similar properties that EPA considers representative. The TSD facility must be assured and will generally inquire, and may require certification from generators, that representative sampling was employed on which to base accurate waste characterization. This representative sample must address variation of a waste over time and also place, e.g., as in a pit, pond or lagoon. Representative sampling is somewhat less variable as a TSD facility given that the waste is received in a DOT specification "package"; the package must be sampled to address stratification or the propensity of some liquids or semi solid wastes to settle into phases during transportation.

Inherent in sampling is the concept of "grab" versus "representative" or multiple sampling events of a whole; this will undoubtedly be addressed and become a Part B permit consideration and probable requirement should the TSD facility need to confirm BDAT. BDAT confirmation is based on a "grab" sample while other sampling events are generally based on "representative" sampling.

TSD facilities must also address what portion of waste received will be sampled. Most, if not all at this writing, require 100% sampling of incoming waste to preclude the possibility of mixing incompatible wastes. Again, this will become a Part B negotiated concept.

(4) The frequency of repeated analysis to maintain up-to-date data;

The TSD facility will frequently ask the generator to "re-certify" at least on a yearly basis that the process giving rise to the waste has not changed and that the analytical or other information on file still constitutes accurate representation of their waste. This is the only mechanism available to the TSD facility to assure consistently current information. Additionally, most TSD facilities will require "re-characterization" of a waste including a certification, should they receive material that gives to rise a discrepancy as to type.

(5) The analyses the generator has agreed to supply;

This can be limited or broad within the allowable RCRA waste characterization depending upon the acceptable arrangement (business-contractual) entered into by the generator and TSD facility. If the TSD facility relies upon the generator's knowledge for waste characterization, there may be substantial data requested with (probable) increased QA,QC upon receipt of the waste.

(6) Any additional waste analysis methods to comply with the following specific waste management methods:

264.17 General Requirements for Ignitable, Reactive or Incompatible Wastes

When a TSD facility treats these general classes of waste, the facility's waste analysis plan must identify the method by which treatment is conducted under circumstances that assure that all unwanted side

reactions and precautions have been addressed to prevent potential threats to human health and the environment.

264.314 Special Requirements for Bulk and Containerized Waste

This requirement is specific to landfills; the absence of liquids must be demonstrated using SW846 Method 9095, Paint Filter Liquids Test in accordance with the frequency as defined in the site's RCRA Part B Permit.

264.341 Incinerator Waste Analysis

As required by either a trial burn or the facility's Part B, the waste feed analysis must be sufficient to provide an analysis of each waste or mixture to be burned including the heat value and composition of the waste to be burned, viscosity or physical form and an identification of organic constituents listed in 40 CFR Part 261, Appendix VIII, as expected to be present, and an approximate quantification of the hazardous constituents. Also, throughout operation, waste analysis must be conducted to verify that the waste feed is within the physical and chemical composition as specified in the permit.

264.1034(d) Subpart AA Air Emission Standards for Process Vents

This requires a TSD facility to evaluate process vents associated with hazardous waste distillation, fractionation, thin film evaporation, or air/or steam stripping operation, may (or may not) be subject to the requirements of this subpart based on an initial determination that a time-weighted, annual average total organic concentration of the waste managed of the unit is less than 10 ppmw.

264.1063(d) Subpart BB Air Emission Standards for Equipment Leaks

Requires the owner or operator of a TSD facility to, for each piece of equipment, assess whether it contains or contacts a hazardous waste with organic concentration that equals or exceeds 10 percent by weight (in order to identify if they are impacted by these requirements).

268.7 Waste Analysis -- Land Disposal Restriction

The land disposal restrictions requirements bring focus to the need for accurate RCRA waste identification as contained in generator requirements (40 CFR) 262.11 and TSD facility requirements (40 CFR) 264.13 for waste determination and Waste Analysis Plans respectively.

TSD facilities that treat or dispose of restricted wastes must detail in their Waste Analysis Plan how and when wastes or treatment residue will be tested to determine if they meet the applicable treatment standards or prohibition level. Thus, even though generators are required to determine if a waste is restricted and if it meets treatment standards or prohibition levels, the disposal facility must conduct tests to confirm compliance prior to disposing of the waste. The third-third rule clarified when treatment or disposal facilities may rely on generators to provide waste analysis data. The preamble to the rule identified that treatment and disposal facilities may generally rely on information provided to them by the generators or treaters of the waste. However, treatment and disposal facilities must conduct periodic detailed physical and chemical analyses on their wastestreams to assure that the appropriate Part 268 treatment standards are being met.

The treatment facility as generator of a restricted waste must establish that the treatment residue does not exceed values as shown in Table CCWE-Constituent Concentrations in Waste Extract (40 CFR) 268.41, or that wastes have been treated according to specified technologies (40 CFR) 268.41, or that the waste treatment residual (not an extract) must meet the concentrations in Table CCW Constituents Concentrations in Wastes (40 CFR) 268.42 and be accompanied by the appropriate paperwork and analyses as necessary if the material is to be disposed (as required) at a RCRA Subtitle C landfill.

Conclusion

Waste Analysis Plans are a cornerstone of the RCRA program for a TSD facility. They essentially define site-specific waste management options and identify the hazardous wastes that can be treated, stored or disposed in/at each option. A well conceived Plan is required to establish compliance with permit requirements; it is a necessary and effective training tool for new employees and is an excellent mechanism to familiarize State and EPA inspectors with all site activities because of its pervasive nature. Generators, now required if they manage, i.e., treat a restricted waste in tanks or containers, would be well advised to establish a "Plan" by gathering together all data, including memos, trial tests, and other permitted information used as the basis for decision and analytical information, into one comprehensive document confirming accurate waste determination.

This is a general overview of RCRA TSD Facility Waste Analysis Plan requirements. It does not address the myriad of specific case-by-case evaluations necessary for compliance with this complex hazardous waste management program. Additionally, this is a discussion of Federal RCRA requirements, each state should be consulted for differing, generally more stringent, requirements.

HAZARDOUS WASTE STORAGE

John Peoples
Tri-State Steel Drum

INTRODUCTION

Storage regulations are a vital issue to all hazardous waste generators. The storage of hazardous waste is regulated by the U.S. Environmental Protection Agency (EPA), as well as virtually all State agencies charged with regulating environmental programs. Since state regulations vary widely and must be at least as stringent as federal regulations, we will focus on EPA regulations. State agencies as well as local regulations and organizations such as NFPA should be consulted to determine applicable storage requirements.

To determine what storage regulations apply to a given situation, you must first determine what your generator status is and what waste accumulation times you are proposing. Accumulation time begins when the first drop in a drum as waste enters a drum or a bulk storage tank. (The first drop in a drum as start of accumulation start date has caused some problems. The regulations do not specify start date for drums. This was defined in the preamble to regulations on January 11, 1982, but preambles are not codified in the regulations). The accumulation start date for wastes in satellite filling areas begins when the 55-gallon drum is full. After the drum is full, 72 hours are allowed before the drum must be moved to the storage area.

Your status as an exempt small quantity generator, a small quantity generator, a generator, or a generator requiring a storage permit will determine your storage time.

Generator

EPA regulates the storage of hazardous waste through the Code of Federal Regulations Volume 40 (40 CFR). 40 CFR parts 260 through 272 contain the majority of the regulations regulating hazardous waste activities under the Resource Conservation and Recovery Act (RCRA). These have been previously discussed. EPA regulates the storage of hazardous waste if a generator generates more than 100 kilograms (220 pounds) in any one calendar month. Some exceptions are generators of characteristic wastes, namely flammable fuel products for use as supplemental fuels under 40 CFR 266, recyclable material utilized for precious metal recovery under 40 CFR 266 and some exempt small quantity generators generating acute hazardous waste or mixing their waste with fuels. We will only discuss the latter since we are primarily concerned with storage requirements.

There are basically three categories of storage regulations based upon the volume of hazardous waste generated and the time the hazardous waste is accumulated. They are small quantity generators greater than 100 kilograms but less than 1000 kilograms in any calendar month, generators generating greater than 1000 kilograms per calendar month and accumulating for less than 90 days, and generators generating greater than 1000 kilograms per calendar month and accumulating for longer than 90 days. Before we discuss these categories let's examine the exempt small quantity generator and how in certain cases the exempt small quantity generator is no longer exempt.

Exempt Small Quantity

40 CFR Part 261 -- Identification and Listing Hazardous Waste, defines what EPA considers to be a hazardous waste under RCRA. 40 CFR Part 261.5 states that ". . . A generator is a conditionally exempt small quantity generator in a calendar month if he generates no more than 100 kilograms of hazardous waste in that month. . . ." Further, ". . . a conditionally exempt small quantity generator's hazardous wastes are not subject to regulation under Parts 262 through 266, 268, and Parts 270 and 124 of this chapter, and the notification requirements of section 3010 of RCRA, *provided the generator complies with the requirements of paragraphs (f), (g), and (j) of this section. . . .*" As in most cases involving complex government regulations, there are exceptions to every rule.

Let's examine these exceptions.

The first paragraph (f), references paragraph (e) and essentially states that if you generate more than *one (1) kilogram* of an acute waste per 40 CFR 261 or 100 kilograms of a spill residue (including soil or contaminated debris) from an acute waste in any one calendar month, you must comply with the regulations contained in 40 CFR Part 262, which will change your classification to regulated small quantity generator. If you are a generator of acute wastes, please read these regulations carefully to insure compliance.

The second exception, paragraph (g), requires that you determine in all cases if your waste is hazardous by compliance with 40 CFR 262.11 and that if your accumulation in any one calendar month exceeds 100 kilograms, you comply with 40 CFR 262.34 which would effectively change your status to regulated small quantity generator.

The third and last exception, paragraph (j), requires compliance with 40 CFR 266 if your waste is mixed with used oil to be burned for energy recovery. These regulations contain storage provisions for energy recovery products which we will not cover here.

As you can see, some conditionally exempt small quantity generators may have to comply with the small quantity generator storage requirements.

Small Quantity Generator Storage Requirements

A small quantity generator is a generator who generates greater than 100 kilograms per calendar month but less than 1000 kilograms per calendar month. This definition can be found in 40 CFR 262.34(d). It allows storage of hazardous waste for 180 days or less without a permit, provided some conditions are met. You may also be eligible to store your waste up to 270 days provided you utilize an offsite treatment or disposal, do not exceed 6000 kilograms of waste stored at any one time, and the offsite treatment or disposal facility is over 200 miles from your facility.

All small quantity generator storage requirements are based on interim status standards for owners and operators of hazardous waste treatment, storage, or disposal facilities, namely 40 CFR 265. They include Subpart

C, Preparedness and Prevention; Subpart I, Use and Management of Containers; and Subpart J, Tank Systems.   In addition, 40 CFR 262.34(d)(5) stipulates some emergency response preparation activities which must take place.   Subparts C, I, and J will be discussed in the section to follow on 90 day storage.   We will only summarize 40 CFR 262.34(d)(5) in this section since there are additional requirements placed on the small quantity generator.   Remember Subparts C, I, and J do apply to the small quantity generator who stores hazardous waste.   40 CFR 265.201 contains special requirements for small quantity generators storing waste in tanks.   Since most small quantity generators store their waste in drums, we will not review these requirements.   If you are a small quantity generator storing waste in tanks, please review these regulations to insure compliance.

Section 40 CFR Part 262.34(d)(5) requires:

- An emergency coordinator must be onsite or on call at all times.

- The emergency coordinator's name and telephone number must be posted by the telephone.   The fire department number must also be posted unless the fire department has a direct alarm.

- The generator must insure that employees are familiar with proper waste handling and emergency response procedures applicable to their position.

- The emergency coordinator must respond to and report all incidents in accordance with EPA regulations.

Less Than 90 Day Storage

40 CFR 262.34 states that a generator may accumulate hazardous waste onsite for 90 days or less without a RCRA permit or interim status provided the generator complies with certain subparts of the interim status standards found in 40 CFR 265.   EPA's intent was to insure that the waste was stored and handled properly without the need for permit applications and other items such as closure-post closure and financial assurances.   The subparts which do not apply, with some subsections excluded, include Subpart C, Preparedness and Prevention; Subpart D, Contingency Plan and

Emergency Procedures; Subpart I, Use and Management of Containers; and Subpart J, Tank Systems. It should be noted that many references to other subparts are contained in these subparts which essentially require compliance with most parts of RCRA. The advantages of less than 90 day storage: no permit is required, no closure-post closure and financial assurance requirements apply, and the less stringent interim standards apply.

The following highlights the major points of each subpart. For more detailed information, please consult 40 CFR Part 265.

Note: 40 CFR 265 applies to interim status facilities while 40 CFR 264 applies to Part B permitted facilities.

Subpart C - Preparedness and Prevention requires:

- Facility must be operated and maintained to minimize the possibility of releases to the environment.

- The facility must have internal communications, telephone or two way radios, portable fire extinguishers and adequate water supply.

- All of the above equipment must be maintained and must be tested to insure proper operation.

- Access to alarms and communication equipment must be maintained.

- Aisle space must be maintained.

- Arrangement with local authorities for response must be made.

Subpart D - Contingency Plan and Emergency Procedures requires:

- A Contingency Plan, detailing actions to be taken, must be prepared.

- All employees must be briefed on the contents of the facility's Contingency Plan and all evacuation routes.

- Copies of the Contingency Plan must be maintained at the facility and submitted to all local police, fire departments, and hospitals, as well as state and local emergency response groups.

- The Contingency Plan must be updated when changes occur.

- An emergency coordinator must be established.

- Specific emergency reporting requirements must be followed.

Subpart I - Use and Management of Containers requires:

- Containers must be in good condition.

- Containers must be compatible with the materials they contain.

- Containers must be stored, closed and handled in a manner to prevent rupture.

- Containers must be inspected at least weekly.

- Containers containing ignitable waste must be stored at least 50 feet from the facility property line.

- Incompatible waste must be stored in areas segregated by dikes, berms, walls, or other devices.

Subpart J - Tank Systems requires:

- Assessment of existing tanks storing hazardous waste are required.

- Specific requirements for design and installation of new tank systems and components.

- Specific containment and detection releases.

- Specific inspection of tanks and components.

- Specific actions to be taken in response to leaks or spills and disposition of leaking or unfit-for-use tank systems.

- Specific special requirements for incompatible wastes.

The preceding summarizes the components of the basic requirements for storage of hazardous waste for less than 90 days.

Interim Status/Part B Storage

40 CFR 264.34(b) states that a generator who accumulates hazardous waste for more than 90 days is an operator of storage facility and is subject to the requirements of 40 CFR Parts 264 and 265 and the permit requirements of 40 CFR Part 270. Thirty (30) day extensions to the 90 day rule can be obtained from the Regional Administrator on a case-by-case basis, due to unforeseen circumstances. Storage facilities in existence at issuance of regulations had until November 8, 1988 to submit a Part B application. All new facilities must apply for a RCRA storage permit. The following is required to develop a written Part B permit application to obtain a RCRA permit to store hazardous waste in quantities greater than 6000 kilograms for periods exceeding 90 days.

- General Facility Standards

  a. Waste analysis and waste analysis plans
  b. Facility security
  c. Inspection requirements
  d. Personnel training

- Prevention and Preparedness Plan

- Contingency and Emergency Plan

- Manifest and Recording System

- Groundwater Protection

- Closure and Postclosure

- Financial Requirements

     a.   Closure limit estimate
     b.   Liability insurance

- Container Management Plan

CONCLUSIONS

Hazardous waste storage has become heavily regulated by the U.S. EPA and other agencies and organizations regulating treatment, storage, and disposal of hazardous waste. The above is a quick overview of the requirements and is intended to make you aware of their complexity. In addition, it should help you to determine what regulations apply to a particular situation with respect to the storage of hazardous waste.

It can not be overemphasized that a thorough review of the actual regulations and discussion with the regulators must take place to insure compliance. Do not forget to determine the applicability of state and local regulations, including zoning, as well as building and fire prevention codes when proposing to store hazardous waste.

TREATMENT AND DISPOSAL OF HAZARDOUS WASTE

William Beranek, Jr., Ph.D.
Indiana Environmental Institute, Inc.

and

David D. Lamm
Waste Management of North America, Inc.

INTRODUCTION

Proper management of hazardous waste is an important business decision for many companies.

Prices for commercial hazardous waste treatment and disposal facilities are escalating and will continue to rise. Federal and State regulations governing management of hazardous waste are tightening, adding new wastes to hazardous categories, restricting management choices, and requiring special worker safety training.

The role of the waste manager has never been more important to the corporation.

This chapter will review the factors to be considered for the fundamental choices in a waste treatment and disposal strategic plan:

1. Regulatory Framework

2. Waste Minimization and Onsite Treatment

3. Use of Commercial Facilities

Regulatory Framework

The good waste manager measures his minimum requirements for waste management against three factors: the Federal regulations, the State enforcement policies of hazardous waste regulations, and the general liabilities. Although commonly a manager will approach his decision in that order, the best managers prepare their company policy considering the factors in the opposite order.

The Federal waste management requirements are the basic rules necessary to follow. As discussed elsewhere in this volume, they are regulations developed from the Resource Conservation and Recovery Act of 1976 (RCRA) and its subsequent amendments.   A waste manager must determine first whether the facility operates in a manner covered by these regulations; if so, is it complying with the regulations?

The Federal regulations will be constantly in revision for the foreseeable future as Congress pressures the system to regulate more waste generators and more types of waste, to promote recovery and to allow less land disposal. The waste manager must stay informed about such changes.

The changing of Federal regulations to protect surface water and air quality from toxic chemicals also can change a hazardous waste manager's options for treatment and disposal.   This susceptibility to regulatory changes is one factor a manager must consider in evaluating major capital investments for waste treatment or disposal equipment.

Often the most important regulators to maintain contact with are the State regulators. Many States have their own regulations controlling hazardous waste which may be stricter than the Federal minimum.   A common example is an additional information requirement on the shipping manifest, treatment permits, or the taxing of waste management activities.

For those States authorized to conduct inspections and enforcement of the Federal RCRA program, it is the State regulators who make the determinations of whether a particular waste has the characteristics of hazardous waste, whether sampling was adequate, whether the operation is adequate and what are the penalties for noncompliance. As much as the Federal Environmental Protection Agency encourages uniformity, there can be variation in interpretation from State to State (and indeed from inspector to inspector).

Finally, and what the wise waste manager considers first when designing a waste strategy, present and future liability has become of paramount importance. The Comprehensive Environmental Response Compensation and Liability Act of 1980, coupled with the existing State legal traditions about landowner responsibility for releases from the property, is driving an open-ended concern about any chemical which might be released in a sudden or in a "nonsudden" fashion to pose an environmental or public health threat.

Stated simply, regardless of what we are "permitted" to do by today's State and Federal regulators, tomorrow we may be responsible to assess the risk and to take appropriate remedial action. Certain States and certain financial institutions already routinely require such actions prior to the sale of real estate. The wise corporation looks first to what strategy is in its best long-term interest.

Waste Minimization and Onsite Treatment

Management Reasons to Promote Operation without Hazardous Waste -- For the following reasons, it is best to promote enough waste reduction to fall below the hazardous waste minimum quantity limits:

1.   The hazardous waste system requires much specific paperwork which a company could do in a simpler fashion.

2.   Companies that are generators are subject to more frequent inspections and enforcement actions under RCRA.

3.   Disposal of hazardous waste tends to be significantly more expensive than disposal of nonhazardous waste.

4.   Companies who have treatment, storage or disposal (TSD) permits now are susceptible to corrective action requirements on any solid waste management unit on their site.

5. The special RCRA worker training requirements must be coordinated with the partially overlapping OSHA Hazard Communication Standard; companies with TSD permits have additional special worker training required by OSHA.

6. The time constraints for removing the waste can be difficult for some operations to manage.

7. Less waste disposed of is less liability.

To help get a perspective on the options available it may be useful exercise for you to do the mass balance required by Superfund Amendments and Reauthorization Act of 1986. Manufacturers who are large chemical users are required to compare the amounts of chemicals purchased each year to the amounts which they can account for leaving the facility. How much leaves by the sewer, into the air, in solid waste, and in the products?

Treatment Onsite -- Reducing the hazard or the quantity of waste reduces disposal costs and liabilities.

The Federal and State rules about whether a RCRA permit is required for certain onsite treatment are under a great deal of discussion. Further, State rules themselves may be stricter than EPA. Check with your State and EPA officials before you make a major investment without a permit.

The current general guidelines for exemption from a treatment permit are as follows:

1. Totally Enclosed Treatment Facility

    Strictly, this means a treatment step in a pipe connected directly as a part of the process pipe. Waste collected in barrels around a plant and carried to one single treatment facility is not exempt from the permit requirement. There are many similar processes for which interpretation is required. However, if you can connect your treatment in the process piping so that waste is never handled before treatment, you should not require a permit.

2. Elementary Neutralization Unit

    This exemption applies to hazardous wastes that are hazardous only because of the characteristic of corrosivity. Thus hazardous waste acids and bases are treated without a permit creating a material which is no longer a hazardous waste. Listed wastes cannot be neutralized without a permit. If the corrosive wastes also contain another hazardous constituent, this exemption does not apply.

3. Permit-by-Rule

    A generator who dewaters or dries the waste before shipping the waste for treatment or disposal does not require a permit for the dewatering treatment facility.

4. Discharges to a Publicly Owned Treatment Works (POTW)

    The wastes which a generator is allowed to discharge to a publicly owned treatment facility (POTW) are not hazardous wastes and neither the wastewater pretreatment facilities nor the POTW need to have a hazardous waste treatment permit.

5. Direct Discharges to Surface Waters

    Wastewater treatment in enclosed vessels (not surface impoundments) regulated under the Clean Water Act is exempt from RCRA hazardous waste treatment permit. The resulting sludge however will need to be tested for hazardous constituents in order to insure it is disposed of properly. In some areas, even though the resulting sludge may be non-hazardous, it may be called "special waste." Generally these types of wastes are non-hazardous industrial wastes that may require special handling for hauling and disposal. Many sludges, asbestos and petroleum contaminated soil are typical types of "special wastes."

Use of Commercial Facilities

Generally regard anybody you deal with to transport, treat or dispose of your waste as somebody with whom you are willing to share a long-term risk, because that is what you are doing. That applies whether the waste is in the hazardous waste system or not.

There are no firm guidelines to use in choosing a commercial vendor beyond those that you would use to choose others you do business with. Nobody (and certainly not the government) shares responsibility for your choice.

Being listed in a State or Federal "directory" of commercial hazardous waste management facilities is no guarantee of the facility's capabilities. Use any prepared list or directory judiciously. The careful waste manager will quickly ascertain that these lists or directories are quickly outdated. Typically, one can find a number of "listed" waste management facilities simultaneously identified as current Superfund projects.

Any list or directory may provide an initial starting point in reviewing waste management options, but a more detailed and thorough screening is necessary before commitments are made.

1.   Check with the State Government

Access to State files is generally much easier than trying to review Federal government information.   A visit to the State regulatory agency with a request to review the facility file is all that is necessary to gain access to all but only the most confidential or enforcement sensitive (attorney-client privilege) information. Most State regulators are glad to assist you in securing adequate and environmentally sound waste management services.   Be sure to check financial assurance (and insurance) information.

In some instances, should it prove necessary, requests can be made for Federal records under the Freedom of Information Act (FOIA). The cost of a lunch may be a wise investment in your corporate waste management future.

Is the facility generally in compliance or is it generally out-of-compliance with the agency? Review the State file on the facility.

2. Visit the Facility

No one can predict how any business will be doing five years from now, but we can check now on corporate attitudes and ability towards orderliness and housekeeping. Treatment and disposal businesses in trouble frequently are not doing a good job of accepting, cataloging, storing, treating and disposing of wastes. A large quantity of barrels waiting treatment or disposal or poorly stored barrels can be very bad signs.

Determine what the facility management feels about unannounced corporate client inspections. Is there a willingness to show you the operations, or do you hear that the corporate relation staff isn't in, or their insurance prohibits it, or the system is down?

Almost any facility at one time or another has been cited by State or Federal regulators for a violation. Will the facility talk with you about them? Have they been corrected? Were they major or minor violations? Do they have proper insurance and will they show it to you?

3. Talk with Other Generators

Conversations with other generators may be made easier if the facility is willing to share some of its customers with you during an interview. If not, the State records most certainly will have documents (manifests or biannual reports) from which other generators may be determined.

What has been their experience with this facility? Do they make regular corporate compliance inspections?

Surprisingly, it is not uncommon for several units (plants) of the same corporation to be using the same waste management facility (or different ones) without ever sharing this information. Check with your other plants to see what they are doing.

Does the facility routinely check chemical composition of wastes received at the gate? Does the facility turn back unacceptable loads?

4. Be Certain You Know Exactly Where Your Waste Will Go.

    Knowing where your waste is or obtaining a "certificate of destruction" may be extremely valuable in the future.

If you are using a landfill as a disposal facility, ensure that the facility is capable of determining and documents the exact location of your waste, using an established grid/reference system. Being able to pinpoint potential trouble spots is critical both to the facility and to you. For instance, should a waste characterization analysis prove faulty, the ability to exhume a specific section of a landfill, rather than several acres, is important. As a matter of good practice, waste analysis should be performed on a routine basis by both the corporate waste manager as well as the waste management facility just as to preclude such a possibility. Good management practice doesn't just start at the gate of the waste management facility.

If you are using an incinerator, be sure that you can get a "certificate of destruction" or some documentation that shows date and time of incineration. Note carefully (through onsite visits and historical records) the amount and type of storage capacity for the particular facility. In particular, what are their contingency plans for your waste in the event of a plant shutdown for whatever reasons? Can they handle wastes at other facilities or do your wastes sit or continue to pile up while repairs are made?

A number of hazardous waste streams, because of their BTU value, have potential for use in a "fuels program." That is, they may be used individually, or blended with other flammable wastes and used as auxiliary fuel sources in boilers and furnaces. Although this may be a legitimate practice, it may become a difficult one for the corporate waste manager to assure adequate documentation. Recent changes in the federal hazardous waste regulations found in the February 21, 1991, Federal Register Volume 56 #35 tighten the regulations concerning the burning of these fuels in industrial boilers and furnaces. These new requirements seek to bring these facilities into compliance with the more stringent requirements established for hazardous waste incinerators.

Quality controls, and quality assurance procedures, proper manifesting, and even shipping and sales receipts may become an important part of any corporate waste management strategy that utilizes a "fuels program" as an alternative to incineration or reclamation.

As a corporate waste manager, you must, in concert with other corporate staff, identify and understand short and long-term costs and liabilities associated with whatever management option is selected. The corporate "comfort level" is directly proportional to many of the activities/questions outlined in this paper. Continuous attention to detail is important to minimize future liability and potential double handling (at tremendous cost) of your own waste material.

MANAGING UNDERGROUND STORAGE TANKS

Elizabeth Phillips
U.S. Department of Energy
Savannah River Project

Updated by

Pat Eddy, CHMM
Allison Division-General Motors Corporation

INTRODUCTION

Leaking Underground Storage Tanks (USTs) have become an increasing source of groundwater contamination. Corrosion and improper installation of systems are the major causes of leaking underground tanks and their piping. Because of the increasing numbers of water supplies being contaminated by toxic substances stored in underground tanks, regulations concerning tanks, their construction, installation, use, cleanup, and closure have been promulgated and finalized.

This paper contains excerpts of the final Federal regulations for storage tanks for the management of hazardous waste and the newly finalized regulations for inventory monitoring, leak testing, corrosion protection, secondary containment, corrective action, and financial responsibility.

On October 21, 1976, Congress enacted the Resource Conservation and Recovery Act (RCRA) to protect human health and the environment. Under Subtitle C of the Act, EPA was directed to promulgate regulations to identify hazardous waste and regulate its control. On January 12, 1981, the agency promulgated standards for hazardous waste storage and treatment tanks that *could be entered for inspection*. These regulations were codified as 40 CFR Part 264, Subpart J. On November 8, 1984, the Hazardous and Solid Waste Amendments (HSWA) were enacted (Public Law 98-616). Section 3004(w) of the amendments required EPA to promulgate final standards for hazardous waste storage tanks that *cannot be entered for inspection*. As a result, on July 14, 1986, EPA amended hazardous waste regulations 40 CFR Parts 260, 261, 262, 264, 265, 270, and 271 for regulating storage and treatment of hazardous waste in tank systems. These amendments became effective on January 12, 1987.

In the HSWA amendments of 1984, the United States Congress also enacted Subtitle I out of concern for the risks that leaking underground tanks posed to the nation's groundwater resources.

Subtitle I provided for the development and implementation of a *comprehensive* regulatory program for underground tanks. Proposed regulations for underground storage tanks storing either petroleum products or hazardous chemicals were issued on April 17, 1987. The final regulation appeared in the September 23, 1988, Federal Register and became effective on December 22, 1988. Financial Responsibility requirements appeared on January 24, 1989. The remainder of this paper will be divided into two sections -- Subtitle C regulations, which cover hazardous waste tanks and Subtitle I regulations, which cover petroleum products and hazardous substances.

Subtitle C -- Regulations for Hazardous Waste Storage and Treatment Tanks

On July 14, 1986, EPA proposed final hazardous waste standards applicable to accumulation tank systems, interim status tank systems, and permitted tank systems. These regulations were codified as 40 CFR Parts 264 and 265, Subpart J, and became effective on January 12, 1987.

The regulations covered by this Subpart apply to tank systems used for treatment or storage of hazardous wastes. Included are aboveground, onground, and underground tank systems.

Exceptions to the regulation include:

1. Tanks used to store or treat a hazardous waste which contains no free liquids and are situated inside a building with an impermeable floor.
2. Tanks that are a part of a "closed-loop" recycling system.
3. Tanks that are themselves a part of a secondary containment system.

Basic requirements for existing tank systems that *do not* have secondary containment include the following requirements:

1. Undergo an initial integrity check by January 12, 1988, to determine that the tank system is not leaking or is unfit for use.
2. Obtain a written assessment by an independent professional engineer to document the tank system's integrity. This assessment must consider design standards, compatibility, corrosion protection, age of the tank, and prior integrity checks.
3. If a tank system is found to be leaking or unfit for use, the owner or operator must comply with the requirements for spills and leak response.

Owners or operators of *new tank systems or components* must:

1. Obtain and submit to the Regional Administrator a written assessment, reviewed and certified by a professional engineer, attesting that the tank system is acceptable for storing and treating a hazardous waste. Minimum requirements are addressed in 40 CFR 264.192(a).
2. Ensure proper handling procedures are adhered to in order to prevent damage to the system during installation.
3. Ensure clean, noncorrosive backfill is used during installation and compacted so that the tank and piping are uniformly supported.
4. Conduct tightness testing on tanks and ancillary equipment prior to covering with backfill.
5. Provide corrosion protection as recommended by an independent corrosion expert.
6. Maintain all records associated with the installation, certification, operation, etc. of the hazardous waste tank system.

Measures to Prevent/Detect Releases of Hazardous Wastes to the Environment

Complete secondary containment must be installed in the following situations:

1. All new hazardous waste tank systems or components.
2. All existing tank systems used to store or treat EPA hazardous waste codes F020 through F027, within two years after January 12, 1987.
3. For tank systems for which the age cannot be documented, within eight years of January 12, 1987.

Secondary containment systems must be:

1. Designed, installed, and operated to prevent migration of waste to the soil or groundwater at any time.
2. Capable of detecting and collecting releases.
3. Capable of meeting the design standards specified in 40 CFR 264.193(c), (d), and (e) or 265.193(c), (d), and (e) except for:

   a. Aboveground piping that is visually inspected for leaks on a daily basis.
   b. Welded joints and connections that are visually inspected daily.
   c. Pumps without seals or magnetic coupling pumps that are visually inspected daily.
   d. Pressurized aboveground piping systems with automatic shut-off devices.

Variances for secondary containment of tank systems and/or ancillary equipment may be obtained from the Regional Administrator if the owner/operator can demonstrate an acceptable alternative.

General Operating Requirements for Hazardous Waste Tank Systems

As a general practice, hazardous wastes must not be placed in a tank system if they could cause the tank or ancillary equipment to leak, corrode or otherwise fail.

The owner or operator of hazardous waste tank systems must take precautions to prevent spills and overflows. These include:

1. Spill prevention controls
2. Overfill prevention controls
3. Maintenance of sufficient freeboard in uncovered tanks
4. Compliance with corrective action requirements in case of a spill or release

Inspection schedules must be developed for all hazardous waste tank systems. At a minimum they must address inspections of:

1. overfill devices,
2. aboveground portions of the tank system,
3. data gathered from monitoring and leak detection equipment, and
4. cathodic protection devices.

Responses to Leaks or Spills of Hazardous Waste from a Tank System

A tank or secondary containment system from which there has been a leak or spill, or which is unfit for use, must be removed from service and the owner or operator must satisfy the following requirements:

1. Discontinue the flow of waste into the tank and inspect for leaks
2. Remove waste from the tank or secondary containment system
3. Contain any visible release of waste to the environment
4. Initiate notification reports to the Regional Administrator within 24 hours
5. Initiate repairs in accordance with 40 CFR 264.196(e)(2) through (4) or 265.196(e)(2) through (4)
6. Obtain certification from an independent professional engineer that the repaired system is capable of handling hazardous waste

Closure and Postclosure Requirements

At closure of a tank system, the owner or operator must remove or decontaminate all waste residues, contaminated containment system components, contaminated soils, structures, and equipment contaminated with waste, and manage them as a hazardous waste.

The closure plan, closure activities, cost estimates and financial responsibility for tank systems must meet the requirements specified in 40 CFR 264 or 265, Subparts G and H.

Special Requirements for Ignitable, Reactive, or Incompatible Wastes in Tanks

The following requirements apply when handling specialized wastes:

1. Ignitable or reactive wastes must not be placed in tank systems unless:

    a. the waste is treated after placement in the tank so it no longer meets the definition of ignitable or reactive, or
    b. the waste is stored or treated in such a way that it is protected from conditions that would cause the waste to ignite or react, or,
    c. the tank is used only for emergencies.

2. The owner or operator of tank systems used to treat or store ignitable or reactive wastes must comply with the requirements for protective distances as specified in the National Fire Protection Association's "Code for Flammable and Combustible Liquids."
3. Incompatible wastes must not be placed in the same tank system.
4. Hazardous waste must not be placed in a tank system that has not been decontaminated and that previously held an "incompatible" waste or material.

Subtitle I -- Final Regulations for Underground Storage Tanks Storing Petroleum Products or Hazardous Substances

APPLICABILITY (40 CFR 280, Subpart A) - Applies to owners and operators of UST systems

A UST is any tank and associated piping system used to contain regulated substances which has at least 10 percent of its volume below ground. This definition does not include:

1. farm or residential tanks of 1100 gallons or less, used for storing motor fuel for noncommercial purposes

2. tanks used for storing heating oil for consumptive use on the premises where stored
3. septic tanks
4. pipeline facilities
5. surface impoundments, pits, ponds, or lagoons
6. stormwater or wastewater collection systems
7. flow-through process tanks
8. liquid traps or associated gathering lines related to oil or gas production and gathering operations
9. storage tanks situated on an underground area, if the tank is upon or above the surface of the floor (i.e., a basement, cellar, or shaft)

The regulations apply to owners and operators of USTs storing either petroleum products or hazardous substances under the Comprehensive Environmental Response, Compensation, and Liability Act (CERCLA) of 1980. The definition of "petroleum" includes used oils.

Some UST systems are excluded from the requirements of Part 280 including:

1. UST systems holding hazardous wastes and regulated under Subtitle C.
2. Wastewater treatment tank systems regulated under Sections 402 or 307(b) of the Clean Water Act.
3. Equipment or machinery that contains regulated substances for operational purposes such as hydraulic lift tanks or electrical equipment tanks.
4. Underground storage tank systems of less than 110 gallons capacity.
5. UST systems containing *de minimus* concentrations of regulated substances.
6. Emergency spill or overflow containment UST system that is expeditiously emptied after use.

Some UST systems are deferred from regulation: Subparts B, C, D, and G do not apply to the following (only Subpart F on Corrective Actions):

1. Wastewater treatment tank systems.
2. USTs containing radioactive material.

3.   USTs part of emergency generator system at nuclear power plant.
4.   Airport hydrant fuel distribution systems.
5.   Field constructed UST systems.

In addition, Subpart D does not apply to UST systems storing fuel solely for use by emergency power generators.

Interim prohibition for deferred UST systems. Deferred UST systems shall not be installed for storing regulated substances unless the system meets new construction standards:

1.   Will prevent releases due to corrosion or structural failure for the operational life of the tank.
2.   Are cathodically protected against corrosion, constructed of noncorrodible material, steel clad with a noncorrodible material, or designed in a manner to prevent releases.
3.   The material used in construction or lining of the tanks is compatible with the material to be stored.

Design, Construction, Installation, and Notification (40 CFR 280, Subpart B)

The following standards are required for new UST systems to prevent releases due to structural failure, corrosion, or spills and overfills.

1.   Each tank must be designed, constructed, and protected from corrosion as specified below:

    a.   constructed of fiberglass reinforced plastic, or
    b.   constructed of coated steel with a corrosion protection system, or
    c.   constructed of a steel-fiberglass reinforced plastic composite, or
    d.   constructed of metal without additional corrosion protection provided that a corrosion expert determines the site is not corrosive and documents demonstrating compliance are maintained.

2.   Underground piping must also be designed and constructed as to prevent a release to the environment as specified below:

    a.   constructed of fiberglass-reinforced plastic, or

    b.   constructed of cathodically protected steel as specified in the regulation, or

    c.   constructed of metal without additional corrosion protection provided that a corrosion expert determines the site is not corrosive and documents demonstrating compliance are maintained.

3.   Equipment must be utilized to prevent spilling and overfilling associated with product transfer and must consist of: (Alternate equipment approved by the implementing agency may be acceptable in lieu of),

    a.   Spill prevention equipment that will prevent release of product to the environment when the transfer hose is detached from the fill pipe, and

    b.   Overfill prevention equipment that will automatically shut off flow into the tank when 95% full or alert the transfer operator when the tank is 90% full by restricting flow or triggering an alarm.

4.   Installation of tanks and piping must be in accordance with a code of practice developed by a nationally recognized association.

5.   All owners and operators must submit information demonstrating compliance with the installation requirements and certify compliance on the UST notification form.

No later than December 22, 1998, all existing UST systems must comply with the performance standards for new UST systems, upgrade existing systems as indicated below, or close in accordance with Subparts G and F.

Upgrading of UST System

1.   Tanks may be upgraded by adding an interior lining, adding cathodic protection, or a combination of both. Upgrades must be in accordance with nationally recognized standards and require periodic monitoring to assure tightness.

2. Metal piping may also be upgraded by adding cathodic protection. Upgrading must be in accordance with nationally recognized standards.

3. Spill and overfill prevention equipment may be added to existing UST systems in accordance with industry standards.

Notification -- Owners/operators who bring an underground tank system into use after May 8, 1986, must submit notification to the local agency within 30 days. The notification requires the owner/operator to certify compliance for proper installation of tanks and piping, cathodic protection, financial responsibility and release detection.

General Operating Requirements (40 CFR 280, Subpart C)

Specifically included are requirements for spill and overfill control, operation, and maintenance of corrosion protection, tank repairs, and recordkeeping.

All owners/operators must ensure that releases due to spills and overflows do not occur. Owners must:

1. Ensure that the volume available in the tank is greater than the volume of product to be transferred.

2. Ensure that a person is present at all times during transfer to observe the transfer.

3. Report, investigate, and clean up any spills and overfills.

Owners/operators of steel UST systems with corrosion protection must ensure releases due to corrosion are prevented by:

1. Proper operation and maintenance of the corrosion protection system.

2. Inspection of cathodic protection systems by a qualified independent corrosion expert according to frequencies specified in 280.31(b) or,

3. UST systems with impressed current systems must be inspected every 60 days to ensure the equipment is running.

4. Records of operation and maintenance must be maintained.

UST systems must be made of, or lined with, materials that are compatible with substance stored in the tank.

Owners/operators must ensure that repairs will prevent releases due to structural failure or corrosion.

1. Repairs of UST systems must be properly conducted in accordance with nationally accepted standards.
2. Repairs of fiberglass-reinforced plastic tanks may be made by a manufacturer's representative or in accordance with national standards.
3. Metal pipe sections and fittings that have caused a release must be replaced. Fiberglass pipes and fittings may be repaired.
4. Repaired tanks and piping must be tightness tested within 30 days (exceptions allowed).
5. Within 6 months following repair of a cathodic protection system, the system must be tested to assure proper operation.
6. Owners must maintain records for each repair for the remaining operating life of the UST system.

Reporting and Recordkeeping

1. Reporting -- the following information must be submitted to the implementing agencies.

    a. Notification for all UST systems, including installation certification for new systems.
    b. Reports of all releases.
    c. Corrective action plans.
    d. Notification before closure or change-in-service.

2. Recordkeeping -- the following information must be maintained.

    a. Corrosion expert's analysis of site corrosion potential if corrosion equipment is not used.
    b. Documentation of operation of corrosion equipment.
    c. Documentation of UST repairs.
    d. Compliance with leak detection requirements.
    e. Results of the site investigation at the time of permanent closure.

3. Availability and Maintenance of Records -- must be kept.

a. At the UST site and immediately available for inspection.

b. At a readily available alternate site.

c. In case of permanent closure, owners may mail closure records to the implementing agency.

Release Detection (40 CFR 280, Subpart D)

1. General Requirements -- Owners of UST systems must provide a method of release detection that:

   a. Can detect a release from any portion of the tank and piping.

   b. Is installed, calibrated, operated and maintained in accordance with manufacturer's instructions.

   c. Meets performance requirements (specific EPA approved methods)

   When release detection indicates a leak, the operator shall notify the implementing agency.

   Schedule for compliance with release detection:

   --Tanks installed before 1965.....................December 22, 1989
   --Tanks installed between 1965-1969............December 22, 1990
   --Tanks installed between 1970-1974............December 22, 1991
   --Tanks installed between 1975-1979............December 22, 1992
   --Tanks installed between 1980-1988............December 22, 1993

2. Owners and operators of petroleum UST systems must provide release detection for tanks and piping as follows:

   a. Tanks -- Must be monitored at least every 30 days by one of the following methods specified in 280.43(d) through (h) except that:

      (1) UST systems that meet performance standards (280.20 or .21) and the monthly inventory control requirements, may use tank tightness testing every 5 years until December 22, 1998 or until 10 years after the tank is installed or upgraded.

(2) UST systems that do not meet performance standards (280.20 or .21) may use monthly inventory controls and annual tightness testing.

(3) Tanks with a capacity of 550 gallons or less may use weekly tank gauging.

b.   Piping -- Must be monitored for releases by one of the following methods.

(1) Pressurized Piping
--automatic line leak, detector
--annual tightness testing
--monthly monitoring

(2) Suction Piping -- Tightness test every 3 years or monthly monitoring. No release detection needed if:
--below-grade piping operates at less than atmospheric pressure.
--below-grade piping is sloped so contents of pipe will drain back to tank.
--only one check valve is included in each suction line.
--check valve is located below and as close as possible to the suction pump.

Owners and operators of hazardous substance UST systems must provide release detection systems as for petroleum products and in addition new systems must:

1.   Include secondary containment, double walled tanks, or external liners and be designed, constructed, and installed to contain leaks.

2.   Underground piping must also be equipped with secondary containment.

3.   By December 22, 1998, all existing hazardous substance UST systems must meet requirements for secondary containment (See the regulation for details of each method).

Methods of Release Detection for Tanks

1.   Inventory Control

Conducted monthly to detect a release of at least 1% of the flow-through plus 130 gallons on a monthly basis by:

   a.   Input, withdraw, and amount remaining in the tank is recorded each operating day.
   b.   The equipment used is capable of measuring the level of product over the full range of the tank's height to the nearest one-eighth of an inch.
   c.   Tank inputs are reconciled with delivery receipts by measurement of tank inventory volume before and after delivery.
   d.   Deliveries are made through a drop tube that extends to within one foot of the tank bottom.
   e.   Product dispensing is metered and recorded as a method of release detection.
   f.   Measurement of any water is made to the nearest one eighth of an inch.

2.   Manual Tank gauging -- requirements:
     (Doesn't address piping leaks).

   a.   Level measurements are based at the beginning and ending of a period of at least 36 hours during which no liquid is added to or removed from the tank.
   b.   Level measurements are based on an average of two consecutive stick readings (beginning and end).
   c.   Equipment is capable of measuring over the full range of the tank and to the nearest one-eighth inch.
   d.   A loss of material over a specified amount is subject to corrective action.
   e.   Only tanks 550 gallons or less can use tank gauging as a sole method of release detection. Tanks 551 to 2,000 gallons may use tank gauging in addition to periodic tightness testing. Tanks greater than 2,000 gallons may not use the method.

3.   Tank tightness testing -- capable of detecting a 0.1 gallon per hour leak rate from any portion of the tank that routinely contains product.

4. Automatic tank gauging.
5. Vapor monitoring.
6. Groundwater monitoring.
7. Interstitial monitoring.
8. Other approved methods.

Release Detection for Piping Which May be Utilized

1. Automatic line leak detectors
2. Line tightness testing
3. Applicable tank methods

Owners/operators must maintain records to demonstrate compliance with Subpart D. Records shall include:

1. Written performance claims pertaining to release detection systems. Records must be kept for at least 5 years.
2. Results of any sampling, testing, or monitoring be retained for at least one year.
3. Written documentation of calibration, maintenance, and repairs must be maintained at least one year.

Release Reporting Investigation and Confirmation (40 CFR 280, Subpart E)

Owners must report to the implementing agency within 24 hours any of the following:

1. Discovery of a release of a regulated substance.
2. Unusual operating conditions, i.e., sudden loss of material.
3. Monitoring results indicating a release.

Determination of off-site impact of a release, (i.e., discovery of free product or vapors in soils, basements, wells) must also be made if required by the implementing agency.

Owners must immediately investigate and confirm all suspected releases within 7 days using the following steps.

1.   System check -- determine if a leak exists in that portion of the tank that routinely contains product or in the attached piping.
2.   Site check -- measure for the presence of a release where contamination is most likely to be present at the UST site.

Owners must contain and immediately clean up a spill or overfill and report to agency within 24 hours if:

1.   The spill results in a release to the environment that exceeds 25 gallons of petroleum.
2.   The spill results in a release of a hazardous substance that exceeds its reportable quantity under CERCLA.

Release Response and Corrective Action (40 CFR 280, Subpart F)

In response to a confirmed release from a system containing petroleum, the owner must initiate these corrective actions within 24 hours:

1.   Report the release to implementing agency.
2.   Take immediate action to prevent any further release.
3.   Identify and mitigate fire, explosion and vapor hazards.

Initial Abatement Measures and Site Check

Owners must perform the following abatement measures:

1.   Remove regulated substances from the tank to prevent further release.
2.   Visually inspect any aboveground release or exposed belowground releases and prevent further release.
3.   Continue to monitor and mitigate any fire or safety hazards.
4.   Remedy hazards posed by contaminated soils that are excavated.
5.   Measure for the presence of a release where contamination is most likely.
6.   Investigate the presence of free product and begin removal as soon as practicable.

Within 20 days after release confirmation owners must submit a report to the agency summarizing the initial abatement techniques.

Owners must assemble site and release information gained while confirming the release or completing the initial abatement by:

1. Determining the nature and estimated quantity of the release.
2. Investigating surrounding populations, location of wells and water quality.
3. Compiling the results of the site check.
4. Compiling the results of free product investigations.

Within 45 days owners must submit the information collected to the agency.

At sites which indicate the presence of free product, owners must remove the free product to the maximum extent practicable and must:

1. Minimize the spread of contamination.
2. Use abatement of free product migration as a minimum objective for design of a removal system.
3. Handle flammable products safely.
4. Submit a free product removal report to the implementing agency within 45 days.

In order to determine the full extent and location of contaminated soils, this report shall include:

1. The names of those responsible for free product removal measures.
2. The estimated quantity, type, and thickness of free product observed.
3. The product recovery system used.
4. Whether there will be any onsite or offsite discharge during recovery.
5. Treatment of discharge and effluent quality expected.
6. Permits which may be necessary.
7. Disposition of the recovered free product.

Owners must conduct investigations of the release, the site and surrounding area if:

1. Groundwater wells have been affected by the release.
2. Free product is found to need recovery.
3. There is evidence that contaminated soils may be in contact with groundwater.
4. The agency requests an investigation.

The information collected must be submitted to the implementing agency. The agency may, after reviewing release information, require the owner to submit a *corrective action plan* for responding to contaminated soils and groundwater. In addition, the owner may choose to submit a plan after completing release investigations.

The agency will approve the plan only after ensuring that implementation of the plan will protect human health, safety and the environment.

Upon approval of the plan, owners must implement the approved plan.

Owners may begin cleaning up of soil and water before the plan is approved if:

1. The agency is notified.
2. The owner complies with all conditions imposed by the agency.
3. The self-initiated measures are incorporated into the corrective action plan.

For each confirmed release that requires a corrective action plan, the agency must provide notice to the public to reach those directly affected by the release and the corrective action.

Decisions concerning the corrective action must be made available to the public for inspection upon request. The implementing agency may hold a public meeting to consider comments on the proposed plan, and must provide public notice if the corrective action does not achieve the established clean up levels.

Out-of-Service UST Systems and Closures (40 CFR 280, Subpart G)

When a UST system is temporarily closed, owners must continue operation and maintenance of corrosion protection and release detection.

When the UST system is temporarily closed for three months or more, owners must:

1. Leave vent lines open and functioning.
2. Cap and secure all other lines, pumps, and manways.

When a UST system is temporarily closed for more than 12 months, owners must permanently close the system if it does not meet new UST standards.

At least 30 days before beginning either permanent closure or change-in-service, owners must notify the agency of the intent to close. Assessment of the excavation zone must be performed after notifying the agency, but before completion of closure. To permanently close, tanks must be emptied and cleaned by removing all liquids and accumulated sludges. Continued use of a UST system to store non-regulated substances is considered change-in-service.

Before closure is complete, owners must measure for the presence of a release where contamination is most likely to occur. (This requirement is met if one of the acceptable external release detection methods is in operation).   If contaminated soils, groundwater, or free product is discovered, owners must initiate corrective action.

Owners of UST systems permanently closed before December 23, 1988, must assess the excavation zone and close in accordance with this Subpart if releases from the UST could pose a threat to human health or the environment.
Owners must maintain records which demonstrate compliance with closure requirements. Records must be maintained for at least 3 years after closure.

Financial Responsibility (40 CFR 280, Subpart H). Published in the Federal Register dated October 26, 1988.

Subpart H establishes requirements for demonstrating financial responsibility for taking corrective action and compensating third parties for bodily injury and property damage caused by sudden and non-sudden accidental releases arising from the operation of underground storage tanks containing petroleum. This subpart applies to petroleum UST systems that are in operation after the effective dates as listed below:

1.   Petroleum marketing firms owning 1,000 or more USTs and all other UST owners that report a tangible net worth of $20 million or more -- *January 24, 1989.*
2.   Petroleum marketing firms owning 100-999 USTs -- *October 26, 1989.*
3.   Petroleum marketing firms owning 13-99 USTs -- *April 26, 1990.*
4.   All petroleum UST owners not described above, including government entities -- *October 26, 1990.*

The amount of money for which owners/operators must show financial responsibility depends on the type of business, the amount of tank throughput, and the number of tanks.

1.   If the UST is used in petroleum production, refining or marketing, or handles an average of more than 10,000 gallons per month, there must be $1 million per occurrence coverage.
2.   There must also be coverage for an annual aggregate amount of financial responsibility to cover all leaks which might occur in one year. Annual aggregate limits depend on the number of tanks:

   a.   1 to 100 tanks -- $1 million annual aggregate.
   b.   101 or more tanks -- $2 million annual aggregate.

3.   If USTs are located at a facility not engaged in petroleum production, refining or marketing, but has a monthly throughput of more than 10,000 gallons, then the requirement is $1 million per occurrence. If the facility has a monthly throughput less than 10,000 gallons, there must be $500,000-per-occurrence coverage and $1 million or $2 million annual aggregate depending on the number of tanks.

UST owners/operators may use any one or combination of the financial mechanisms listed below to demonstrate financial responsibility (for specific details see the regulation).

1.   Test of self-insurance based on net worth.

2.   Insurance and risk retention coverage.
3.   Guarantee
4.   Surety bond
5.   Letter of credit
6.   Trust fund
7.   State funds
8.   Other state approved mechanisms

If financial responsibility is cancelled, the owner/operator must find a replacement mechanism within 60 days. If this cannot be achieved, the implementing agency must be notified.

Records of financial responsibility must be maintained by the owner/operator. Certification of financial responsibility must be maintained until tanks are properly closed. Copies of records and certification need to be mailed to the implementing agency only in the following cases:

1.   Within 30 days after a UST system is confirmed to be leaking.
2.   If the owner/operator receives notice of cancellation on existing financial coverage and is unable to obtain alternate coverage.
3.   Upon installation of a new tank system.
4.   At the specific request of the implementing agency.

Approval of state underground storage tank programs (40 CFR Part 281), specifies the requirements that state programs must meet for EPA approval. The final regulation for State programs can be found in *Federal Register* Volume 53, dated September 23, 1988.

HAZARDOUS MATERIALS TRANSPORTATION ACT (HMTA) AND HAZARDOUS WASTE TRANSPORTATION (RCRA)

Gary F. Lindgren, CHMM
Heritage Environmental Services, Inc.

INTRODUCTION

The offsite shipment of hazardous waste requires the hazardous materials manager to deal with the regulatory program of the U.S. Department of Transportation (DOT), as it meshes with that of the U.S. EPA under RCRA. The EPA regulations for generators (40 CFR Part 262) and transporters (40 CFR Part 263) make frequent reference to the DOT Hazardous Materials Transportation Regulations (49 CFR Parts 171-180). In fact, the EPA standards for offsite shipments of hazardous waste are indecipherable without a copy of the DOT regulations. The purpose of this chapter is to explain the hazardous materials transportation program established by DOT, in the context of hazardous waste shipments.

The EPA/DOT standards for generators who ship offsite are deceptively simple. The generator has the responsibility for determining where the waste will undergo treatment, storage, or disposal (TSD), and that the transporter and designated facility have EPA Identification Numbers and proper permits to accept the generator's particular type of waste. The generator must properly describe the waste using DOT shipping descriptions, and ensure that the containers are marked and labeled, suitable for the particular material and in proper condition for transportation. The waste must be accompanied by a shipping document called a manifest, the transportation vehicle must be appropriately placarded and the generator must verify that the waste is actually received by the designated TSD facility. The many pages of DOT regulations merely apply this scheme to the variations made possible due to the many types of hazardous materials, types of containers, and modes of transportation.

The U.S. Department of Transportation has the authority to regulate both the interstate transportation of hazardous materials and the inter- and intra-state transportation of hazardous wastes, under the authority of the Hazardous Materials Transportation Act (HMTA). DOT promulgated regulations under the authority of HMTA, at 49 CFR Parts 171-180. Their purpose is to promote the uniform enforcement of law among the states, while minimizing barriers to interstate commerce, and minimizing the dangers to life and property incident to the transportation of hazardous materials. DOT established requirements in these regulations for shipping papers, proper containers, marking and labeling of containers, placarding of vehicles, and incident reporting. The DOT regulations address all modes of transportation (air, rail, highway, waterway and pipeline). DOT's Hazardous Materials Regulations apply to the transportation of hazardous materials, regardless of their end use or ultimate disposition. DOT considers hazardous wastes to be a subset of hazardous materials, and thus regulated by their program.

It is important to remember that the purposes of the DOT regulations (i.e., to minimize the dangers to life and property during transit) are somewhat different than those of the hazardous waste regulations (i.e., protection of human health and the environment from hazardous waste mismanagement). This and other factors result in somewhat different terminology, as well as different hazard class definitions between the two programs. For example, DOT uses the terms "shipper" and "carrier" for parties identified by EPA as "generator" and "transporter." DOT and EPA have different definitions of empty container.

For transportation purposes, it is important to remember that hazardous wastes are a subset of hazardous materials. Recent changes to the DOT regulations under the HM-181 rulemaking have not altered this relationship, but they have resulted in some changes in how hazardous wastes and materials are described, packaged, marked, labeled, and placarded. As this chapter was written, new DOT rules comprehensively revising the Hazardous Materials Regulations (HMR) were being phased in. These rules, generally termed HM-181 (the DOT Regulatory Docket Number) and/or performance-oriented packaging standards ("POPS"), were intended to simplify and reduce the length and complexity of the previous HMR, as well as to enhance safety and better facilitate international commerce in hazardous materials. These objectives were said to be achieved by aligning DOT hazard class definitions and shipping descriptions with those of the United Nations (UN) Committee of Experts' Recommendations on the Transport of Dangerous Goods, and by the substitution of UN performance-oriented packaging standards for the detailed specifications for package manufacture that previously existed. The effective dates for various elements of the HM-181 transition are found at the end of this chapter.

The structure of the DOT regulations is shown in Figure 1. The hazardous materials transportation regulations are issued by the Research and Special Programs Administration (RSPA) of the DOT. The definitions utilized by DOT for certain key terms are found at 49 CFR 171.8 and should be reviewed by the hazardous materials manager.

SHIPPING DESCRIPTION SELECTION

The initial step is to determine the appropriate shipping name, hazard class or division, identification number, and packing group, if any. These four elements are referred to as the "basic description." Selecting an appropriate shipping description for a hazardous waste can be difficult, because such waste materials are often variable mixtures of several chemicals, are spent or have become diluted with water or oil, and/or consist of multiple phases. As a result, technical name/chemical name entries in the Hazardous Materials Table are often inappropriate for shipping name purposes.

To select the proper shipping description for hazardous wastes, one must be familiar with the definitions of the various DOT hazard classes/divisions, and to know how to utilize the DOT Hazardous Materials Table (HMT) found at 49 CFR 172.101. Selection of a proper shipping description requires knowledge of the physical properties and the chemical characteristics of the waste material *vis-à-vis* the DOT hazard class/division definitions and the available entries in the HMT. Figure 2 lists the DOT hazard classes/divisions.

The generator will have some knowledge of the waste material to be shipped from several sources:

1. Analytical result(s) from laboratory testing for the hazardous waste characteristics and/or land disposal restriction (LDR) purposes;

2. Analytical result(s) from laboratory testing by the designated facility for treatment/disposal purposes;

3. Material Safety Data Sheet (MSDS) information for the purchased components of the waste material; and

4. Knowledge of the hazard characteristics of the waste in light of the materials and process(es) involved.

This information is necessary, but may not be sufficient to determine the appropriate shipping description. It is critical that sufficient information be obtained to determine into which DOT hazard class(es)/division(s) the waste material is best classified. If a hazardous waste does not meet any of the technical (chemical name) descriptions in the HMT, hazardous waste may be assigned a shipping description from the HMT based on the hazard class/division definitions, the hierarchy of hazard classes, and the shipper's knowledge of the waste material.

Hazardous Materials Table

Selection of the shipping description is done by reference to the Hazardous Materials Table (HMT) found at 49 CFR 172.101. The HMT designates those materials to be treated as hazardous materials, for transportation purposes. The HMT is the key to determining the DOT requirements for packaging, labeling, and marking a waste material fitting a particular shipping description. The use of the Hazardous Materials Table (and the Appendix of Hazardous Substances and Reportable Quantities) should be mastered by generators/shippers of hazardous wastes.

The HMT consists of ten major columns. These columns give specific information and/or references to the following information:

Column 1:   Regulated mode(s) of transportation and
             shipping description considerations
Column 2:   Proper shipping name
Column 3:   Hazard class or division
Column 4:   DOT identification number
Column 5:   Packing group
Column 6:   Label(s)
Column 7:   Special provisions
Column 8:   Packaging authorizations
Column 9:   Quantity limitations for rail and air transport
Column 10:   Vessel stowage requirements

Columns (9) and (10) deal with requirements and limitations for air, passenger-carrying rail, or water shipments, and will not be discussed further. The List of Hazardous Substances and Reportable Quantities appears as an Appendix to the HMT.

The DOT regulations give little guidance in respect to the selection of the most appropriate shipping description for hazardous wastes. When selecting a proper shipping name for a particular material, the entry in the HMT that most accurately and specifically identifies the material must be used. For waste materials, especially mixtures, the correct technical (chemical) name of a material is not entirely accurate because use of technical names is not appropriate for mixtures of two hazardous materials, unless specifically listed in the HMT. For other waste materials consisting of proprietary chemicals, a technical (chemical) name is unavailable or may not be identified in the HMT. Another situation exists when a waste chemical has been so diluted or has become so spent that the waste material described by a technical (chemical) name no longer meets the definition of the associated hazard class. In the event that the correct technical name is not listed, is not accurate, or is not accurately described by the associated hazard class/division, the next most specific entry must be determined from the other types of descriptions corresponding to the specific hazard class(es)/division(s) of the material to be shipped. If an appropriate listing by technical (chemical) name is not found, listings by chemical family are evaluated. If no such listings are found or are appropriate, the listings by end use description corresponding to the hazard class/division of the material are reviewed. At this point, the hazard class, n.o.s. descriptions are evaluated.

When evaluating hazard class n.o.s. descriptions, it is necessary to remember the hierarchy of hazard classes ("hazard precedence" per §173.2) when using hazard class n.o.s. descriptions for materials meeting the definition of more than one hazard class. The hazard precedence, and the Precedence of Hazards Table are found at 49 CFR 173.2. Except when there are hazard class n.o.s. listings which specifically include all hazard classes posed by a material with multiple hazard classes, (e.g., flammable liquid, poisonous, n.o.s.), the hazard class n.o.s. entry corresponding with the highest hazard class of the material, per the precedence of hazards, is to be selected. Some hazardous wastes are appropriately described by more than one of the hazard classes (including corrosives, certain poisons, and flammable liquids) within level 8 of the §173.2a hazard precedence hierarchy. In such cases, the Precedence of Hazards Table at §173.2b is utilized when there is not an HMT entry (e.g., flammable liquids, corrosive, n.o.s.) identifying the multiple level 8 hazard class(es)/division(s) possessed by the waste.

The last resort with respect to shipping descriptions are the Class 9 listings. Class 9 listings are for describing those hazardous materials not meeting any other DOT hazard class definitions. Class 9 listings include:

Environmentally Hazardous Substance, liquid *or* solid, n.o.s. *and* Hazardous Waste, liquid *or* solid, n.o.s.

These entries are to be utilized only after all other levels of the shipping description hierarchy have been evaluated, and found not to contain an appropriate entry. Hazardous wastes not meeting the definition of any other hazard class are *by definition* Class 9, since hazardous wastes are *by definition* a subset of hazardous materials. DOT established the Class 9 hazard class for those materials regulated by EPA as hazardous substances or hazardous wastes, but that would not otherwise pose the level of hazard in transportation requiring DOT regulation.

Once the basic description, namely an appropriate shipping name/hazard class/identification number/packing group (if any) entry has been selected from the HMT, it is necessary to note the considerations which apply to how the description will appear on manifests and on containers. Recent revisions to the DOT regulations have added to these considerations when hazardous substances and hazardous wastes are shipped.

The first of these considerations is that the proper shipping name for a hazardous waste must include the word "waste" preceding the shipping name (e.g., waste acetone) unless the word "waste" is included in the description in the HMT (Ref. 172.101(c)(9)).

The second consideration is whether the shipment involves hazardous substances, as defined by DOT *for transportation purposes*. DOT has adopted the Reportable Quantities (RQs) that EPA established for hazardous substances under CERCLA. All listed and characteristic hazardous wastes have RQs, for transportation purposes. The DOT List of Hazardous Substances and Reportable Quantities is found as an Appendix to the HMT. For hazardous wastes, the generator/shipper should determine its RQ by referring to the entry in the Appendix for the Hazardous Waste Number (if the waste is a listed hazardous waste), or the hazardous waste characteristic(s) of the waste. The entries for listed hazardous wastes are at the end of the Appendix, following the alphabetical hazardous substance entries. The four entries for the characteristically hazardous wastes are identified together in the alphabetical entries, all preceded by the phrase "Unlisted Hazardous Wastes Characteristic of ...".

DOT treats RQs somewhat differently than EPA does under CERCLA. Under CERCLA, hazardous wastes are *by definition* hazardous substances, with an RQ for each listed and characteristic waste. DOT considers hazardous wastes to be a hazardous substance *for transportation purposes* only when an amount equal to or exceeding the Reportable Quantity is shipped *in a single package* (i.e., container, roll-off box, or tank truck). The entire amount shipped may greatly exceed the RQ. However, RQ designations on the manifest and containers only become mandatory when an amount equal to or exceeding the RQ is placed in a single package. The letters "RQ" must be entered on the shipping paper either before or after the basic description for each hazardous substance.

Except for radioactive materials, if the proper shipping name for a material that is a hazardous substance does not identify the hazardous substance by name, one of the following descriptions is to be entered, in parentheses, in association with the basic description:

1.   The name of the hazardous substance;
2.   The hazardous waste number (F, K, P, U, or D numbers from 40 CFR Part 261); or
3.   For characteristically hazardous wastes, the letters "EPA" followed by the word "ignitability", "corrosivity", "reactivity", or "toxicity" as appropriate can be used instead of the D-series hazardous waste number(s). (Ref. 172.203(c)).

Please note that when the EPA hazardous number(s) must appear with the shipping description, appearance of the hazardous waste number(s) in Item I - "Waste No." of the Uniform Hazardous Waste Manifest is not an acceptable substitute.

The DOT Emergency Response Communication Standard (49 CFR Part 172 - Subpart G Emergency Response Information) affects the shipping descriptions of hazardous waste shipments properly described by one of the HMT n.o.s. (not otherwise specified) entries identified at §172.203(k)(3).

Unless otherwise excepted, the general rule is that materials properly described by one of the identified n.o.s. entries must have the technical name of the hazardous material entered, in parentheses, in association with the basic description. Technical name(s) when appropriate are to be entered in parentheses either between the shipping name and hazard class or following the basic description. An appropriate modifier such as "contains" or "containing" may be used (Ref. §172.202(d) and §172.203(k)).

Shipments correctly described as "Hazardous waste, liquid *or* solid, n.o.s.," are allowed the option of either including the technical name or the EPA hazardous waste number in association with the basic description. For reference, the following sections of the DOT regulations impact shipping descriptions: 49 CFR §172.202(d), §172.203(c), §172.203(k), and §172.203(m).

Other considerations apply to waste materials that DOT considers to be poisons. First, the word "Poison" shall be entered on shipping papers in association with the shipping description where the material meets the DOT definition of poison, but that fact is not reflected in the proper shipping name or hazard class entry (Ref. §172.203(m)(1) and §172.203(k)(1)). Second, if the technical name of the compound or principal constituent that causes a material to meet the DOT definition of poison is not included in the proper shipping name, the technical name shall be entered in parentheses in association with the basic description (Ref. §172.203(m)(2)). Third, Division 2.3 materials and Division 6.1 materials that are poisonous by inhalation per §173.133(a)(2) shall have the words "Poison - Inhalation Hazard" and the words "Hazard Zone" "A", "B", "C", or "D" as appropriate entered on the shipping paper in association with the shipping description. The word "Poison" need not be repeated if it is already part of the shipping description. (Ref. §172.203(m)(3)).

For mixtures of a hazardous material identified by technical name and a *non*-hazardous material, "mixture" or "solution", as appropriate, can be added to the proper shipping name, provided the mixture or solution is not specifically identified in the HMT, and the hazard class of the mixture or solution is the same as that of the hazardous material's HMT entry. For mixtures of two or more hazardous materials, the use of a technical (chemical) name and "mixture" or "solution" is not appropriate, unless the mixture is specially identified in the HMT. In the instances of mixtures of two or more hazardous materials, an appropriate shipping description must be selected, using the hierarchy of shipping descriptions.

Before continuing further with the packaging, marking and labeling requirements, it may be useful to repeat some basic concepts in deriving appropriate shipping descriptions. Any material meeting the definition of a hazard class other than the one specified with a shipping name entry *must* be described by a shipping name that appropriately corresponds with its actual hazard class. The only exceptions are for those entries preceded by a Plus (+) in column (1) of the HMT. Also, when utilizing a hazard class n.o.s. description for a waste with multiple hazards, it is necessary to refer to the hierarchy of hazard classes.

PACKAGING OF HAZARDOUS MATERIALS

Column 8 of the HMT, entitled "Packaging Authorizations", contains references to packaging information for the hazardous material description in Column 2. Column 8 consists of three (3) subcolumns. Exceptions to the required use of authorized packaging are made in Column 8A. Authorized non-bulk packaging options are found in Column 8B and authorized bulk packaging options are found in Column 8C. Numerical entries in Columns 8A, 8B, and 8C are to be read as if preceded by "49 CFR 173.____."

Some packages are "excepted" from some parts of the regulations provided they meet certain requirements. Column 8A contains a reference to the applicable regulatory section, if any, dealing with excepted packaging. Often, the word "NONE" will appear in Column 8A, indicating that there are no exceptions to the use of authorized packaging.

If Column 8A contains the entry "NONE" *or* if the excepted packaging options specified are not acceptable or feasible, then authorized (formerly termed "specification") packaging must be used. Column 8B of the HMT refers to the section in 49 CFR Part 173 containing the authorized packaging requirements for non-bulk shipments, while column 8C addresses bulk packaging options. Please note that the appropriate Packing Group must be determined to identify the appropriate authorized packaging alternatives, if the hazardous material description in Column 2 is associated with multiple packing group entries in Column 5.

General requirements for shipments and packagings are found in Part 173. All packages of hazardous materials must meet certain general packaging requirements. These are found at 49 CFR 173.24. Materials forbidden for transportation are identified generally at 49 CFR 173.21, and specifically in Column 3 of the HMT. Most hazard classes have both general and specific packaging requirements. The authorized packaging alternatives from Columns (8B) and (8C) refer to UN specification packages identified in 49 CFR Part 173, Subparts E and F, respectively, except for Class 1 explosives and Class 7 radioactive materials.

Certain other aspects of the DOT regulations have a direct impact on packaging of hazardous wastes. DOT allows, at 49 CFR 173.12(a), the use of equivalent authorized open head drums for hazardous wastes containing solids and semisolids, where the use of the required authorized closed head drum would be impracticable.

DOT allows the use of overpack or salvage drums for damaged, defective, or leaking packages containing hazardous materials, under certain circumstances. This exception from authorized packaging is found at 49 CFR 173.3(c).

DOT allows the reuse of authorized non-bulk packaging for hazardous waste shipments at 49 CFR 173.28(b)(6) and §173.12(c). Such containers can be reused once for hazardous waste shipments, prior to reconditioning or disposal. There are certain conditions to reuse under these provisions, including:

1. Except as authorized, the waste must be packaged and offered for transportation in accordance with the regulations.
2. Transportation by highway only.
3. Package stands closed for 24 hours prior to shipment.
4. Each package is to be inspected for leakage immediately prior to being offered for transportation.
5. Each package is loaded by the shipper and unloaded by the consignee, unless the carrier is a private or contract carrier.

Please note that any inconsistent markings and labels should be removed or painted over prior to such reuse.

MARKING OF PACKAGES

The requirement to mark bulk and non-bulk packages of hazardous materials with certain information is found at 49 CFR Part 172 Subpart D - Marking. Packages having a maximum capacity of 450 liters (119 gallons) or less are considered non-bulk packages, and are to be marked with the proper shipping name and DOT identification number, preceded by "UN" or "NA" as appropriate. Technical names become part of the marking requirements for generic and n.o.s. shipping descriptions, subject to the provisions of §172.203(k). Containers of certain poisonous materials are also to be marked "Inhalation Hazard," in association with the required labels, as outlined at §172.313.

If an amount of hazardous waste equal to or exceeding its Reportable Quantity (RQ) is shipped within a single non-bulk package, then the letters "RQ" are to be marked on the package in association with the proper shipping name. If the shipping name does not identify the hazardous substance by name, the generator is given the option of marking either the name of the hazardous substance, or the EPA Hazardous Waste Number on the package, in parentheses, in association with the proper shipping name. For characteristically hazardous wastes, the EPA Hazardous Waste Number can be so marked, or the letters "EPA" followed by the specific characteristic, as appropriate. Normally, marking of the EPA Hazardous Waste Number, in parentheses, will be much less cumbersome.

EPA has additional marking requirements, found at 40 CFR 262.32, for containers of 110 gallons or less. These requirements are to be met prior to transportation. Such containers are to be marked with the following words and information:

> "HAZARDOUS WASTE - Federal Law Prohibits Improper Disposal. If found, contact the nearest police or public safety authority or the U.S. Environmental Protection Agency.
> Generator's Name and Address _____.
> Manifest Document Number _____."

Normally, the DOT and EPA marking requirements are satisfied with a commercially-printed decal. The word "Waste" need not be part of the shipping description marking if these EPA marking requirements are met.

LABELING OF PACKAGES

The requirements for labeling of hazardous material packages are found at 49 CFR 172 - Subpart E. Labeling refers to placing DOT-specification diamond-shaped decals on packages indicating the hazard class/division of the contents. Packages, including containers, of hazardous materials are to be labeled as specified in column (6) of the HMT shipping name entry selected for the hazardous material. If Column (6) shows more than one label for the shipping name and packing group, all such labels must be affixed. Generally, the first label listed is considered the Primary Hazard, and subsequent labels are considered Subsidiary Hazards. Portable tanks are not required to be labeled when they are appropriately placarded.

Hazard class labels are to be placed near the shipping name markings. When both primary and subsidiary hazard labels are required, they must be placed next to each other. For labeling purposes, the Primary Hazard labels are to have the class/division number in the lower corner of the label. Subsidiary Hazard labels are not to display any hazard/division number. There is a subsidiary Hazard Label Table at §172.402(a) to deal with labeling materials with multiple hazards not specifically addressed in the HMT.

Labels on hazardous material packages must reflect the hazard of the hazardous material in the package. *"Precautionary" labeling (i.e., use of flammable liquid label on containers of combustible liquids) is prohibited at 49 CFR 172.401.* The DOT hazard class definitions, found at 49 CFR Part 173, are very specific. Using common sense interpretations or the EPA hazardous waste characteristics as substitutes for determining the appropriate DOT hazard class(es) is ill advised.

PLACARDING OF TRANSPORTATION VEHICLES

Placarding of transportation vehicles is addressed at 49 CFR Part 172 - Subpart F. Placarding is a joint shipper/carrier responsibility. The shipper must either placard the transportation vehicle or offer the carrier the required placards for the material being offered for transportation, unless the carrier's vehicle is already properly placarded for the material.

Placarding does not apply to Infectious Substances/Etiologic Agents (Division 6.2), hazardous materials classed as ORM-D, or hazardous materials offered as Limited Quantities per §172.203(b). Placards must only be used for materials defined as hazardous materials, and must represent the hazard(s) of the material being transported. Placards must be placed on each side and on each end of the transport vehicle.

The various DOT categories of materials (hazard class or division and additional descriptions, as appropriate) are split into Table 1 and Table 2, for placarding purposes (49 CFR 172.504). Any quantity of hazardous materials classified as:

Division 1.1, 1.2, or 1.3 Explosives
Division 2.3 Poisonous Gas
Division 4.3 Dangerous when wet material
Division 6.1 Poisonous material, Packing Group I, inhalation hazard
Division 7 Radioactive (Yellow-III label)

must be placarded as provided in Table 1 of 49 CFR 172.504. Very few hazardous wastes would be subject to Table 1 placarding requirements. Most hazardous waste shipments would be subject to Table 2 placarding requirements.

Table 2

Category of material (Hazard class or division number and additional description, as appropriate)	Placard Name
1.4	EXPLOSIVES 1.4
1.5	EXPLOSIVES 1.5
1.6	EXPLOSIVES 1.6
2.1	FLAMMABLE GAS
2.2	NON-FLAMMABLE GAS
3	FLAMMABLE
Combustible Liquid	COMBUSTIBLE
4.1	FLAMMABLE SOLID
4.2	SPONTANEOUSLY COMBUSTIBLE
5.1	OXIDIZER

5.2	ORGANIC PEROXIDE
6.1 (PG I or II, other than	POISON
PG I inhalation hazard)	
6.1 (PG III)	KEEP AWAY FROM FOOD
6.2	(None)
8	CORROSIVE
9	CLASS 9
ORM-D	(None)

When the gross weight of all hazardous materials covered by Table 2 is less than 1001 pounds (451 kg), no placards are required on the transport vehicle. For mixed shipments (requiring different placards) of Table 2 materials, the DANGEROUS placard may be used in place of separate placarding for each class. *However,* when 5,000 pounds (2,268 kg) or more of one class of material is loaded at a single facility, the placards specified in Table 2 for that class must be applied. Do *not* combine Table 1 and Table 2 items when determining placarding.

Additional placards may be required for Poison-Inhalation Hazard materials and for materials which have the subsidiary hazard of being dangerous when wet.

THE UNIFORM HAZARDOUS WASTE MANIFEST

The transportation of hazardous wastes to offsite TSD facilities is to be accompanied by a document called the Uniform Hazardous Waste Manifest (EPA Form 8700-22). The Uniform Hazardous Waste Manifest is the mandatory format for shipping papers that must accompany hazardous waste shipments. In its simplest form, the manifest is a four-part shipping document which serves to track hazardous wastes to ensure delivery to the designated TSD facility. There is a continuation page available (EPA Form 8700-22A) for shipments of more than four types of hazardous wastes. The manifest serves both shipping document and tracking document purposes.

The Uniform Hazardous Waste Manifest (Figure 3) is the mandatory format for hazardous waste shipping papers. However, it is not a universal form, as state hazardous waste management agencies are allowed to require the use of state-supplied manifest forms. Typically, requirements to use a state-supplied manifest form are accompanied by additional parts of the manifest, as well as by requirements for the generator and/or the designated facility to mail signed manifest parts or copies to the state regulatory agency.

There is a hierarchy to be followed in determining the appropriate manifest form (not format) to use for shipments of hazardous waste to out-of-state TSD facilities. If the State in which the designated facility is located (the consignment State) supplies the manifest and requires its use, then that State's manifest form must be used. If the consignment State does not supply the manifest, but the State in which the generator is located (generator State) supplies the manifest and requires its use, then the generator State's manifest must be used. If neither the consignment State or generator State supplies the manifest, then any manifest with sufficient parts or copies meeting the mandatory format of EPA Form 8700-22 can be used.

The Uniform Hazardous Waste Manifest must consist of sufficient copies (sometimes referred to as parts) to provide the generator, each transporter, and the designated facility with one copy each for their records and another copy to be returned to the generator by the designated facility, acknowledging acceptance of the waste shipment. State-supplied manifests typically have at least two additional copies: one to be mailed to the state regulatory agency by the generator and another to be mailed to the state regulatory agency by the designated facility. Generators required to use State-supplied forms will typically be informed of same by their state regulatory agency and/or their designated TSD facility. The instructions for State-supplied manifests should be carefully read to ensure compliance with the requirements to provide copies to the State regulatory agency. Such instructions usually include directives to provide additional information in the shaded areas of the manifest.

Completing the Uniform Hazardous Waste Manifest

The Uniform Hazardous Waste Manifest format can be thought of as consisting of three sections. The form itself, consisting of multiple pages, was designed for use on a 12-pitch (elite) typewriter. The form can be completed by hand, using a ball point pen. However, handwritten information typically is illegible on the last few copies of the form. The

DOT regulations on shipping papers (49 CFR 172.201) require all copies to be legible and printed (either manually or mechanically).

The upper section of the manifest consists of items 1 - 10. These items serve to identify all the parties to the shipment: the generator, the transporter(s), and the designated facility. There are spaces for each party's name and EPA Identification Number, as well as the generator's mailing address (where the manifests will be kept) and emergency telephone number. There is also a space for the designated facility's site address. Certain areas of the manifest format are shaded. The federal EPA regulations do not require that any of the items in the shaded area (Items A - K) be completed. States can require the completion of some or all of items A - K, under State regulatory authority. Many of these items, particularly the transporter's telephone number (Items C & F) and the designated facility's telephone number (Item H) should be completed regardless, as a matter of good practice and common sense.

The last five digits of Item 1, following the generator's 12-digit EPA Identification Number, are to be a unique five-digit number assigned to the manifest by the generator. The number must be unique, so the five digits "00000" or "00001" are not to be reused. The regulations formerly required that a sequential manifest document number be assigned. As a matter of routine and to assist in recordkeeping, many generators use the first two digits of the five digit document number to identify the year of the shipment, with the last three digits being sequential numbers (e.g., 92001, 92002, 92003). Completed manifests (those with a signed copy returned by the TSD facility) are then filed by year.

The final point with respect to the upper third of the manifest is Item 2. Unless continuation sheets (EPA Form 8700-22A) are used, this should be completed as "Page 1 of 1".

The middle section, consisting of Items 11 - 15, integrates the DOT Hazardous Material shipping paper requirements into the manifest form. The U.S. DOT shipping description(s), discussed earlier in this chapter, for the waste(s) to be shipped is to be entered in Item 11 a-d, as necessary. Unless specifically authorized or required, the shipping description may not contain any code or abbreviation. The inclusion of additional information, such as technical names and hazardous waste numbers was discussed earlier in this chapter, as was the significance of hazardous substance shipments.

Item 12 requires the entry of the number of containers of each waste, as well as the type of container(s) used. Mandatory abbreviations are given for the various types of containers. These abbreviations are:

DM = Metal drums, barrels, kegs
DW = Wooden drums, barrels, kegs
DF = Fiberboard or plastic drums, barrels, kegs
TP = Tanks portable
TT = Cargo tanks (tank trucks)
TC = Tank cars
DT = Dump truck
CY = Cylinders
CM = Metal boxes, cartons, cases (including roll-offs)
CW = Wooden boxes, cartons, cases
CF = Fiber or plastic boxes, cartons, cases
BA = Burlap, cloth, paper or plastic bags

Item 13 requires that the total quantity of waste be described, in conjunction with item 14 - the unit of weight or volume used to describe the total quantity. Mandatory abbreviations are also specified for the units of measure entered on the manifest.

G = Gallons (liquids only)
P = Pounds
T = Tons (2000 lbs)
Y = Cubic yards
L = Liters (liquids only)
K = Kilograms
M = Metric tons (1000 kg)
N = Cubic meters

Items I - Waste Number, Item J - Additional Descriptions for Materials Listed Above, and Item K - Handling Codes for Wastes Listed Above, can and are often required to be completed under State regulatory authority. These areas can be used by the generator along with Item 15 - Special

Handling Instructions and Additional Information, to make the manifest transmit desirable types of additional information and special instructions. Such information can include:

1. The identification of the person to whose attention manifest return copies are to be mailed.
2. The identification of the generator's contact person or contractor, as well as appropriate 24 hour telephone numbers, for emergency purposes or for further information. The appropriate Guide Number from the DOT Emergency Response Guidebook could also be specified.
3. Instructions to return the shipment to the generator if it or any part is rejected by the designated facility.
4. Identification of an alternate designated facility, site address and EPA Identification Number, in the event an emergency prevents delivery of the waste to the primary designated facility.
5. Identification of the common names for the waste materials being shipped, along with any TSD facility - assigned waste product codes, contract numbers, or scheduling numbers, sometimes called work order numbers.
6. Identification of appropriate Purchase Orders for the treatment/disposal of the waste shipment or other special billing instructions.
7. Verification as to how the transport vehicle was properly placarded after loading, or that the appropriate placards were offered to the transporter.
8. Specification of the method of treatment or disposal to be used by the designated facility on the waste being shipped, as well as any special precautions or other instructions.
9. Land Disposal Restriction (LDR) information, per 40 CFR Part 268, although typically the amount of required information for most LDR notifications will require the use of a separate form. Many TSD facilities require the use of land disposal restriction forms of their own design, in order to simplify their recordkeeping.

The lower third of the manifest, Items 16 - 20, is where the parties to the shipment sign the manifest by hand, acknowledging or certifying specific conditions. All parties are to print or type their name, sign their name, and date their signature. In Item 16, the generator, typically an employee of the generator in a responsible position, is certifying two statements. First, a certification is made that the shipment is properly described, packaged, marked and labeled, and is otherwise ready for transportation in accordance with applicable DOT regulations. Second, a certification is made that the generator is complying with waste minimization requirements, and that the method of treatment or disposal selected minimizes present and future threats to public health and environmental quality. Employees of the generator that sign the manifest are allowed to write the words "On behalf of" in the signature block prior to signing their names. This is allowed so as to address the concerns of employees regarding personal liabilities for any environmental or public health problems resulting from the waste shipment.

Transporters must acknowledge receipt in Item 17 of the wastes described by the manifest. This is done by entering the name of the person accepting the waste, typically the driver. The transporter's signature is then placed on the manifest, as well as the date of acceptance. EPA Manifest Form 8700-22 allows for the use of two transporter companies. If a second transporter is used, then the first transporter must obtain the name, signature, and date of acceptance from the second transporter. Of course, if two transporters are used, Item 7 - Transporter 2 Company Name and USEPA ID Number - must be completed as well.

Items 19 and 20 are for use of the designated facility owner or operator. If there are any significant discrepancies between the shipment as received, and the shipment as described on the manifest, the authorized representative of the designated facility's owner or operator is to note the details in Item 19. Significant discrepancies include any differences in the container count, as well as variations of more than 10 percent in weight for bulk shipments. Significant discrepancies can also exist with respect to the type of waste received, when it differs from the type of waste described on the manifest. Significant discrepancies can result in rejected shipments, which are then returned to the generator, or sent to an alternate designated facility selected by the generator.

If the waste shipment is accepted, or is accepted except as noted in Item 19, the name of the person accepting the waste on behalf of the designated facility must be entered in Item 20, along with their signature and date of acceptance. The certification in Item 20 only acknowledges receipt of the manifested shipment, except as noted in the discrepancy indication space (Item 19). It is not certification that the wastes have been or will be properly managed or treated or disposed of by any particular technology.

Using the Manifest

The generator is to complete the appropriate Uniform Hazardous Waste Manifest form, using State-supplied forms when appropriate. The generator is well-advised to read the instructions typically printed on the back of State-supplied manifest forms, or the instructions found in the Appendix to 40 CFR Part 262. The generator must ensure that the required information is legible on all pages or copies of the manifest. Carbon pages or carbonless forms are typically used. Some State-supplied manifest forms have up to seven identical pages, so using a typewriter becomes necessary to ensure legibility on the bottom copies of the manifest. Any last minute changes should be initialed by the person signing the manifest.

Upon obtaining the appropriate pre-shipment acceptance by and making any other necessary arrangements with a commercial TSD facility regarding the particular waste to be shipped, the generator then typically schedules the shipment with both the transporter and designated TSD facility.

The transporter typically inspects the shipment prior to loading, verifying that the containers are in good condition, closed, marked and labeled. An accurate container count is established, and the containers are loaded, and properly blocked and braced to avoid problems during transportation.

The generator then signs and dates the manifest certification. The printed name, signature, and date of acceptance is obtained from the driver. The driver will leave one copy of the manifest for the generator's records, and may need to leave an additional copy for the generator to mail to a state regulatory agency. State-supplied forms often specify which copy or copies are to be left with the generator, either by color or by copy number. LDR forms appropriate to the wastes being shipped are to accompany the shipment. Copies of LDR forms, which must reference the manifest document number, are to be retained by the generator for LDR compliance purposes.

The transporter must take the remainder of the manifest with the shipment, as the manifest serves as the hazardous materials shipping paper, for DOT purposes. The first transporter then must deliver the entire shipment to the second transporter, if specified in Item 7, or to the designated facility identified in Item 9. The transporter cannot (and should not be allowed to) select the designated facility for the waste. Remember that the manifest, with the exception of the required signatures, is to be completed by the generator/shipper.

The transporter must obtain the signature of the second transporter, if any, and date of delivery or the signature of the designated facility and the date of delivery. The transporter then retains one copy of the manifest with the appropriate signatures, and gives the remaining copies to either the second transporter or the designated facility. The facility retains one copy for its records, and sends to the generator a copy of the manifest with the handwritten signature of the owner or operator of the designated facility. When a State-supplied manifest form is used, then a copy typically is mailed to the state regulatory agency as well.

If the generator does not receive a copy of the manifest with the handwritten signature of the designated facility's owner, operator, or designated representative within 35 days of the date of shipment, the generator is to contact the transporter and/or the designated facility to determine the status and disposition of the waste shipment. If a manifest copy with the handwritten signature of the designated facility is not received within 45 days of the date of shipment, the generator must file an Exception Report with the Regional Administrator of the U.S. EPA or the authorized State regulatory agency. The Exception Report must include a copy of the manifest for which no confirmation of delivery was received (termed an "open" manifest), as well as a letter signed by the generator explaining the efforts taken to locate the waste shipment, and the results of those efforts.

Having an open manifest beyond the 45 day period allowed is serious business. In effect, it means that the shipment of hazardous waste is lost, despite efforts to determine its status or ultimate disposition. If regulatory agencies discover an open manifest after the 45 day period allowed for obtaining the signed return copy has expired, an enforcement action will be forthcoming. EPA considers open manifests to be a Class I violation, of serious consequence. Generators are well-advised to have a tickler file for manifest copies left by the transporter, pending receipt of the manifest copy signed by the designated TSD facility.

Land Disposal Restriction Notices

Generators are required to provide notification to any offsite TSD facility with respect to wastes subject to the Land Disposal Restrictions found at 40 CFR Part 268. This notification becomes, in effect, part of the manifest requirements because such notices are to accompany each offsite shipment of restricted waste.

These notices are required even if the waste is being sent to a treatment or reclamation facility. Shipments of restricted wastes to land disposal facilities must be accompanied by a notice and certification that the waste meets the applicable treatment standards. Alternatively, the generator must send a notice with the shipment to the land disposal facility that the restricted waste is subject to a case-by-case extension, an exemption, or nationwide variance.

Many commercial TSD facilities have placed the information elements of the mandatory restricted waste notices on their own forms, and require customers to use the appropriate form developed by the TSD facility.

Recordkeeping

The land disposal restriction (LDR) notices are, in effect, part of the manifest requirements and should be considered to be subject to the same recordkeeping requirements. Generators are required at 40 CFR 262.40 to keep a copy of each manifest signed by the transporter for three years, or until a copy is received with the signature of the authorized representative of the designated TSD facility which accepted the waste. This latter manifest must be retained at least three years from the date the waste was received by the initial transporter.

The LDR program has a longer records retention period. Generators are required, at 40 CFR 268.7(a)(6), to maintain copies of all notices, certifications, demonstrations, waste analysis data, and other documentation (for knowledge of waste-based determinations) for at least five (5) years from the date the waste was last sent to on-site or off-site treatment, storage or disposal. Generators are also to document where restricted waste was treated, stored, or disposed. This applies to both off-site and on-site waste management.

The records retention period for manifests and LDR information is automatically extended during any unresolved enforcement action or as requested by the EPA or authorized State regulatory agency. As a practical matter, manifests, waste analyses, and other supporting information should be kept indefinitely, storage space permitting. Such records are often the only means of determining whether EPA claims of liability are justified, with respect to the generator's involvement at any facility subject to EPA enforcement under CERCLA.

CONCLUSION

The offsite shipment of hazardous waste requires careful consideration of both DOT and EPA regulatory requirements. Mastering the use of the Hazardous Materials Table in selecting the most appropriate shipping description is critical to determining the appropriate DOT requirements. This information, in conjunction with knowledge of the use of the Uniform Hazardous Waste Manifest, and the Land Disposal Restriction notices, allows the preparation of the proper shipping papers. Selection of the transporter and treatment/disposal facility is then necessary to minimize statutory and regulatory liabilities.

SUMMARY OF DOT HM-181 TRANSITIONAL PROVISIONS
(49 CFR 171.14)

September 18, 1991 *Federal Register* (56 *FR* 47158-47163)

Effective October 1, 1991

New explosives must be classified, described on shipping papers, marked on packages, and labeled according to the new system. Classification criteria in § 173.115(c) are effective for gases which are poisonous by inhalation. For these gases, the words "Poison-Inhalation Hazard" or "Inhalation Hazard", as appropriate must be entered on shipping papers, as required by either §172.203(m) or Special Provision 13 to the §172.101 Table. Except for cultures of infectious substances (etiologic agents) of 50 ml or less total quantity in one package (the "50 ml exception"), revised hazard communication (shipping papers, marking, and labeling) and classification requirements are effective for infectious substances. Infectious substances (etiologic agents) currently excepted under the "50 ml exception" in §173.386(d)(3) are granted a one-year extension of the effective date, until October 1, 1992.

Effective October 1, 1992

Revised hazard communication requirements (i.e., descriptions on shipping papers, package marking, labeling, and vehicle placarding) are effective for all materials meeting the criteria for poisonous by inhalation, including those assigned Special Provision 13 in column 7 of the §172.101 Table. Also, revised hazard communication (shipping papers, marking and labeling) and classification requirements are effective for cultures of infectious substances (etiologic agents) of 50 ml or less total quantity in one package.

Effective October 1, 1993

Except for placarding, compliance with new classification and hazard communication requirements is required for all other hazardous materials. Packaging requirements are effective for all materials meeting the criteria of poisonous by inhalation. Model requirements are effective, and hazardous materials must be loaded and segregated as required in §174.81 and §177.848 for transportation by rail car and motor vehicle, respectively.

Effective October 1, 1994

Non-bulk packagings are required to be manufactured in compliance with UN performance standards. Also, conversion to the new placarding system is required for the transport of all hazardous materials except materials poisonous by inhalation (for which placarding requirements are effective October 1, 1992).

Effective October 1, 1996

DOT specification packagings rendered obsolete by the December 21, 1990 final rule may no longer be used. Other transitional provisions are established in §171.14(c). Paragraph (c)(1) allows packages filled with hazardous materials before October 1, 1991, to (1) retain original markings and labeling; and (2) not comply with the UN packaging standards if these packages are transported prior to October 1, 2001. However, as of October 1, 1992, the "Inhalation Hazard" marking specified in §172.313(a) must be applied to packages filled with materials meeting the criteria of poisonous by inhalation. Until October 1, 1994, carriers may use either new "UN-based" or old placards, as indicated in the placard substitution table provided in paragraph (c)(2). RSPA sets forth "mix and match" guidelines in §171.14(c)(3) for operating within a dual system during the various transition periods.

Figure 1
DOT REGULATIONS REGARDING
HAZARDOUS MATERIALS AND WASTES

49 CFR Chapter I - Research and Special Programs Administration
Subchapter C - Hazardous Materials Regulations

Part 171 - **General Information, Regulations and Definitions**
Part 172 - **Hazardous Materials Table and Hazardous Materials Communication Requirements**

    Subpart A - General
    Subpart B - Table of Hazardous Materials and Special Provisions
    Subpart C - Shipping Papers
    Subpart D - Marking
    Subpart E - Labeling
    Subpart F - Placarding
    Subpart G - Emergency Response Information

Part 173 - **General Requirements for Shipments and Packagings**

    Subpart A - General
    Subpart B - Preparation of Hazardous Materials for Transportation
    Subpart C - Definitions, Classification and Packaging for Class 1 (Explosives)
    Subpart D - Definitions, Classification, Packaging Group Assignments and Exceptions for Hazardous Materials Other than Class 1 and Class 7
    Subpart E - Non-Bulk Packaging for Hazardous Materials Other than Class 1 and Class 7
    Subpart F - Bulk Packaging for Hazardous Materials Other than Class 1 and Class 7
    Subpart G - Gases, Definition and Preparation
    Subpart I - Radioactive Materials
    Appendices - Test Methods and Classification Guidelines

Part 174 - **Carriage by Rail**
Part 175 - **Carriage by Aircraft**

Part 176 - Carriage by Vessel
Part 177 - Carriage by Public Highway
Part 178 - Specifications for Packagings
Part 179 - Specification for Tank Cars
Part 180 - Rules for Continuing Qualification and Maintenance of Packagings

Figure 2
DOT Hazard Classes/Divisions

Class/Division Number	Name of Class or Division	49 CFR Reference Definition
1.1	Explosives	173.50(b)(1)
1.2	Explosives	173.50(b)(2)
1.3	Explosives	173.50(b)(3)
1.4	Explosives	173.50(b)(4)
1.5	Explosives	173.50(b)(5)
1.6	Explosives	173.50(b)(6)
2.1	Flammable Gas	173.115(a)
2.2	Non-flammable, compressed gas[1]	173.115(b)
2.3	Poisonous gas	173.115(c)
3	Flammable Liquid	173.120(a)
	Combustible Liquid	173.120(b)
4.1	Flammable Solid	173.124(a)
4.2	Spontaneously combustible material	173.124(b)
4.3	Dangerous when wet material	173.124(c)
5.1	Oxidizer	173.127(a)
5.2	Organic peroxide	173.128(a)
6.1	Poisonous material	173.132(a)
6.2	Infectious substance (Etiologic agent)	173.134(a)
7	Radioactive material	173.403
8	Corrosive material	173.136(a)
9	Miscellaneous hazardous material	173.136(a)
		173.140(a)
		173.140(b)
ORM-D	ORM-D	173.144
None	Forbidden materials	173.21

Note: 49 CFR also has Classification Codes and Compatibility Groups for Explosives (173.52).

---

[1] Includes non-flammable, non-poisonous Compressed Gases, Liquified Gases, Pressurized Cryogenic gases, and Compressed Gases in Solution that do not meet the definition of either 2.1 or 2.3.

Figure 3

Please print or type. (Form designed for use on elite (12-pitch) typewriter.) Form Approved OMB No. 2050-0039. Expires 9-30-88

UNIFORM HAZARDOUS WASTE MANIFEST

1. Generator's US EPA ID No. Manifest Document No
2. Page 1 of

Information in the shaded areas is not required by Federal law.

3. Generator's Name and Mailing Address

A. State Manifest Document Number

B. State Generator's ID

4. Generator's Phone ( )

5. Transporter 1 Company Name
6. US EPA ID Number

C. State Transporter's ID

D. Transporter's Phone

7. Transporter 2 Company Name
8. US EPA ID Number

E. State Transporter's ID

F. Transporter's Phone

9. Designated Facility Name and Site Address
10. US EPA ID Number

G. State Facility's ID

H. Facility's Phone

GENERATOR

	HM	11. US DOT Description *(Including Proper Shipping Name, Hazard Class and ID Number)*	12. Containers No.	Type	13. Total Quantity	14. Unit Wt/Vol	I. Waste No.
a.							
b.							
c.							
d.							

J. Additional Descriptions for Materials Listed Above

K. Handling Codes for Wastes Listed Above

15. Special Handling Instructions and Additional Information

16. **GENERATOR'S CERTIFICATION**: I hereby declare that the contents of this consignment are fully and accurately described above by proper shipping name and are classified, packed, marked, and labeled, and are in all respects in proper condition for transport by highway according to applicable international and national government regulations.

If I am a large quantity generator, I certify that I have a program in place to reduce the volume and toxicity of waste generated to the degree I have determined to be economically practicable and that I have selected the practicable method of treatment, storage, or disposal currently available to me which minimizes the present and future threat to human health and the environment; **OR**, if I am a small quantity generator, I have made a good faith effort to minimize my waste generation and select the best waste management method that is available to me and that I can afford.

Printed/Typed Name | Signature | *Month Day Year*

TRANSPORTER

17. Transporter 1 Acknowledgement of Receipt of Materials

Printed/Typed Name | Signature | *Month Day Year*

18. Transporter 2 Acknowledgement of Receipt of Materials

Printed/Typed Name | Signature | *Month Day Year*

FACILITY

19. Discrepancy Indication Space

20. Facility Owner or Operator: Certification of receipt of hazardous materials covered by this manifest except as noted in Item 19.

Printed/Typed Name | Signature | *Month Day Year*

Style F15REV-6 Labelmaster, Div. of American Labelmark Co. Inc. 60646

EPA Form 8700-22 (Rev. 9/86) Previous editions are obsolete.

WORKER RIGHT-TO-KNOW LAW

Donald E. Witt, B.S.ChE., M.S., P.E.
Tennessee Department of Labor

INTRODUCTION

Hazardous materials are useful to society, and if used properly should not present a threat to occupational safety and health. The use of chemicals in today's economy began without adequate study of hazardous effects on workers and adherence to safe practices and exposures. The Hazard Communication Standard focuses on communication of these hazards to the worker. The degree of exposure is not the issue, since it is already regulated by OSHA. It is the knowledge of the hazards of chemicals in normal conditions of use, Material Safety Data Sheets, labels and other forms of warning, effective information and training programs, written hazard determination and communication programs.

Numerous State and municipal governments' worker Right-to-Know laws resulted in the promulgation of a Federal Right-to-Know law entitled the Hazard Communication Standard, 29 CFR 1910.1200. The objective of this law is to communicate to the worker the presence and effects of hazardous chemicals in the workplace which are known to be present in such a manner that employees may be exposed under normal conditions of use or in a potential emergency. With a few exceptions (labeling on pesticides, foods, distilled spirits and consumer products, and total exemptions on regulated hazardous wastes, tobacco, wood and foods, drugs or cosmetics intended for personal use), all workers must be informed, and training for worker identification evaluation and protection must have been in place by May 25, 1986.

Training

To accomplish this training, each employer must establish a hazardous chemical list. This list is defined in a written hazard determination program developed by each employer. The format for this program is suggested in the Standard in Section (d). Chemical hazards are generally classified in two groups: physical and health. Physical hazards generally include combustibility, flammability, compressibility (of gases), explosivity, stability, or reactivity. Health hazards include acute and chronic effects on the body that may result in cancer, birth defects, toxic effects such as damage to the lungs, skin, eyes, mucous, blood, liver, kidney, central nervous system, and irritation of skin, corrosion, and sensitivity. According to the Standard all chemicals mentioned in (1) OSHA, (2) the latest ACGIH-TLV Publication, (3) IARC or NTP and OSHA as carcinogens or potential carcinogens, (4) Appendix A of the Standard Health Hazard Definitions, and (5) Appendix B -- Hazard Determination, are hazardous. Only the use of significant available evidence for hazardous effects is required for this standard. No animal experimentation is needed.

The chemical list required by each employer (in Standard Industrial Classification Codes 20-39) is composed of (1) hazardous chemicals as determined from the Material Safety Data Sheets (MSDS) from chemical manufacturers, distributors and importers, in the "hazardous ingredients" section, and (2) in-house reaction products such as welding fumes, carbon monoxide from lift trucks, wood dust, and chemical intermediates. A walk-through of the plant is initially suggested, and all chemicals used (compressed gases and dusts included) or developed should be noted. MSDS should be requested from suppliers for all incoming materials used and developed and evaluated for reaction products by a qualified person such as a chemist or industrial hygienist. The content of the MSDS is given in Section (g) of the Standard. There is no form that is required, only the format. Forms give the appearance of requiring certain information (often not required), and allow too little space for needed information. A good indication of whether the MSDS is current is if it states whether the chemical is listed in NTP, IARC, or OSHA [see Section(g)(2)(vii)] as a carcinogen. Most chemicals used in industry are mixtures of pure chemicals whose hazardous properties have not been determined as a whole. Therefore, the hazardous properties of each chemical (if over 1 percent for a hazardous chemical, and over 0.1 percent for a carcinogen) must be given. Physical hazards of chemical as well as health hazards must be addressed. Chemical names may be withheld under certain conditions [see Section (i)] as long as all other information is presented. Qualified people such as physicians or health professionals may obtain immediate revelation if necessary. Physicians generally treat health problems symptomatically and the immediate knowledge of the chemical name is not generally necessary. In some instances, symptomatic treatment only exacerbates the condition.

Employee recall is perhaps the most effective measurement of communication. The required information must be in simple and understandable language, as used by the worker. The MSDS probably cannot be used directly as the medium of communication since the language is often too technical. The information must be simplified, summarized and communicated. In some parts of the country, 20 percent of the working force cannot effectively read or write. Written information transfer is not the acceptable method. Supervisor-to-worker communication is essential using visual aids and dialogue. A bell-shaped statistical curve will describe adequate recall. The basic areas of the employee knowledge according to Section (h) are:

1.   Purpose
2.   What
3.   Where
4.   Effect on body
5.   Detection
6.   Protection
7.   Written Program & MSDS

Employees are not only responsible for a written plan for determining whether chemicals they use or store are hazardous (which must be shown and explained to the worker) they must develop a written program of the plan they will use to affect the hazard communication program -- Section (e). This plan should designate a person in charge of the various responsibilities and generally explain how they will be carried out. These responsibilities are: (1) attainment and maintaining of MSDS, (2) attainment and maintaining of labels, (3) execution and sources for a good training program, (4) production of a hazardous chemical list, (5) the methods the employer will use to inform employees of the hazards of non-routine tasks (for example, the cleaning of reactor vessels), and the hazards associated with chemicals contained in unlabeled pipes in their work areas, and (6) the methods the employer will use to inform any contractor employees working in the employer's workplace of the hazardous chemicals they may be exposed to while performing their work, and any suggestions for appropriate protective measures. The written hazard communication program may be combined with these responsibilities as a seventh section.

Employees should be made aware of their responsibilities for an effective program. Unless they fully participate in fellow employee health, the program will not attain its intended goal of a safe and healthy working place for everyone. It should also be emphasized that management commitment and enthusiasm dictates to a large degree the effectiveness of the program.

Lab Standard Supplement (29 CFR 1910.1450)

The application of the Right-to-Know Law for laboratories is defined in OSHA's "Occupational Exposure to Hazardous Chemicals in Laboratories," 29 CFR 1910.1450. Either the Hazardous Communication Standard or the Laboratory Standard applies to all "laboratory" operations. The formaldehyde standard (29 CFR 1910.1048) when used in laboratories, supercedes the jurisdiction of any other standard. Even though the laboratory standard differs slightly with the hazard communication standard, the intent that workers must know about the chemicals they use or are exposed to under normal conditions or in a foreseeable emergency is identical. A written program as defined in Section (g) requiring a chemical hygiene officer, criteria for determining and implementing control measures to reduce employee exposure to hazardous chemicals, must be clearly defined, and all chemicals not identified and evaluated must be considered hazardous. Individual worker recall of basic information concerning hazardous effects on the body, detection, prevention of exposures by engineering means, personal protection and work practice is the key to any effective right-to-know program.

OSHA REQUIREMENTS PERTAINING TO HAZARDOUS MATERIALS MANAGEMENT

Belton G. Aldrich
Retired

INTRODUCTION

Approximately 25 million workers -- about one of four in the nation's workforce -- are exposed to one or more chemical hazards. There are an estimated 575,000 existing chemical products, and hundreds of new ones are introduced annually. This poses a serious problem for exposed workers.

Chemical exposure may cause or contribute to many serious health effects such as heart ailments, kidney and lung damage, sterility, cancer, burns, and rashes. Some chemicals may also be safety hazards and have the potential to cause fires and explosions and other serious accidents. In light of these facts, the Occupational Safety and Health Administration (OSHA) was created by the United States Congress within the Department of Labor to administer the Occupational Safety and Health Act of 1970.

In 1971, OSHA promulgated its initial Occupational Safety and Health Standards, which were derived primarily from National Consensus Standards originally developed by voluntary nongovernmental organizations. The emphasis in these standards was on safety, and many of these so-called nuisance standards have since been revoked at the insistence of Congress. OSHA was also aware of the link between cancer and the workplace. This was first established in 1775 when an English surgeon, Sir Percival Pott, reported on the high rate of scrotal cancer among London chimney sweeps.

The first new health standard under the act reduced the permissible level of worker exposure to asbestos to five fibers longer than five micrometers per cubic meter of air, effective July 1972, and to two fibers, effective July 1976. (An Emergency Temporary Standard (ETS) was established in November 1983, reducing asbestos exposure to one-half fiber per cubic centimeter (cc) of air averaged over an eight-hour time period. The exposure is now 0.2 fiber/cc). This was the beginning of what is known as the Subpart Z Standards. Since the asbestos standard, OSHA has promulgated several other health standards. OSHA also has proposed 21 other health standards which have not yet been promulgated.

29 CFR 1910 Subpart H -- Hazardous Materials

Subpart H covers regulations pertaining to the safe handling and storage of compressed gases, flammable and combustible liquids, and explosives and blasting agents.

29 CFR 1910.101 -- Compressed Gases
(General Requirements)

Inspection of Compressed Gas Cylinders

> Each employer shall determine that compressed gas cylinders under his control are in a safe condition to the extent that this can be determined by visual inspection. Visual and other inspections shall be conducted as prescribed in the Hazardous Materials Regulations of the Department of Transportation (49 CFR Parts 171-179 and 14 CFR Part 103). Where those regulations are not applicable, visual and other inspections shall be conducted in accordance with Compressed Gas Association Pamphlets C-6-1968 and C-8-1962.

Compressed Gases

> The implant handling, storage, and use of all compressed gases in cylinders, portable tanks, rail tank cars, or motor vehicles cargo tanks shall be in accordance with Compressed Gas Association Pamphlet P-1-1965.

Safety Relief Devices for Compressed Gas Containers

Compressed gas cylinders, portable tanks, and cargo tanks shall have pressure relief devices installed and maintained in accordance with Compressed Gas Association Pamphlets S-1.1-1963 and 1965 ADDENDA and S-1.2-1963.

29 CFR 120 Subpart I -- Personal Protective Equipment

Regulations in this subpart which are of interest in hazardous materials management are 1910.133 -- Eye and Face Protection, and 1910.134 -- Respiratory Protection.

29 CFR 1910.120 -- Hazardous Waste Operations and Emergency Response

This final rule provides employee protection requirements for workers engaged in hazardous waste operations including emergency response to hazardous substance incidents. Coverage includes employees involved in responses covered by CERCLA or the "Superfund" Act, operations conducted under permitted RCRA activities, and emergency responses to accidental releases to the environment involving hazardous substances.

29 CFR 1910.132 -- General Requirements

Application

Protective equipment, including personal protective equipment for eyes, face, head, and extremities; protective clothing, respiratory devices, and protective shields and barriers shall be provided, used and maintained in a sanitary and reliable condition wherever it is necessary by reason of hazards of processes or environment, chemical hazards, radiological hazards, or mechanical irritants encountered in a manner capable of causing injury or impairment of any part of the body through absorption, inhalation, or physical contact.

Employee-Owned Equipment

Where employees provide their own protective equipment, the employer shall be responsible to ensure its adequacy, including proper maintenance and sanitation of such equipment.

Design

> All personal protective equipment shall be of safe design and construction for the work to be performed.

29 CFR Subpart M -- Compressed Gas and Compressed Air Equipment

This subpart deals with the inspection of compressed gas cylinders, safety relief devices, and air receivers.

29 CFR 1910 Subpart Z -- Toxic and Hazardous Substances

Subpart Z deals with the exposure of employees and the general public to toxic and hazardous substances. Tables Z-1, Z-2, and Z-3 of this subpart give exposure limits of the substances listed. Listed below are the health standards which have been promulgated by OSHA.

1910.1000	Air Contaminants
1910.1029	Coke Oven Emissions
1910.1011	4-Aminodiphenyl
1910.1002	Coal Tar Pitch Volatiles; Interpretation
1910.1003	4-Nitrobiphenyl 4-Dimethylaminoazobenzene
1910.1004	Alpha-Naphthylamine
1910.1006	Methyl Chloromethyl Ether
1910.1007	3,3-Dichlorobenzine (and its salts)
1910.1008	Bis-Chloromethyl Ether
1910.1009	Beta-Naphthylamine
1910.1010	Benzidine
1910.1045	Ethylene Oxide
1910.1001	Asbestos
1910.1012	Ethyleneimine
1910.1013	Beta-Pripiolactone
1910.1014	2-Acetylaminoflourene
1910.1016	N-Nitrosodimethylamine
1910.1017	Vinyl Chloride
1910.1018	Inorganic Arsenic
1910.1025	Lead
1910.1043	Cotton Dust
1910.1044	1,2-Dibromo-3-Chloropropane
1910.1045	Acrylonitrile

29 CFR 1910.1200 Subpart Z -- Hazard Communication Standard

The Hazard Communication Standard, published November 25, 1983, is intended to ensure that all employees are apprised of the hazards they work with through a Hazard Communication Program. This is commonly referred to as "Right-to-Know." The principle of "Right-to-Know" is becoming an important element in American industry. Right-to-Know should be an automatic part of safety in the workplace along with hardhats, safety glasses, and other physical protection provided the worker. The standard requires each employer to establish a comprehensive Hazard Communication Program for employees, which includes at least the mandated container labeling, MSDS, and an employee training program. The program is to be written, and is to include how the employer plans to meet the criteria of the standard regarding labels, MSDSs, and training, and a list of the hazardous chemicals in each workplace. The program must also include methods the employer will use to inform employees of the hazards of nonroutine tasks, as well as the hazards associated with chemicals contained in unlabeled pipes in their work areas; and the methods employers will use to inform contractors in manufacturing facilities of the hazards to which their employees may be exposed.

Labels and Other Forms of Warning

Chemical manufacturers, importers, and distributors are required to ensure that containers of hazardous chemicals leaving the workplace are labeled, tagged, or marked with the identity, appropriate hazard warnings, and the name and address of the manufacturer or other responsible party. Additionally, they are to ensure that these labels do not conflict with those applied in accordance with Department of Transportation regulations under the Hazardous Materials Transportation Act. If labels already applied by the manufacturer, importer, or distributor contain the minimum information required by OSHA, additional labels need not be affixed. The standard requires that each container in the workplace be labeled, tagged, or marked with the identity of hazardous chemicals contained therein, and hazard warnings appropriate for employee protection.

The user is not required to label portable containers into which hazardous chemicals are transferred from labeled containers and which are intended only for the immediate use of the employee who performs the transfer.

According to the definition of immediate use, the container must be under the control of the employee performing the transfer, and used within the workshift when the transfer has been made. Where containers are labeled by the manufacturer or supplier, further labeling is not required.

Material Safety Data Sheets

The standard requires chemical manufacturers and importers to develop material safety data sheets (MSDS) for each hazardous chemical they produce or import. Employers are required to obtain an MSDS for each hazardous chemical used in their workplaces.

Copies of the MSDSs for hazardous chemicals in a given work area are to be readily accessible to employees in that work area. In order for the MSDS to serve as a source of detailed information on hazards, it must be located close to workers, and readily available to them during each workshift.

Employee Information and Training

Employees are to establish a training and information program for employees exposed to hazardous chemicals. Such training is to be provided at the time of initial assignment and whenever a new hazard is introduced into the work area. Of course, employees who have not been trained previously must receive training equivalent to the required initial training when this standard takes effect. The standard specifies the information to be transmitted to employees. First they are to be informed of the requirements of this regulation, i.e., that it exists, that employers are required to have Hazard Communication Programs, and the components of the programs in their workplaces.

Employees are also to be informed of any operations in their work area where hazardous chemicals are present, and where the employer will be keeping the written materials required under this standard, including the written hazard evaluation procedures, written program, lists of hazardous chemicals, and MSDSs required by this section.

Employees are also to be trained regarding methods and observations they may use to detect the presence of a hazardous chemical in their work area. Employees are also to be trained about the hazards of the chemicals in their work areas. Training is to include the measures employees can take to protect themselves from the hazards and is to indicate procedures implemented by the employer to provide protection such as work practices and the use of personal protective equipment. In addition, the employer is to explain the Hazard Communication Program implemented in that workplace, including how to read and interpret information on labels and MSDSs, and how employees can obtain and use the available hazard information.

29 CFR Subpart E and Executive Order 12196

If you are employed by any Federal Agency you should read these items. They give Federal employees the same Right-to-Know safeguards as provided to private sector employees.

TOXIC SUBSTANCES CONTROL ACT (TSCA)

Doye B. Cox, P.E., CHMM
Signal Environmental Services, Inc.

INTRODUCTION

The passage of the Toxic Substances Control Act (TSCA) in 1976 culminated five years of intensive effort by Congress to provide a regulatory framework for comprehensively dealing with risks posed by the manufacture and use of chemical substances. Prior to the passage of TSCA, these substances were largely unregulated (except pesticides under the Federal Insecticide, Fungicide, and Rodenticide Act -- FIFRA and certain consumer products under the Federal Food, Drug, and Cosmetic Act -- FFDCA). TSCA was enacted in large part due to the discovery of widespread contamination by Polychlorinated Biphenyls (PCB) and EPA's lack of regulatory tools to control PCB material. TSCA authorizes EPA to: (1) obtain data from industry regarding the production, use, and health effects of chemical substances and mixtures and (2) regulate the manufacture, processing, and distribution in commerce, as well as use and disposal of a chemical substance or mixture.

Because they are regulated by other laws, pesticides, tobacco, nuclear material, firearms and ammunition, food, food additives, drugs, and cosmetics are exempted from the Act.

Premanufacture Notification (PMN) (Section 5)

In May 1979, EPA published its initial inventory of chemical substances. Any chemicals not listed were considered new chemicals subject to premanufacture review as of July 1, 1979. As new chemicals complete premanufacture review and begin to be manufactured they are added to the inventory.

If a chemical is not already listed on the inventory, a PMN must be submitted. This notification must, among other things, identify the chemical, provide information on use, method of dispersal, production levels, worker exposure, and potential by-products or impurities. In addition, the manufacturer must provide any data he possesses on health and environmental effects of the product and a description of known or reasonably ascertainable data. After the submittal of the PMN, EPA has 90 days to complete the review and either approve the production of the chemical or act to ban manufacture. The review period may be extended by EPA for an additional 90 days. If additional time is needed, EPA and the manufacturer may interrupt the 180-day review to develop additional data. To partially counter criticism from the chemical industry that certain classes or amounts of compounds do not pose a significant enough risk to require PMN review, EPA has issued two broad exemptions from the process: (1) high molecular weight polymers and (2) low volume chemicals produced at less than 1000 kg quantities per year. In general, the chemical industry seems to have adapted to the PMN regulations in spite of costs and charges that the statute stifles innovation. However, industry still has a number of significant concerns, including the provision allowing EPA to stop manufacture of a chemical until sufficient data is available.

Significant New Use Rule (SNUR) (Section 5.2)

If a chemical is approved for manufacture, EPA may propose a Significant New Use Rule. Under this rule the use or production volume of a chemical may be restricted. Perhaps because this provision has been opposed by the chemical industry as a continual PMN threat, the SNUR provisions have not been widely applied. SNUR was issued in September 1984 and required EPA notification if use of the specified substance produced exceeded five percent of a consumer product.

Testing Requirements (Section 4)

If EPA determines that there is insufficient data to evaluate whether a chemical poses unreasonable risk to health or the environment, then testing of the material can be required. Section 4(b) of the statute lists many of the studies which may be required, including: carcinogenicity, mutagenicity, teratogenicity, behavioral modification, synergisms, and various types of toxicity. The testing methodologies do not appear in the regulation but rather have been issued as testing protocols or guidelines. The protocols can be more readily modified as better techniques are developed. This allows more flexibility in specifying which tests should be applied to specific chemicals. These guidelines are reviewed and revised annually and are available through the National Technical Information Service in Springfield, Virginia.

Chemicals are selected for testing by an Interagency Testing Committee composed of representatives from eight Federal agencies (EPA, OSHA, CEQ, NIOSH, NIEHS, NCI, NSF and the Department of Commerce). Once selected, these chemicals or groups of chemicals are placed on a priority list for testing which may never contain more than 50 chemicals or chemical groups.

Because toxicity testing is so expensive (up to $1,000,000/chemical) TSCA requires that with minor exceptions all manufacturers and processors of the material must share the costs of testing. The allocation of costs is to be devised by the manufacturers or if they cannot agree, by EPA. As expected, this section of the regulation has been the source of much controversy.

Data Gathering (Section 8)

In order for EPA to perform an adequate risk assessment of a chemical substance, the agency must have access to all available data regarding the substance. Section 8 of TSCA authorizes EPA to require industry to provide such data. The agency requires four types of reporting under this section.

General Data Collection [Section 8(a)] uses a model rule concept whereby data is required to be submitted on chemical substances as they are added to a list.

In this way, EPA can collect basic, readily obtainable data needed for risk assessments. To date, EPA has used this rule to gather information on approximately 350 chemicals. EPA is planning a second model rule called the Comprehensive Assessment Information Rule to collect more detailed information.

Manufacturers routinely test their chemicals for efficiency and safety. Section 8(d): Health and Safety Studies allows EPA to require a manufacturer to provide the agency with copies of such studies. In addition, if the company has copies of, knows of, or reasonably could determine that other reports or studies exist, regardless of their origin, it must also provide copies or lists of these reports. Through the courts, EPA has established that this applies: (1) not only to manufacturers but to independent testing labs, and (2) to chemicals produced in small quantities and not offered for sale.

The myriad reporting requirements of TSCA have resulted in the inundation of EPA with chemical data -- so much data that the agency has little hope of analyzing and interpreting this data in any reasonable timeframe. To minimize the possibility of a chemical tragedy occurring while data remains un-analyzed, Section 8(e) Substantial Risk Notification requires industry to notify EPA if any evidence of substantial risk is identified. In defining substantial risk the regulation excludes from consideration economic or social benefits of use, or cost of restricting use, and strengthens the requirement further by directing that potential for exposure be given little weight in assessing risk.

Section 8(c) of TSCA requires industry to maintain records of significant adverse reactions alleged to have been caused by a chemical because they "may indicate a tendency of a chemical substance or mixture to cause long-lasting or irreversible damage to health or the environment." Records relating to possible health reactions of employees must be kept for thirty years.

The recordkeeping requirement is limited to written or otherwise recorded allegations and applies only to SIC code industries in categories 28 and 2911. Surprisingly, EPA does not require reporting of these allegations, merely right of inspection.

Chemicals Posing Unreasonable Risks (Section 6)

Under Section 6 of the Act, EPA may move to ban the manufacturing and distribution in commerce, limit the use, require labeling, or place similar restrictions on specific chemicals. It may also issue public warnings, require situational notification, recordkeeping, reporting or other measures as the agency deems appropriate. To date, only four such substances are regulated under Section 6. These four actions effectively illustrate the breadth of authority available to EPA under this section.

Asbestos in Schools: To protect students from exposure to friable asbestos fibers, EPA requires school systems to inspect their facilities for the material. The results were not only to be posted but must be reported to EPA, school employees and parents, and to be maintained as records where asbestos was found. As might be surmised, reporting and subsequent public pressure where asbestos was located has resulted in removal of asbestos from schools.

In January 1986 EPA moved to immediately ban the use of asbestos in five of the products in which it was used most. Further, a ten year phaseout of domestic mining and import of asbestos was issued. EPA is considering other steps for control of products not immediately banned.

TCDD: The action taken by EPA in this instance illustrates the ability of the agency to act to control an imminent hazard and to target this action specifically. The dioxin TCDD occurs as a by-product/contaminant in waste produced as a result of the manufacture of the herbicide 2,4,5-trichlorphenoxy acetic acid (2,4,5-T/Silvex). The toxicity of TCDD is well established and has received much notoriety due to health effects at Love Canal in New York and those alleged from Agent Orange. EPA, in response to a large amount of such waste at a Jacksonville, Arkansas, pesticide plant, moved to require notification of disposal methods 60 days prior to disposal. EPA has recently transferred this authority to the Resource Conservation and Recovery Act.

CFC: As hazards to the ozone layer from the use of freon (CFC) products were identified, EPA moved to restrict the use of these compounds only as aerosol propellents. In this case, CFC products are still manufactured and available for use in certain products and processes including refrigeration, cooling, and production of urethane foam. These uses were deemed not to pose a substantial threat to the ozone layer. Certain small uses of CFC as aerosol propellents are still allowed where no reasonable substitute could be identified.

PCB: The regulation of PCB (polychlorinated biphenyls) represents the full extent of powers granted to EPA under TSCA. Nowhere else in environmental statutes is a substance banned by name. Further, what started out to be a rather simple manufacturing and use ban has developed into a complex set of regulations restricting PCB use, requiring inspections, reporting, and recordkeeping; establishing labeling and marking requirements, and outlining disposal criteria.

Part or perhaps all of this complexity emanates from the ubiquitous use of PCB and its propensity for resisting degradation. As an illustration, the PCB regulations address PCB usage in electrical distribution transformers and capacitors, railroad transformers, mining equipment, heat transfer systems, hydraulic systems, carbonless copy paper, pigments, electromagnetic switches and voltage regulators, compressors, liquids of natural gas pipelines, small research and development quantities, microscopy mounting medium and immersion oil, circuit breakers, reclosers, cable, optical liquids, food and feed, and inadvertently generated PCBs.

The keys to PCB regulation are the term "totally enclosed manner" and the selection of 50 ppm as the general cutoff between non-PCB material or equipment and PCB contaminated equipment. Equipment containing 50 to 499 ppm PCB is defined "PCB contaminated equipment" and is subject to special rules. Equipment containing 500 ppm or greater is regulated as PCB. EPA has chosen to allow the continued use of PCB equipment for its useful life if such use is in a totally enclosed manner. The interpretation of "totally enclosed manner" has been the subject of considerable debate. The 50 parts per million limitation has been the subject of similar debate and litigation.

Most PCBs still in use are associated with the generation, distribution, and use of electricity and are about equally divided between transformers and capacitors. EPA's regulations require labeling of this equipment, allow very limited servicing of the equipment, established schedules for retirement and inspection, and provides requirements for transportation, storage, and disposal.

On July 17, 1985, in recognition of the dangers associated with PCB fires (production of Tetrachlorinated Dibenzodioxins and Tetrachlorinated Dibenzofurans), EPA promulgated further restriction of the use of PCB transformers. These restrictions are largely associated with use in commercial buildings but also include more general requirements such as: registration with local fire departments, prohibition of nearby flammable storage, and increased inspection, notification, and spill control requirements.

On April 2, 1987, EPA promulgated a PCB Spill Cleanup Policy (40 CFR 761.120-135). This regulation established a national spill cleanup policy. It requires notification for PCB spills into sensitive areas and for all spills greater than 10 pounds. It also establishes cleanup levels and general methodologies for spills onto both solid surfaces and soils. In addition, recordkeeping requirements are established. It is important to note that all reporting and cleanup levels are established by weight of PCBs, not PCB containing materials (e.g., 90 lb of 10% PCB oils = 9 lb of PCB).

On December 1, 1989, EPA promulgated broad changes to the PCB tracking mechanism of TSCA. These changes include:

(1) A requirement that PCB generators or TSDFs notify EPA and obtain an EPA identification number.
(2) All PCB shipments use the RCRA Uniform Hazardous Waste Manifest
(3) Additional recordkeeping requirements
(4) Commercial PCB storage facilities must receive specific approval and prepare closure plans, cost estimates and financial assurance.

THE COMPREHENSIVE ENVIRONMENTAL RESPONSE, COMPENSATION, AND LIABILITY ACT OF 1980 (CERCLA) WITH 1986 AMENDMENTS

Pat Siefferman Ogle
Cogentrix, Inc.

and

David Richard Gengozian
Tennessee Valley Authority

Revised by

Brian D. Lopez-Cepero
E.I. DuPont De Nemours & Company (Inc.)

INTRODUCTION

The Comprehensive Environmental Response, Compensation, and Liability Act of 1980, commonly known as the "Superfund" Act or as CERCLA, was passed by Congress in response to a growing national concern about the release of hazardous substances to the environment. These concerns were directed primarily at inactive sites, but also from actively managed facilities and vessels which are not subject to the Resource Conservation and Recovery Act (RCRA).

The key purpose of CERCLA is to establish a mechanism of response for the immediate cleanup of hazardous waste contamination from accidental spills or from abandoned hazardous waste disposal sites that may result in long term environmental damage.

In general, if a release to the environment is considered a "Federally permitted release," it is not subject to CERCLA-reporting requirements. Release is defined as any spill, leaking, pumping, pouring, emitting, emptying, discharging, injecting, escaping, leaching, dumping, or disposing into the environment (including the abandonment or discarding of barrels, containers, and other closed receptacles containing any hazardous substance, pollutant, or contaminant).

A Federally permitted release is any discharge that is in compliance with a permit issued under other environmental laws. This exemption applies whether the permit is issued by a Federal, State, or local authority. The intent of CERCLA is to provide for response to, and cleanup of, environmental problems that are not adequately covered by other environmental statutes.

There are three basic types of responses that may be taken under CERCLA: removals, remedial actions, and enforcement actions. All three actions may be taken at any site. Enforcement actions, either administrative or judicial, are always initiated at the time a site is discovered.

The goal of CERCLA is to compel those parties responsible for a non-permitted release to pay for the cleanup of that release. If a potentially responsible party (PRP) cannot be identified quickly enough to address an imminent and substantial endangerment, the Federal Government will respond. If a settlement cannot be reached with a PRP, the Federal Government will take action and then seek to recover from the PRP the costs of response.

The National Priorities List (NPL) is a list of sites that present the greatest danger to public health or welfare of the environment. The list is promulgated by the EPA in section 105(a)(8) of CERCLA. The sites on the NPL are prioritized according to the Hazard Ranking System (HRS).

The cleanup of sites must conform to EPA's National Contingency Plan (NCP). This plan comprises the operating rules for Superfund cleanups promulgated by EPA under section 105(a)(8)(B) of CERCLA.

The National Contingency Plan (NCP)

The NCP specifies the planning, coordination, and communication networks. A national response team chaired by EPA and the Coast Guard and comprising appropriate Federal agencies responds to oil and hazardous substances releases beyond "regional capabilities." The NCP requires that each Federal region prepare regional contingency plans, similar to the NCP. Each EPA region is to have its own regional team and coordinators to oversee responses for oil and hazardous substances removals, as well as remedial project managers to oversee remedial activities involving hazardous substances.

Hazardous Substances and Reportable Quantities

Releases of oil, PCBs, or hazardous substances in excess of reportable quantities must be reported to the National Response Center immediately at 1-800-424-8802. The reportable releases are defined in 40 CFR 110, hazardous substances in 40 CFR 302, and PCBs in 40 CFR 302.4 and 40 CFR 761. In July, 1989, the table in 40 CFR 302.4 was amended by revising the entry of "Radionuclides" under the "Final RQ" column. The Clean Air Act Amendment of 1990 added 189 chemicals to the existing CERCLA list of 700 plus chemicals. All of these chemicals came with a statutory reportable quantity (RQ) of one pound under section 112 of the Clean Air Act. Until such time that the statutory RQ's are changed, it is necessary to report any releases of these chemicals in excess of reportable quantities.

Cleanup Actions

There are two types of cleanup actions under Superfund: removal actions and remedial actions.

1. Removal Actions -- Removal actions are short-term actions designed to protect the public from imminent threats to public health, welfare, or to the environment. Removals can be triggered by burning, leaking, or explosion, among other things. Removal

actions can include installing a security fence, providing an alternate water supply, removing waste and contaminated material, or other measures to stabilize or mitigate the release.

Removal actions can occur at sites listed on the NPL as well as non-NPL sites.   Removal actions focus on site control and stabilization, and are statutorily limited in cost and duration to generally $2 million and one year per site, respectively.

2.   Remedial Actions -- Remedial actions are generally longer-term actions requiring extensive study to select the best option and may cost millions of dollars to implement.   Examples of remedial actions include removal and treatment of contaminants and pumping and treating groundwater or other actions to permanently clean up the site.

Fund-financed remedial actions are limited to NPL sites and focus on permanent remedy/cleanup of the site.   Remedial actions are not statutorily limited in either cost or duration.

All responses taken under CERCLA by the Federal Government, State Government, or PRP must follow the procedures set forth in the NCP which is the central regulation that outlines response powers and responsibilities under CERCLA.

The Remedial Process for Hazardous Waste

The remedial process, as defined by the National Contingency Plan (NCP), includes four phases:

a.   PA/SI (Preliminary Assessment/Site Investigation)
b.   RI/FS (Remedial Investigation/Feasibility Study)
c.   RD/RA (Remedial Design/Remedial Action)
d.   O & M (Operation and Maintenance)

Upon notification of a release or threat of release, the NRC notifies the onscene coordinator (OSC). The OSC in turn notifies the governor of the affected State.

Initial action is a preliminary assessment (PA) which is basically a records search. If the PA does not provide sufficient information to determine if a threat exists or the degree of threat, then a site investigation (SI) is conducted. The PA/SI may conclude that (1) there exists an "imminent hazard" warranting immediate removal action, (2) removal action is not required but remedial action is, or (3) no action is required. Therefore, a site evaluation must take place to determine whether the site should be placed on the NPL. The PA/SI may also end if a responsible party is responding to the situation or if it is determined that no threat exists.

Site evaluations, which are extensions of PA/SI work, are conducted to determine whether the site needs to be placed on the NPL. To be eligible for proposed inclusion, the sites must receive a score of 28.5 or higher on the EPA hazard ranking system. This is accomplished using factors which rate sites on the potential for human and environmental exposure to leaking contaminants through groundwater, surface water, or air. Waste volume, population at risk, and potential for fire and explosion are also considered. The hazard ranking system may include health risk to onsite employees.

A remedial investigation/feasibility study (RI/FS) is undertaken to determine the appropriate remedial response for a site on the NPL. Alternatives are identified and screened according to cost, feasibility, and effectiveness. A remedy is then usually selected based on the ability to meet or exceed environmental and health standards. Situations may occur in which this does not happen because of lacking technologies, unacceptable environmental impacts, or shortage of Federal funds (if remedy is not being funded by responsible party).

The original intent of CERCLA was to have 400 sites on the NPL. As of February 1991, there were 1173 sites on the NPL list, plus 116 NPL Federal Facility Sites. Some of the Federal sites have many potential remediations even though they only have one number. The NPL is dynamic. New sites are added as other sites are removed.

The Superfund Amendments and Reauthorization Act (SARA)

CERCLA has been amended four times. The most recent amendment, the Superfund Amendments and Reauthorization Act of 1986 (SARA), was signed on October 17, 1986. SARA is the first major revision of

CERCLA since it was enacted.   The Act is divided into five titles as follows:

Title I -- Provisions Relating Primarily to Response and Liability

Title II -- Miscellaneous Provisions

Title III -- Emergency Planning and Community Right-to-Know

Title IV -- Radon Gas and Indoor Air Quality Research

Title V -- Amendments of the Internal Revenue Code of 1986

Some of the major issues addressed in Titles I and II of SARA include:

A.   *Cleanup Standards* -- The emphasis is placed on permanent cleanup methods.   Remedial actions, in which treatment that permanently and significantly reduces the volume, toxicity, or mobility of the hazardous substances, are to be preferred.   Offsite transport and disposal without treatment is the least favored method of completing remedial actions.   This provision was adopted to discourage simply moving waste from one location to another without reducing the long-term threat.

B.   *Fund Replenishment* -- The 1986 amendment provides for an $8.6 billion five-year replenishment of the Superfund.   The monies allocated to the Superfund come from a combination of:

1. $2.7 billion in petroleum taxes, imposed on imported oil at a somewhat higher rate than on domestic

2. $1.3 billion in chemical feedstock taxes and a tax on imported chemical derivatives

3. $2.6 billion in a new "environmental tax" on corporations; and

4.   the balance from general revenues, recoveries, and interest.

C. *Settlement Provisions* -- Title I, section 122 deals with provisions which facilitate voluntary settlements by offering a variety of techniques for carrying out such actions. Liability releases that the government may offer as a part of a settlement are also outlined.

D. *Liability* -- There are four categories of people defined as liable under Section 107(a), as amended by SARA. They are liable for response costs incurred as a result of a release or threat of release of a hazardous substance. The categories are as follows:

1. The current owner and operator of a vessel or a facility.
2. The owner or operator at the time of disposal.
3. Any person who by contract, agreement, or other arrangement is responsible for the disposal or treatment of hazardous substances at or transport to a facility from which a release occurred.
4. Transporters who selected the disposal facility.

These people are liable for:

1. all costs of removal or remedial action incurred by the Federal government or a State government as long as is not inconsistent with the NCP;
2. any other necessary costs of response incurred by private parties consistent with the NCP;
3. damages for injury to natural resources; and
4. the costs of any health assessment or health effects study carried out by the Agency for Toxic Substances and Disease Registry (ATSDR).

SARA also provides a new defense for innocent landowners who acquire property without knowledge that it was previously used for waste disposal. However, mere lack of knowledge by the new owner may not be enough. One must demonstrate that appropriate inquiry consistent with good commercial practice was undertaken. Liability under Section 107 cannot be transferred or conveyed away. However, agreements between parties to ensure, hold harmless, or indemnify another against liability under this section are not prohibited. Congress is attempting to limit the liability of lending institutions that did not take an active role in the facilities operation.

E.   *State Participation* -- States now participate with EPA in each stage of the process of identifying NPL sites and the appropriate cleanup remedy. The affected State's comments on a proposed settlement and the resulting consent decree must be obtained by the EPA during settlement negotiations with potential responsible parties. The States are required under SARA to provide assurances to EPA that they have sufficient treatment and disposal facilities complying with RCRA that are adequate to meet the State's need for 20 years.

F.   *Public Participation* -- Title I, Section 117 stipulates that the public must be given an opportunity to comment on both a proposed remedial action and on the consent order settling a case. EPA must respond to these comments. Furthermore, under SARA, a citizen suit provision is established. Private persons may petition the EPA to have risk assessments performed on any site, and technical assistance grants to Superfund site community groups may be made. In essence, the community relations program ensures citizen involvement in all remedial actions and removal actions lasting longer than 45 days.

G.   *Health-Related Authorities* -- Title I, Section 110 greatly expands the expertise in health risk assessment to be utilized at Superfund sites. Responsibility for implementing many of these requirements rests with the Agency for Toxic Substances and Disease Registry (ATSDR), in consultation with EPA. The ATSDR is required to perform health assessments at all NPL sites. Upon request of a State or EPA these assessments must be conducted at other sites. Citizens are also allowed to petition directly to ATSDR for health assessments. The ATSDR is required to prepare toxicological profiles for the 200 hazardous substances it has identified as those most commonly found at NPL facilities. EPA and ATSDR are required to add at least 75 substances over the next three years.

H.   *Federal Facilities Cleanup Program* -- Under new CERCLA Section 120, each department, agency, and instrumentality of the United States is subject to, and must comply with, CERCLA in the same manner as any nongovernmental entity (except for requirements for bonding, insurance, financial responsibility, or applicable time period). Department of Defense (DOD) and the Department of Energy (DOE) facilities may be exempted by Presidential Order from any requirement in Titles I and III of CERCLA as necessary for the protection of National security interests. Certain specifications regarding such an exemption are given in this section.

Title III

Title III or the Emergency Planning and Community Right-to-Know Act of 1986 is a freestanding title. Title III is not a part of CERCLA per se, and differs enough in subject matter that it is discussed in a separate chapter.

Title IV

Title IV of SARA contains the Radon Gas and Indoor Air Quality Research Act of 1986. Due to rising concern over the problem of radon gas, section 403 of SARA outlines a research program which emphasizes the coordination of efforts and the gathering of data. To assist and advise EPA, an advisory committee composed of individuals from the appropriate agencies was established. Reporting requirements and funding details are also provided in this section.

Title V

The 1986 amendments added to RCRA is a comprehensive corrective action program for releases of petroleum from underground storage tanks. The new leaking Underground Storage Tank (UST) Trust Fund is financed at $600 million from a new tax on fuel. Use of the fund for cleanup is limited to situations where no financially solvent owner or operator can be found to do the cleanup or where the cost of cleanup exceeds available resources of the owner or operator.

Section 206 of SARA defines the uses of the UST fund and amends the UST program established under RCRA. EPA is required to establish financial responsibility standards for owners or operators of underground tanks pursuant to regulations promulgated under the RCRA program. The amendments also allow EPA and/or States to take corrective action and sue the owner or operator to recover the cost of cleanup, or to require the owner or operator to conduct the cleanup themselves.

THE EMERGENCY PLANNING AND COMMUNITY RIGHT-TO-KNOW ACT OF 1986

Pat Siefferman Ogle
Cogentrix, Inc.

and

David Richard Gengozian
Tennessee Valley Authority

Revised by

Brian Lopez-Cepero
E.I. DuPont De Nemours & Company (Inc.)

INTRODUCTION

The Emergency Planning and Community Right-to-Know Act of 1986 was signed into law on October 17, 1986. This Act was included as Title III of the Superfund Amendments and Reauthorization Act of 1986 (SARA). Title III of SARA is a freestanding title (not part of the Comprehensive Environmental Response, Compensation, and Liability Act or Superfund). SARA, Title III authorizes a nationwide program of emergency planning as a protection against accidents involving extremely hazardous materials. The Act also requires a comprehensive body of information about hazardous materials to be submitted to various State and local groups.

The four major issues addressed in the Emergency Planning and Community Right-to-Know Act deal with:

1. Emergency planning and release notification (Sections 301 and 304).
2. Community right-to-know reporting on chemicals (Sections 311 and 312).
3. Emissions inventory (Section 313).
4. Miscellaneous provisions (including trade secrets in section 322).

This legislation builds upon EPA's Chemical Emergency Preparedness Program (CEPP) as well as other State and local chemical emergency response programs. In addition to increasing public access to information on the presence of hazardous chemicals in the community and releases of these chemicals into the environment, the community right-to-know provisions of Title III provide essential information for preparing emergency plans.

Emergency Planning

The Act requires each State to establish an emergency response commission. The State Emergency Response Commission is required to form local emergency planning committees to operate at the community level. The local committees are required to develop contingency plans for responding to releases of extremely hazardous substances. Facilities maintaining an inventory of extremely hazardous substances above the threshold level were required to notify the State emergency response commission by May 17, 1987, that they are subject to the emergency planning provisions. EPA maintains a list of 406 extremely hazardous substances.*

Emergency Release Notification

Section 304 significantly expands the emergency release reporting requirements of Superfund. The existing CERCLA emergency release reporting program is supplemented by the establishment of State and local reporting requirements for hazardous and extremely hazardous substances. Specific notification requirements vary depending on whether the substance is (1) an extremely hazardous substance with Reportable Quantity (RQ)

---

*Federal Register. Monday, November 17, 1987, vol. 51, page 401582.

listed under CERCLA, (2) listed under CERCLA but has no RQ or (3) an extremely hazardous substance not listed under CERCLA. These reporting requirements are now in effect.

If a release of a substance beyond facility boundaries requires reporting under CERCLA and the substance is on the list of extremely hazardous substances or is a substance with a RQ under CERCLA, the facility must not only notify the National Response Center (NRC) but must also notify the local emergency planning committee and the State emergency planning commission. The notification to the State commission and local committee is more detailed than the notice required under CERCLA.

If the substance released is covered by CERCLA but has no RQ the facility need only provide the State commission and local committee the same information as required to be submitted to the NRC. After April 30, 1988, the facility must provide the more detailed notification on these substances.

A facility is subject to the emergency planning and release provisions if a substance on the list of 406 extremely hazardous substances is present at the facility in an amount exceeding the threshold planning quantity established for such substance. A governor or State emergency response commission can make additional facilities subject to the emergency planning requirements after public notice and opportunity for comment.

Community Right-to-Know Act (Sections 311 and 312)

This portion of the Act is linked to OSHA's Hazard Communication Standard ("the Standard") by definition of "subject facility" and "hazardous chemical;" therefore, Sections 311 and 312 currently apply to manufacturers and importers of hazardous chemicals and users of those chemicals within Standard Industrial Classification Codes (SIC) 20-39. The SIC codes were expanded, effective September 23, 1987. By May 23, 1988, all employers in the non-manufacturing sector must comply with all provisions of the revised standard.

Facilities subject to Sections 311 and 312 are required to submit a Material Safety Data Sheet (MSDS) for each hazardous chemical present. These must be submitted to the local emergency planning committee, the State emergency response commission, and the local fire department by October 17, 1987 or for non-manufacturing facilities, August 23, 1988. The requirement of this section is not based on a specific list of subject chemicals but rather on a broad definition of "hazardous chemicals" as defined by the OSHA Standard.

Section 311 -- MSDS or List -- In lieu of MSDS's, a list of hazardous chemicals may be submitted. At this time, lists are preferred over MSDS's since lists are more easily processed. The list of hazardous chemicals present at the facility is to be grouped by categories of hazard as listed below and is to include the chemical or common name of each chemical as set forth on the MSDS's.

1.   Immediate (acute) health
2.   Delayed (chronic) health
3.   Fire
4.   Sudden release of pressure
5.   Reactive

As another option, facilities may provide MSDS's for the pure chemicals that constitute the mixtures or for the product mixtures themselves. Those choosing to provide an MSDS for mixtures must still identify the hazardous components of the mixture. This also holds true if the facility has decided to submit a list as opposed to MSDS's. Presently, MSDS's are to be submitted for extremely hazardous substances in quantities equal to or greater than 500 pounds or the threshold planning quantity, whichever is less at the time of submission. MSDS's must be submitted for the first two years for all other hazardous substances in quantities equal to or greater than 10,000 pounds at the time of submission.

Section 312 -- Emergency and Hazardous Chemical Inventory -- Section 312 of the Act required a subject facility to submit an annual "Emergency and Hazardous Chemical Inventory Form" on or before March 1, 1988, or for non-manufacturing facilities, March 1, 1989, and annually thereafter. The report is done for each category of hazardous chemical present at the facility during the previous calendar year in excess of the threshold which may be established (as mentioned in the preceding paragraph). The hazardous chemicals and categories covered by section

312 are the same as those for which an MSDS is required by section 311. The inventory form must also be submitted to the same three entities as the MSDS's, i.e., the State emergency response commission, the local emergency planning committee, and the fire department having jurisdiction over the facility.

The inventory form incorporates a two-tier approach. Tier I, submitted annually, must contain the following information aggregated by category:

> An estimate (in ranges) of the maximum amount of chemicals for each category present at the facility at any time during the preceding calendar year.
>
> An estimate (in ranges) of the average daily amount of chemicals in each category.
>
> The general location of hazardous chemicals in each category.

Upon the specific request of the State commission, local committee, or fire department, a facility must supply the following Tier II information on specific chemicals:

> The chemical name or the common name as indicated on the MSDS.
>
> An estimate (in ranges) of the maximum and average daily amounts of the chemical present at any time during the preceding calendar year.
>
> A brief description of the manner of storage of the chemical.
>
> The location of the chemical at the facility.
>
> An indication of whether the owner elects to withhold location information from disclosure to the public.

The public may also request Tier II information from the State commission and the local committee.

Toxic Chemical Releases to the Environment

Section 313 of the Act requires annual reporting to the Federal and State governments of all releases of "toxic chemicals" to the environment that occur as a result of normal operations. Facilities subject to this requirement must complete a toxic chemical release form for each toxic chemical that was manufactured, processed, or otherwise used in quantities exceeding certain thresholds during the preceding calendar year. The forms must be submitted to the Administrator of EPA and to State officials designated by the governor on or before July 1, 1988 and annually thereafter, with respect to releases during the preceding calendar year.

The range of facilities to which Section 313 applies is somewhat narrower than the MSDS and inventory reporting provisions of Sections 311 and 312. Section 313 applies to owners and operators of facilities that have 10 or more full-time employees, that are in SIC 20-39 (i.e., manufacturing), and that manufactured, processed, or otherwise used a listed toxic chemical in excess of specified threshold quantities.

The reporting threshold for users is different than the thresholds for manufacturers and processors. Furthermore, the thresholds for manufacturers and processors are scaled down over time. The threshold for facilities that use a toxic chemical is 10,000 pounds per year. For facilities manufacturing or processing a toxic chemical, the threshold is 25,000 pounds.

The list of toxic chemicals subject to Section 313 reporting does not correspond to the list of extremely hazardous chemicals or any other list of chemicals in the Act. The list was generated by the Senate Committee on Environment and Public Works by combining lists of chemicals contained in the New Jersey and Maryland right-to-know laws.

The EPA Administrator is authorized to modify the SIC coverage of this requirement, add or subtract chemicals from the toxic chemical list, and revise the reporting thresholds.

The information to be provided on the toxic chemical release form is as follows:

The name, location, and type of business.

Whether the chemical is manufactured, processed, or otherwise used, and the general categories of use of the chemical.

An estimate (in ranges) of the maximum amounts of the toxic chemical present at the facility at any time during the preceding year.

Waste treatment/disposal methods and efficiency of methods for each waste stream.

Quantity of the chemical entering each environmental medium annually.

A certification by a senior official that the report is complete and accurate.

The law requires that the SARA 313 reports for the reporting year 1991 and thereafter include information relating to the recycling, treatment, and disposal of each of the compounds reported on the Form R's. The first such reports would be due in 1992. The information would be released to the public by the Federal government using the same computer database that now exists for SARA 313 release reports.

The EPA will issue rules which will include modifying the SARA 313 forms sometime this year. The basic information required is summarized below. Where numerical information is needed, engineering estimates are generally sufficient. New measurements are generally not required.

(1)   Quantity of chemical entering any waste stream prior to recycling, treatment, or disposal.
(2)   Recycling methods used (if any), the percentage of the material recycled, and the year to year change in the percentage of material recycled.
(3)   "Source reduction" methods utilized for reducing emissions of the chemical.

(4)   Projections for the next two years of how much source reduction and recycling will take place for these chemicals.

(5)   Ratio of product production in current year to previous year.

(6)   Techniques which were used to identify source reduction opportunities (EPA will probably give a list of suggested techniques in the regulations).

(7)   Amount of the chemical released due to episodic or catastrophic events.

(8)   The amount of the chemical which is "treated" and the percentage change from the previous year.

Other Title III Provisions

Trade secrets are addressed in Sections 322 and 323 of Title III. These provisions apply to emergency planning, community right-to-know, and toxic chemical release reporting.

ASBESTOS

Charles A. Waggoner, Ph.D., CHMM
Chattanooga State Technical Community College

INTRODUCTION

The term asbestos is applied to a group of naturally occurring fibrous minerals which have been widely used since the time of the ancient Greeks. Canada and South Africa have provided the world most of its commercial asbestos although it has also been mined in the USSR, Australia, Finland and the United States. There are six recognized asbestiform minerals which can be classified into one of two groups: (1) serpentine or (2) amphibole. These minerals are composed predominantly of magnesium silicate and group classification is based upon crystal structure as well as presence of contaminating metals (Fe, Ca, and Na) within the mineral matrix.

The serpentine group is identified as having a layered or sheet type of crystal structure. Chrysotile (white asbestos) is the sole member of this serpentine classification group. Approximately 95 % of the asbestos found in U.S. buildings is chrysotile. Physical properties of chrysotile asbestos include tube-like fibers which are strong and flexible. These characteristics make it a good composite material as well as allowing it to be spun and woven into fabrics. The soda straw shape of the fibers contributes greatly to the material's ability to absorb or wick water. This is an important property because the wetting of asbestos containing materials (ACM) is a commonly employed practice to prevent release of fibers while working with the material.

The amphibole group is characterized by a chain-like crystal structure along with the presence of metals other than magnesium. Members of this group include amosite (brown asbestos), crocidolite (blue asbestos), and the asbestiform minerals; tremolite, actinolite, and anthophylite. Amphibolers are more resistent to degradation by either heat or chemicals than is chrysotile. Due to these qualities, amosite and crocidolite have been frequently employed in boiler and high temperature insulation applications. Another differing characteristic particularly of amosite is that amphiboles do not wet or absorb water easily. This necessitates the addition of surfactants to water used in wetting amosite materials before attempting removal.

The variation in physical properties of the different types of asbestos establishes two goals for the analysis of bulk samples of materials suspected to be ACM. Samples must be analyzed to determine both the types and concentrations of asbestos present. Regulatory classification of a suspect material as ACM or non-ACM is a function of the concentration of asbestos fibers in the sample. Management of ACM during a removal action requires knowledge of not only the asbestos concentration but also the type asbestos present in order to properly wet the material for reduction of fiber releases.

The chemical and physical properties of asbestos coupled with its cost of production caused it to be widely used in construction. The different forms of asbestos have been used as thermal, fireproof, and acoustical insulation. It has also been woven into fabrics for use in expansion joints of ductwork as well as for fire-proof curtains. It has been used as a strengthening agent in concrete, floor tile, mortar, grout, and drywall spackling compounds. Some of the unique properties of asbestos also made it an ideal material to be used in brake pads and for different types of gasket materials.

Methods of Analysis

Asbestos identification is normally accomplished using microscopic techniques. Analysis of samples can be accomplished using either light or electron microscopy. The analytical method employed is chosen as a function of the type sample being analyzed. Two types of samples are submitted for analysis: bulk samples and air samples.

Bulk samples are gross samples of a material suspected of containing asbestos and are currently analyzed by polarized light microscopy (PLM). PLM, using dispersion staining, is capable of distinguishing the different types of asbestos present in the sample. Sensitivity of this method is one percent by weight and leads to the definition of ACM as being materials which "contain greater than one percent asbestos." Analysis is done using the point count method of PLM as established by the National Institutes for Standards and Testing (NIST). These analyses can be expected to cost on the range of $20-$35 each.

Air samples are collected by drawing measured quantities of air through a filter cassette and are analyzed using either phase contrast microscopy (PCM) or transmission electron microscopy (TEM). The advantages of PCM are that analysis is fast, inexpensive, and can be done on site if necessary. PCM is limited, however, in that it is not capable of distinguishing between asbestos and other fibers. The frequently used NIOSH 7400 method calls for the use of PCM to analyze air samples and any structure (fiber) with a length-to-width (aspect) ratio of 3:1 is considered to be an asbestos fiber. This, of course, causes PCM to err on the conservative side (i.e. give a fiber count higher than the true value for the sample). TEM, on the other hand, is capable of distinguishing between asbestos and non-asbestos fibers. It is also capable of "seeing" particles orders of magnitude smaller than those visualized by use of a light microscope. The most limiting factor for the use of TEM is cost which may vary from $350 to 700 per sample. We should note that air samples are collected for one or two purposes; (1) monitoring exposure of individual workers via personal monitoring pumps, or (2) evaluating ambient fiber concentrations in an enclosed area using high volume floor pumps. A common intent of such sampling is to determine the adequate level of respiratory protection for workers. Air sampling is also undertaken at the end of a response action or abatement project to determine if the work area has been sufficiently cleaned. This is referred to as a clearance testing and the samples for this purpose are collected using aggressive techniques. Aggressive air sampling involves use of a one horsepower leaf blower in concert with electric fans to stir up any dust or particulates present while floor pumps are collecting the samples. The NIOSH 7400 method has been used to analyze both personal and clearance air samples. As will be discussed more fully later, the majority of clearance testing must presently be done using TEM.

Finally, mention should be made concerning use of scanning electron microscopy (SEM) for analyzing asbestos samples. SEM has been employed as a research tool to study physical characteristics of asbestos fibers; however, there is no accepted protocol available to use SEM as a quantitative analytical tool. Therefore, SEM does not enter into the picture as a tool for asbestos monitoring or management.

HEALTH EFFECTS

Asbestos has been suspected of causing adverse health effects for nearly as long as it has been used by man. Greek slaves were believed to have become ill as a result of asbestos exposure. Mesothelioma, which will be described later in this section, was first identified in South African mine workers. Shipbuilders were also observed to have asbestos-related diseases as early as 1920.

As with any sort of toxic material, individuals can be exposed to asbestos by dermal contact, ingestion, or inhalation. Inhalation is considered the most dangerous mode of exposure, followed by ingestion, and then dermal contact. The great majority of asbestos related maladies are a result of inhaling small asbestos fibers. Exposure via ingestion is believed to be linked to an increased incidence of cancer in various regions of the alimentary canal. Hands of abatement workers may develop a condition called asbestos warts. These warts tend to disappear after exposure is ended and no other adverse effect has been observed due to dermal exposure.

Although dermal exposure to asbestos is not believed to produce dangerous or irreversible effects, protective clothing is universally recommended and used when working with or around asbestos. Use of protective clothing is predominately intended to facilitate worker decontamination and prevent spread of fibers outside the work area, thereby exposing other individuals.

As previously stated, the greatest risk to health is via inhalation of microscopic asbestos particles. Six disorders have been identified as resulting from exposure to airborne asbestos: lung cancer, asbestosis, mesothelioma, pleural effusion, pleural plaque, and pleural thickening. Each of these diseases is progressive and has a lengthy latency period. The toxic effects of asbestos seem to stem from particle size and shape more than from chemical composition.

Inhalation of asbestos fibers has been directly linked to the development of all types of lung cancer, a malignancy of the covering of the bronchial tubes. As with most asbestos-related diseases, lung cancer follows a dose-response relationship. Risk to the individual increases as the length of exposure time increases and as levels of exposure increases. A latency period of twenty to thirty years can be expected between initial exposure to airborne asbestos fibers and declaration of the disease. A very important point to note is that there exists a synergistic effect between smoking tobacco and exposure to airborne asbestos fibers. Exposure to industrial concentrations of asbestos fibers produces an approximate five-times increase in the likelihood of lung cancer. Smoking causes in the neighborhood of a ten-times increase in such risk. Exposure to asbestos by individuals who also smoke results in a 50 to 100 times increase in the risk of lung cancer.

Asbestosis is the most commonly discussed of the asbestos related diseases and is a scarring or fibrosis of lung tissue. The symptoms produced by asbestosis are similar to those of emphysema. All forms of asbestos have demonstrated the ability to cause asbestosis. The latency period for asbestosis ranges from fifteen to thirty years and follows a dose-response relationship. In most cases, individuals will not develop asbestosis unless exposed to high concentrations of airborne fibers for an extended period of time (years). Risk of contracting asbestosis can be reduced by lowering either exposure concentration or exposure time and therefore, represents one of the most preventable of the asbestos-related diseases.

A third asbestos-related disease is mesothelioma; a malignancy of the lining of the chest or abdominal cavity. Pleural mesothelioma is a malignant growth of the exterior lining of the lungs (pleura). Peritoneal mesothelioma is a malignancy of the peritoneum of the abdominal cavity. Either form of the disease spreads quickly and is always fatal. Pleural mesothelioma gained public notoriety when Steve McQueen was diagnosed and later died of it. The disease has a latency period of greater than thirty years and represents a severe management problem because it does not follow a dose response relationship. Mesothelioma is the most rare of diseases caused by exposure to asbestos fibers; however, lack of a dose response relationship between exposure and incidence of this disease implies there is no known safe level of exposure.

Three other diseases associated with asbestos exposure are pleural effusions, diffuse pleural thickenings, and pleural plaques. Pleural effusion is a collection of fluid around the lung and is the most common effect of inhalation of asbestos dust. It is probably the only effect which occurs during the first ten years of exposure. Diffuse pleural thickening is often associated with the occurrence of pleural effusions. It is a thickening of the visceral (lung) and/or parietal (chest wall) pleura. The thickening can vary from 0.5 to 2 cm in thickness and results in increased difficulty in breathing.

Pleural plaque is a thickening of tissue under the parietal pleura, which can become calcified. An associated latency period of twenty years exists and the condition is typically asymptomatic. Pleural plaques are the most important x-ray abnormalities found as a result of asbestos exposure and are used as diagnostic signposts.

The best non-invasive method for monitoring exposure of patients is by radiographic examination with pleural plaques being the most predominant of conditions identifiable using x-rays. Only fifteen percent of the pleural plaques found in asbestos workers during autopsy were capable of being diagnosed by pre-autopsy x-ray examination. This underscores the fact that in addition to being a brown human carcinogen, asbestos exposure leads to physiological changes in a majority of individuals who are significantly exposed.

Asbestos-related diseases are somewhat characterized by long latency periods which may vary from ten to forty years. These long latency periods cause many workers to become cynical as to the danger of exposure. Although not an immediate health risk, asbestos does cause adverse health effects and worker education is necessary to minimize unwarranted exposure. All asbestos-related diseases are progressive and treatment, therefore, is intended to retard the rate at which a patient's condition degrades. It is important to note that most of the asbestos-related diseases are asymptomatic, that is, the patient never demonstrates physical symptoms. In summary, exposure to airborne concentrations of asbestos fibers leads to the significant incidence of respiratory diseases. Unfortunately, only the most serious cases are ever diagnosed and it is impossible to screen workers to determine individual susceptibility. Moreover, the lengthy latency periods and asymptomatic nature of most asbestos-related diseases contributes to high levels of worker complacency. Education and effective workplace monitoring are necessary to protect workers from the hazards of airborne asbestos fibers.

ASBESTOS REGULATIONS

A wide variety of federal regulations address the manner in which asbestos can be used or handled. Regulated activities include mining and milling of asbestos ores, manufacturing of asbestos containing materials, use of asbestos containing materials in construction, removal of asbestos containing materials from buildings, and disposal of asbestos containing waste. Workers are protected from exposure to asbestos under a variety of standards. Two sets of regulations have also been established dealing specifically with asbestos in schools.

The bulk of discussion in this section will focus on regulations dealing with worker protection along with disposal of asbestos waste materials. These regulations are most easily grouped with respect to the agencies which administer them. Three federal agencies that have regulatory jurisdiction over asbestos will be discussed; the Department of Transportation (DOT), the U.S. Environmental Protection Agency (EPA), and the Occupational Safety and Health Administration (OSHA).

DOT Requirements

DOT regulations represent a good starting point since they are the most brief. Under the Hazardous Materials Transportation Act, asbestos is considered a hazardous material and is categorized as an ORM-C. Crocidolite (blue asbestos) has been designated as UN 2212 and chrysolite (white asbestos) as UN 2590. Asbestos has a reportable quantity (RQ) of one pound. As waste ACM, material should be identified as waste hazardous substance (asbestos), solid nos. UN 9188, ORM-E RQ 1 lb. (asbestos).

Containers appropriate for shipment of asbestos are listed in 49 CFR 173.1090. Such containers can be rigid or non-rigid but must be air-tight. The exception for this requirement is ACM which has been fixed in a natural or artificial binder such as cement or plastic so as to be non-friable.

Standards which are intended to limit exposure of transportation personnel can be found in 49 CFR 177.844. Asbestos containing materials must be loaded, handled, and unloaded in a manner that will minimize occupational exposure to airborne particles. In regard to asbestos abatement projects, this translates to insuring that waste materials are thoroughly wetted prior to transport and that such waste materials are placed in DOT approved containers. One of the most common DOT violations for transport of asbestos containing waste materials is that the waste has not been properly wetted. This produces a dilemma for the environmental professional as to the extent to which water can be used while preparing wastes for disposal. The material should be thoroughly wetted, yet free water should not be present in the containers since free liquids are banned from landfills.

OSHA Requirements

The Occupational Safety and Health Administration (OSHA) also has established several standards directed at protection of workers from exposure to asbestos. Due to its carcinogenic nature, asbestos is considered a hazardous chemical and, therefore, covered under the hazard communication standard (29 CFR 1910.1200). Aside from this, there are also OSHA standards specific to activities which could involve exposure to airborne asbestos. The most notable of these are the asbestos construction standard (29 CFR 1926.58) and the general industry standard for asbestos (29 CFR 1910.1001).

The OSHA Standard found in 29 CFR 1926.58 applies to all construction work. This includes demolition or salvage of asbestos containing materials, removal or encapsulation of asbestos containing materials, construction, alteration, repair, maintenance, or renovation of structures where ACM will be disturbed. Emergency response to spills containing asbestos, as well as transportation, storage, and disposal of contaminated debris, is also covered under this standard. The permissible exposure limit (PEL) for airborne asbestos fibers is currently listed as 0.2 fibers per cubic centimeter (cc) of air and the action level (AL) is 0.1 fibers/cc. Both exposure limits are based on an eight hour time weighted average. A final protective standard has been established for short term exposure of workers to airborne asbestos fibers, the EL or excursion limit. The EL is presently set at 1 fiber/cc on a 30 minute time weighted average.

For the past two years, OSHA has been considering revision of the existing asbestos PEL and AL. The proposed value for a new PEL is 0.1 f/cc with deletion of the AL. Final notice for these changes are scheduled for July 1991.

Employers covered under these OSHA standards are required to establish regulated work areas where airborne concentrations of asbestos fibers might be expected to equal or exceed the PEL. The establishment and supervision of a regulated area is to be under the direction of a "competent person." Responsibilities of this competent person will be to establish negative pressure enclosures where necessary, supervise exposure monitoring, designate appropriate personal protective equipment as well as to ensure training of workers with respect to proper use of said equipment, establishment and use of hygiene facilities, and ensuring that proper engineering controls are used throughout the life of the project. OSHA is currently preparing a more descriptive statement of the training requirements necessary for these competent persons.

Employers are required to provide respirators to all workers who may be exposed to greater than the PEL of airborne asbestos fibers during their work activities. The employer must also ensure the provided equipment is capable of giving adequate protection to the exposed individuals. Respirator selection for asbestos exposure is to be accomplished in accordance with the OSHA guideline listed in 29 CFR 1926.58(h). A written respiratory protection program shall also be put into place as described in 29 CFR 1910.134. Selection of proper respiratory protective equipment is based on air sampling or monitoring which is required prior to and throughout the life of the construction project in areas where airborne concentrations of asbestos might be reasonably expected. Sampling and analysis conducted for this purpose is to follow the NIOSH 7400 method (PCM). All employees covered by this protective program are to be notified of the results of personal exposure monitoring either by personal contact or the posting of the test results.

Presently all employees who (1) are exposed to concentrations of asbestos fibers at or above the action level for 30 days or more each year or (2) are required to wear a negative pressure respirator, must be included in a medical monitoring program. The medical examinations are to include collection of a medical history, completion of a standardized questionnaire contained in Appendix D of 29 CFR 1926.58, a chest x-ray, examination of the pulmonary and gastrointestinal system, as well as, a pulmonary function test by either forced vital capacity or forced expiratory volume. Examinations are to be completed yearly with the cost being borne by employers.

An OSHA standard has also been established to protect workers in the general industry category who may work around asbestos (CFR 1910.1001). This standard applies to all occupational exposures to asbestos fibers covered by the Occupational Safety and Health Act with the exception of those activities subject to the construction industry standard (29 CFR 1926.58).

EPA Requirements

In addition to worker protection standards established by OSHA, EPA has promulgated a number of rules intended to limit environmental release of asbestos fibers. The most frequently encountered EPA asbestos regulation is the asbestos NESHAP found in 40 CFR 61 Subpart M (see Clean Air Section for NESHAP explanation). Asbestos has also been explicitly addressed under the Toxic Substances Control Act (TSCA). These asbestos standards are located in 40 CFR 763. Two commonly referenced rules can found in part 763: (1) asbestos in schools regulations and (2) the Worker Protection Rule. The EPA has additionally established bans on the manufacture or importation of asbestos containing products. This restrictive ruling is to be implemented in three phases and calls for elimination of 94 percent of all asbestos containing materials from the U.S. marketplace by 1997.

We will now look more specifically at the asbestos NESHAP. The currently enforced rule was published in final form on November 20,

1990 (55 FR 48406) and contains some significant revisions. A number of definitions have been either revised or added (see 40 CFR 61.141) including those for adequately wet, nonfriable, regulated ACM, and waste shipment record.

In general, the asbestos NESHAP addresses four basic points: (1) fugitive emissions from work sites, (2) required removal before demolition, (3) notification requirements before disturbing ACM, and (4) standards disposal of asbestos containing waste materials in landfills. The "no visible emissions" statement for releases from mining, milling, and manufacturing processes is probably the most commonly quoted part of the asbestos NESHAP. This restriction extends to renovation and building demolition projects as well as those previously stated. It is important to distinguish between the OSHA PEL and the EPA "no visible emissions level." OSHA establishes exposure standards for inside the work space while EPA establishes limits for non-point source emissions to the environment. The EPA no visible emissions limit is not intended to serve as a worker protection standard.

A second requirement of the asbestos NESHAP is that all regulated asbestos containing materials (RACM) must be removed from a building prior to demolition. The reader should note that this is the only place in federal regulations in which asbestos removal is required. Additionally, before any renovation, remodeling, or removal activities involving disturbance of RACM can be undertaken, the state agency responsible for Clean Air Act enforcement must be provided written notification ten days in advance of beginning work. This advance notification is required in the event that 160 linear feet or 260 square feet of RACM will be effected or if 35 cubic feet of asbestos containing waste material will be generated. Should the starting date of the removal project change prior to initiation of work, a revised notification form must be submitted and ten working days must separate submission of this form from the start of work. Finally, the delegated state agency must be provided with project updates in the event the amount of asbestos effected changes by 20 percent.

Asbestos containing waste materials are not considered hazardous wastes and can be disposed of in approved landfills. The asbestos NESHAP establishes guidelines for proper disposal of such asbestos wastes. These guidelines include provisions for restricting emissions, adequate wetting of waste materials, use of hazard warning labels, indelible marking of each container with information about the generator, and use of waste shipment records in a fashion analogous to the uniform manifest for hazardous waste disposal. This documentation of waste shipments includes the requirement to submit an "exception" report if written verification of disposal of the asbestos waste is not received from the designated disposal facility within 45 days.

Asbestos is one of five groups of chemicals specifically regulated under the Toxic Substances Control Act (TSCA). Asbestos regulations promulgated pursuant to TSCA are located in 40 CFR 763. Three major areas of concern are addressed in this regulatory reference: (1) reporting of commercial and industrial uses of asbestos, (2) asbestos in schools, and (3) asbestos abatement projects. Notifications and reports which must be submitted by miners, primary processors, secondary processors, manufacturers, and importers, are outlined in 763 Subpart D. In certain cases information must also be submitted to the Consumer Product Safety Commission as well as the EPA.

As we have already discussed, abatement activities conducted by private sector personnel are subject to the OSHA Construction Industry Standard (29 CFR 1926.58). When OSHA was first created, its purview was limited to the private sector. Federal agencies were incorporated into OSHA's sphere of authority in 1979 via executive order of the President. In addition to this, approximately half the states in our nation have passed statutes placing their state and local government agencies subject to OSHA standards. Obviously, there remains a group of state employees who would not be subject to protective standards when performing work on an asbestos removal project. EPA addressed this small group of OSHA exempt workers in something commonly referred to as the worker protection rule (40 CFR 763 Subpart G). It is directed specifically at state and local employees not subject to OSHA and is basically equivalent to the construction industry standard.

The presence of asbestos in school buildings has been a popular topic of discussion and has been also addressed by EPA. In 1982, an Asbestos in Schools Rule was passed which required schools to identify friable asbestos containing materials in buildings. This rule was replaced in 1986 by the Asbestos Hazard Emergency Response Act (AHERA) which goes far beyond the old Asbestos in Schools Rule. AHERA was initially applicable to schools; however, its applicability has recently been expanded to include all public buildings. Environmental professionals who may deal with asbestos should become familiar with AHERA because it establishes accreditation requirements for individuals involved with inspection, management, removal, or design of removal projects. AHERA also establishes state of the art management practices for asbestos in buildings.

A discussion of basic principles of AHERA must start with some important definitions (see 40 CFR 763.83). An asbestos-containing material (ACM) is considered to be any material or product containing greater than one percent asbestos. An asbestos-containing building material (ACBM) is defined to be ACM found in or on interior structural members or other parts of a building and is grouped into one of three categories: (1) surfacing materials, (2) thermal system insulation, and (3) miscellaneous ACM. Each of these categories of ACBM can be further described as being either friable or non-friable. Friable ACM is defined as material which, when dry, may be crumbled, pulverized, or reduced to powder by hand pressure. There are also definitions for removal, enclosure, encapsulation, and repair for which the management professional should be familiar.

Another important aspect of AHERA to cover in this initial discussion would be training/accreditation requirements for workers and professionals. AHERA has established five areas of accreditation as the appropriate training requirements for individuals who would: (1) perform building inspections, (2) prepare management plans for buildings, (3) supervise abatement projects, (4) serve as workers on abatement projects, or (5) design abatement projects. Accreditation in each of these areas is achieved by attending an EPA approved course and passing a written examination. In addition to this, most states presently require registration or licensure of asbestos professionals.

Looking now at the inspection procedure, floor plans along with record drawings and specifications of construction projects are reviewed to identify locations of suspected ACBM. Homogeneous areas defined as "an area of surfacing material, thermal system insulation material, or miscellaneous material which is uniform in color and texture" are then established for the purposes of sampling. Bulk samples are taken from each homogeneous area in a statistically random fashion with the number of samples collected based upon the square or linear footage present in the homogeneous area. Each sample must be collected by an accredited inspector and analysis must be completed using the PLM point count method in a laboratory which has been accredited by the National Institutes of Standards and Testing (NIST). If one sample from a homogeneous area is determined to contain greater than one percent asbestos, the homogeneous area must be classified as ACBM. In lieu of sampling and analyzing suspected ACM, the building owner is allowed to assume the material is ACM and manage it accordingly.

The final stages of inspecting a building will include an assessment of the physical condition of all materials which have been identified or assumed to be ACBM. Based upon this physical assessment, the accredited inspector will assign each homogenous area to one of seven assessment categories. The inspection report submitted to the building owner will include the sampling scheme, sample locations, names of inspectors collecting samples, analysis reports for all samples, classification of homogeneous areas as ACBM or non ACBM, and physical assessment of all homogeneous areas.

According to AHERA, an accredited management planner will review information contained in the inspection report and then conduct a hazard assessment for each homogenous area of ACBM or suspected ACBM. The assessment completed by the management planner is more detailed than the physical assessment done by the inspector and is intended to serve as an indicator of risk for building occupants. Based upon this hazards assessment, the management planner will recommend a response option for each homogeneous area; enclosure, encapsulation, removal, repair, or maintenance. In conjunction with these response option recommendations, the management planner will also prescribe an operation and management plan for all ACBM left in the building.

Since an operations and maintenance plan will be carried out by facility personnel, AHERA also establishes training requirements for those individuals. Any custodial or maintenance personnel working in a building containing ACBM must be given two hours of awareness training, whether they work with ACBM or not. Those individuals who may disturb ACBM during their duties must receive an additional fourteen hours of training. All employee training must be site specific and include locations of ACBM in each building.

The role played by an accredited project designer should also be explained. Obviously, a large scale abatement project would be designed by such an individual; however, small projects may also require the services of an accredited project designer. Any response to a major fiber release must be completed by accredited personnel: project designer, project supervisor, and project workers. A major fiber release is defined to have occurred when greater than three square or linear feet of ACBM becomes dislodged from its substrate.

In the event a major fiber release occurs, the facility environmental manager should immediately conduct a number of actions. The area in which the release occurred should be isolated by modifying or shutting off the heating, ventilation, and air conditioning (HVAC) systems. Entry to the affected area should be restricted and signs posted warning of the hazard. An air sampling firm should be contacted to have non-isolated areas tested for airborne asbestos fibers. Finally, an accredited project designer should be contacted to coordinate the remediation.

Still another way in which AHERA has impacted asbestos abatement activities is the manner by which response actions receive clearance. Prior to AHERA, clearance testing was conducted using the NIOSH 7400 method (PCM). AHERA stipulates use of a TEM method involving collection of 13 samples for each work area. Until a NIST laboratory accrediting program for TEM is operational, analysis must be done by labs using the protocol listed in Appendix A of 40 CFR 763 Subpart E.

Finally, in no way does AHERA supersede those requirements established by OSHA standards, the Asbestos NESHAP, or the EPA Worker Protection Rule. EPA has begun integrating concepts of AHERA into other asbestos regulations as is reflected by the updated NESHAP.

AHERA has become the "state-of-the-art" in asbestos management and abatement.

CROSS-REFERENCE TO ASBESTOS REGULATIONS

AGENCY	REFERENCE	STANDARD
EPA	40 CFR 61, Subpart M	Asbestos NESHAP
	40 CFR 763, Subparts E,F	Asbestos in schools (AHERA)
	40 CFR 427	Effluent standards (asbestos manufacturing)
	40 CFR 763, Subpart G	EPA Worker Protection Rule
OSHA	29 CFR 1910.1001	General industry asbestos standard
	29 CFR 1926.58	Construction industry asbestos standard
MSHA	30 CFR 57, Subpart D	Surface mining asbestos standard
	30 CFR 57, Subpart D	Underground mining asbestos standard
DOT	49 CFR 171 and 172	Hazardous Materials Transportation Act

FEDERAL INSECTICIDE, FUNGICIDE, AND RODENTICIDE ACT (FIFRA)

Earl R. Burns
Tennessee Valley Authority

Revised by

Edward E. (Gene) Burgess, Ph.D.
University of Tennessee
Agricultural Extension Service

INTRODUCTION

The first version of the Federal Insecticide, Fungicide, and Rodenticide Act (FIFRA), was passed by Congress in 1947. The primary purpose of the Act was to require registration of pesticides to protect consumers from misbranded, adulterated, and/or ineffective pesticides. Jurisdiction was originally placed with the United States Department of Agriculture, but was transferred to the Environmental Protection Agency (EPA) in 1970.

In 1972 FIFRA was amended by the Federal Environmental Pesticide Control Act. This amended Act completely restructured the Federal pesticide regulatory scheme and redefined its thrust. FIFRA was changed from a labeling law into a comprehensive regulatory statute to control the manufacture, distribution, and use of pesticides. The primary purpose of the 1972 amendments was to ensure that pesticide use would be subject to a thorough review of environmental and human health hazards.

This was to be accomplished by requiring all pesticides sold or distributed in the United States to be registered by EPA. The administrator of EPA,

229

hereinafter referred to as the "Administrator," was also given authority to suspend, cancel, or restrict pesticides that posed a risk to the environment. The requirements of this Act are enforced through inspections, labeling, notices, and regulation by State authorities. FIFRA was extended in 1975 by public law 94-140 and extended again in 1978 by public law 95-396. Key sections of the amended FIFRA and regulations (CFR 40) are discussed in more detail later.

Section 2: Definitions

(e)   CERTIFIED APPLICATOR, ETC.

(1)   *Certified applicator* -- A "certified applicator" is any individual who is certified under section $4^{2.1}$ as authorized to use or supervise the use of any pesticide which is classified for restricted use.

(2)   *Private applicator* -- A "private applicator" is a certified applicator who uses or supervises the use of any restricted-use pesticide for purposes of producing an agricultural commodity on property owned or rented by him, his employer or (if applied without compensation other than trading of personal services between producers of agricultural commodities) another person.

(3)   *Commercial applicator* -- A "commercial applicator" is an applicator who uses or supervises the use of any restricted-use pesticide for any purpose or on any property other than as provided by paragraph (2).

(4)   *Under the direct supervision of a certified applicator* -- Unless otherwise prescribed by its labeling, a pesticide shall be considered to be applied by a competent person acting under the instructions and control of a certified applicator who is available if and when needed, even though such certified applicator is not physically present at the time and place the pesticide is applied.

(p)   LABEL AND LABELING

    (1)   *Label* -- The term "label" means the written, printed, or graphic matter on, or attached to, the pesticide or device or any of its containers or wrappers.

    (2)   *Labeling* -- The term "labeling" includes all labels as well as other written, printed, or graphic matter.

(u)   PESTICIDE -- The term "pesticide" means (1) any substance or mixture of substances intended for preventing, destroying, repelling, or mitigating any pest, and (2) any substance or mixture of substances intended for use as a plant regulator, defoliant, or disiccant, except that the term "pesticide" shall not include any article that is a "new animal drug" within the meaning of section 201(w) of the Federal Food, Drug, and Cosmetic Act (21 U.S.C. 321(w)).

(bb)   UNREASONABLE   ADVERSE   EFFECTS   ON   THE ENVIRONMENT -- The term "unreasonable adverse effects on the environment" means any unreasonable risk to man or the environment, taking into account the economic, social, and environmental costs and benefits of the use of any pesticide.

Section 3: Pesticide Registration

Section 3(3) of the Act provides that, except as otherwise provided by the Act, no person in any State may distribute, sell, or otherwise place into commerce, any pesticide which is not registered with the EPA.

Each applicant for registration of a pesticide must file with the Administrator a statement (3(c)1) which includes: the name and address of the applicant, the name of the pesticide, a complete copy of the labeling, a statement of claims, directions for use, and, if requested by the Administrator, a full description of tests and results on which claims are based.   The complete formula for the pesticide and a request for classification of use is also required. The Administrator publishes (3(c)2) specifying the kinds of information required to support registration.

Upon completion of application for registration and review of supporting data, the Administrator may approve (3(c)5) or deny (3(c)6) registration. To approve registration, the Administrator must determine [considering restrictions imposed under subsection (d)] that the material warrants the claims for it, its labeling and other material required to be submitted comply with requirements of the Act, it will function as intended without unreasonable adverse effects on the environment, and, when used in accordance with widespread and commonly recognized practice, it will not generally cause unreasonable adverse effects on the environment.

If a pesticide can be used by an untrained person according to directions without unreasonable adverse effects on the environment or applicator, it is classified for general use. A pesticide that may generally cause unreasonable adverse effects on the environment or injure the applicator even when being used according to directions is classified for restricted use.

If the Administrator classifies a pesticide for restricted use because of environmental or health hazard to the applicator or other persons, the pesticide may only be used for any use to which the restricted classification applies only by or under the direct supervision of a certified applicator. A pesticide product which is classified for restricted use shall bear a label containing a statement of restricted use classification and directions for use which are consistent with the terms of the restriction.

Section 4:   Reregistration of Registered Pesticides (FIFRA 1988 Amendments)

The reregistration provisions of FIFRA 1988 establish mandatory time frames and duties for reregistration of pesticides. The law now requires EPA to complete, over approximately a nine year period, the reregistration review of each registered product containing any active ingredient registered before November 1, 1984.

Congress directed EPA to carry out reregistration in five phases (4[b]).

Phase 1: Listing of Active Ingredients (4[c])

Phase 1 required EPA to publish lists of pesticide active ingredients subject to reregistration and to ask registrants of pesticide products containing those ingredients whether they intended to seek reregistration.

Phase 2: Declaration of Intent and Identification of Studies (4[d])

Phase 2 required registrants to declare (within three months after publication of each chemical list) whether they intended to seek reregistration of their products. If so, they had to notify EPA, identify applicable data requirements and missing studies, commit to submitting new studies or replacing inadequate existing data, and pay the first installment of the reregistration fee. If a registrant did not seek reregistration, EPA cancelled the appropriate product registrations.

Many pesticides were not supported by their registrants during this phase and were cancelled.

Phase 3: Summarization of Studies (4[e])

Registrants were required to resubmit existing studies that had been reformatted and summarized according to Agency guidance, to certify the availability of raw data, to "flag" studies that indicate adverse effects, to make additional commitments to satisfy all applicable data requirements, and to pay the final installment of the reregistration fee.

Phase 4: EPA Review and Data Call-In's (4[f])

During Phase 4, EPA must review all Phase 2 and 3 submissions and determine independently whether all applicable data requirements have actually been satisfied.

Phase 5: Reregistration Decisions (4[g])

In Phase 5, EPA must conduct a comprehensive review of all the studies.

Criteria for Reregistration Eligibility

Before a pesticide product may be reregistered, its active ingredient(s) must be declared "eligible" for reregistration. When EPA determines that an active ingredient is eligible for reregistration (4[g]2), the Agency issues a Reregistration Eligibility Document (RED), summarizing the studies reviewed and the findings reached. Once such data and labeling are received and accepted, and when all their uses are eligible, individual pesticide products are reregistered. Reregistered pesticides will be reassessed as new data is received or new concerns are identified. New information received by the Agency may trigger a Special Review or cancellation actions, at any time.

Reregistration Fees

For each active ingredient used on major food or animal feed crops, registrants were required to pay a one-time reregistration fee totalling $150,000 (h[i][2]B). For pesticide active ingredients not intended for major food or feed uses, registrants had to pay a fee of not more than $150,000 and not less than $50,000. The exact fee depended on, among other things, whether a Registration Standard had been issued for the pesticide and the extent of data required for reregistration (h[i][3]B).

Maintenance Fees

Unlike the one-time reregistration fee, which is levied on the basis of active ingredients, the annual maintenance fee is assessed for each individual pesticide product.

Section 5: Experimental Use Permits

Under FIFRA the Administrator is given the authority to issue and set terms for the experimental use of a pesticide in order to obtain data to support registration. The Administrator may establish a temporary pesticide residue tolerance level for the pesticide before issuing the experimental use permit.

Section 6: Administrative Review: Suspension

This section sets forth the procedure for changing classification, suspension, or cancellation of registration if the Administrator has reason to believe a registered pesticide does not comply with the Act or if when "used in accordance with widespread and commonly recognized practice," generally caused unreasonable adverse effects on the environment.

Section 6 also states that the Administrator shall cancel the registration of any pesticide at the end of five years from the date of registration unless the registrant or other interested party requests that the registration be continued in effect.

Section 7: Registration of Establishments

Each establishment which produces pesticides must be registered with the Administrator. Producers are required to inform, within 30 days after initial registration and annually thereafter, which pesticide is currently produced, which has been produced in the past year, and which has been sold or distributed during the past year.

The Administrator assigns the establishment an establishment number. The number of the final establishment at which a specific pesticide product was produced must appear somewhere on the pesticide label.

Section 8: Books and Records

All producers of pesticides and active ingredients used in producing pesticides are required to keep a variety of information on record. Records include: name and quantity of pesticides produced; receipt and shipment of all pesticides, active ingredients and devices; inventory; copies of advertisements of restricted use pesticides; copies of guarantees; export records; disposal methods, dates, locations, sites, and types and amounts of pesticides disposed; any tests conducted on human beings; and research data relating to registered pesticides.

These records must be available for inspection by EPA and/or state officials, after presentation of appropriate credentials, and a written statement of the reason for inspection.

Section 9: Inspection of Establishments, Etc.

For the purpose of enforcing the Act, officers or employees designated by the Administrator may, upon presentation of a written statement as to the reason, enter any establishment or other place where pesticides are held for distribution or sale for the purpose of inspecting and obtaining samples of pesticides, containers, labels, etc.

Section 10: Protection of Trade Secrets and Other Information

This section prohibits disclosure of data or information related to trade secrets or commercial or financial information required by the Act to the public or to foreign producers by the Administrator and other Federal employees.

Section 11: Use of Restricted Use Pesticides; Applicators

Any State who desires to certify applicators of restricted use pesticides must have an approved State Plan (a[1]).

The EPA Administrator may require any person engaging in commercial application or sale of restricted use chemicals to maintain records and submit reports concerning the commercial application, sale or distribution of restricted use pesticides (a[1]).

EPA shall prescribe standards for the certification of applicators of pesticides. To be certified, an individual must be determined to be competent with respect to the use and handling of pesticides, or to the use and handling of the pesticide or class of pesticide covered by the individual's certification (a[1]).

The certification standard for a private applicator shall be deemed fulfilled by his/her completing a certification form. The form may include an affirmation that the private applicator has completed an approved training program, but cannot require, pursuant to a requirement prescribed by the Administrator of EPA, the private applicator to take any examination to establish competency in the use of pesticides (a[1]).

No regulations prescribed by the Administrator of EPA for carrying out the provisions of this Act shall require any private applicator to maintain any records or file any reports or other documents (d). However, in the 1990 Farm Bill, there are provisions that require all certified applicators, including the private, of restricted use pesticides to maintain records comparable to records kept by commercial applicators of pesticides. These records are to be available to any Federal or State agency that deals with pesticide use. USDA and EPA are to survey the records of pesticide use and publish an annual comprehensive report concerning agricultural and non-agricultural pesticide use. Voluntary compliance is expected in 1991, but this law should be enacted in 1992.

Section 12: Unlawful Acts

This section specifies unlawful acts regarding distribution and use of pesticides. In general, it states that it is unlawful for any person in any state to distribute, sell, offer for sale, hold for sale, ship, deliver of shipment, or receive and (having so received) deliver or offer to deliver to any person any pesticide in a manner inconsistent with the requirements of the Act, or to use a pesticide in a manner inconsistent with its labeling.

Section 13: Stop Sale, Use, Removal, and Seizure

Stop Sale Orders -- If the Administrator has reason to believe, based on inspection and tests, that a pesticide is being or is intended to be distributed or sold in violation with any provisions of the Act, or when the registration of the pesticide has been canceled by a final order or has been suspended, the Administrator may issue a written Stop Sale, Use or Removal Order to any person who owns, controls, or has custody of the pesticide. After receipt of such order, no person shall sell, use, or remove the pesticide except in accordance with provisions of the order.

Section 14: Penalties

The Act provides for both civil and criminal penalties for violators of the Act. Civil penalties for commercial applicators, registrants, dealers, etc., shall not be more than $5,000 for each offense. Any person who knowingly violates any provision of the Act is guilty of a misdemeanor and upon conviction may be fined not more than $25,000 or imprisoned for not more than one year, or both, for each violation.

Civil penalty for private applicators is a maximum fine of $1,000 for each offense. Private applicators convicted of knowingly violating the Act are guilty of a misdemeanor and may be fined not more than $1,000 or imprisoned for not more than 30 days, or both, for each violation.

This section also provides that any person who intends to defraud, or uses, or reveals information relative to product formulas acquired under authority of section 3 shall be fined not more than $10,000 or imprisoned for not more than three years, or both.

Section 15: Indemnities

If the registration of a pesticide is canceled to prevent an imminent hazard, the owners of the pesticide shall be paid an indemnity if they suffered a loss because of the cancellation, unless the Administrator finds that they had knowledge of facts that would have shown the pesticide did not meet registration requirements and continued thereafter to produce the pesticide without giving timely notice to the Administrator.

Section 17: Imports and Exports

Pesticides produced solely for export to any foreign country and prepared or packed according to the specification and directions of the foreign purchaser will not be deemed in violation with the Act except that the pesticide must be subject to section 8 of the Act concerning records.

The Administration is required to notify foreign governments through the State Department whenever a registration, cancellation, or suspension of the registration becomes effective or ceases to be effective.

Pesticides which are imported are subject to inspection, and those which violate the Act will be refused entry or seized and destroyed.

The Administrator may exempt any Federal or State agency from any provision of the Act if emergency conditions exist.

Section 19: Disposal, Storage, and Transportation

This section gives the authority to the Administrator to establish procedures and regulations for disposal and storage of packages and containers of pesticides, for disposal or storage of excess amounts of pesticides, and to accept at convenient locations for safe disposal, pesticides which have had registrations canceled under section 6(c), if requested by the owner of the pesticide.   The Administrator is also responsible for providing advice and assistance to the Secretary of Transportation with respect to the transportation of hazardous materials.

Regulations under 40 CFR Part 165 outline procedures recommended and not recommended for disposal and storage of pesticides and containers. Pesticides or containers should *not* be disposed of or stored in a manner inconsistent with their labels. Open dumping, open burning (except open burning by the user of small quantities of combustible containers formerly containing organic or metallo-organic pesticides except organic mercury, lead, cadmium, or arsenic compounds), water dumping, and other procedures which violate Federal or State pollution control standards, or any provisions of the Act, are prohibited.

Recommended Procedures for Disposal of Pesticides

1. Organic pesticides (except organic mercury, lead, cadmium, and arsenic compounds) should be disposed of by:

   - incineration in a pesticide incinerator;
   - if incineration facilities are not available, buried in a specially designated landfill;
   - if adequate incineration or specially designated landfill facilities are not available, pesticides and containers should be stored temporarily until proper disposal can be achieved.

2. Metallo-organic pesticides (except organic mercury, lead, cadmium, or arsenic):

   - treat compounds by appropriate chemical or physical means to recover metals, then incinerate in a pesticide incinerator;
   - if appropriate treatment and incineration facilities are not available, bury in a specially designated landfill.

3. Organic mercury, lead, cadmium, arsenic, and all inorganic pesticides should be disposed of by:

   - chemical deviation to nonhazardous compounds and recovery of metals;
   - if chemical deactivation facilities are not available, such pesticides should be encapsulated and buried in a specially designated landfill. Records should be kept to a permit location for retrieval.

4. If above options are not available, pesticides should be placed in suitable containers and stored until adequate disposal facilities or procedures are available.

Recommended Procedures for Disposal of Pesticide Containers and Residues:

1. Group I pesticide containers are combustible containers which formerly contained organic or metallo-organic pesticides, except organic mercury, lead, cadmium, or arsenic. They should be

disposed of by incineration or buried in a specially designated landfill.

Small quantities of such containers may be burned in open fields or buried singly in open fields by the user provided due regard is given to protection of surface and subsurface water.

2.   Group II containers (noncombustible containers which formerly contained organic or metallo-organic pesticides except organic mercury, lead, cadmium, or arsenic) should first be triple-rinsed. After rinsing they may be returned to the pesticide manufacturer, formulate, or drum reconditioner for reuse with the same chemical class of pesticide previously contained. Other rinsed metal containers should be punctured and transported to a recycling facility or disposal site. All rinsed containers may be crushed and disposed of by burial in a sanitary landfill or in the field by the pesticide user. Unrinsed containers should be disposed of in a specially designated landfill or incinerator.

3.   Group III containers (those which formerly contained organic mercury, lead, cadmium or arsenic or inorganic pesticides) should be triple-rinsed, punctured and disposed of in a sanitary landfill. Unrinsed containers should be encapsulated and buried in a specially designated landfill.

4.   Residue and rinse liquids should be added to spray mixtures in the field. If not, they should be disposed of in the manner prescribed for each specific type of pesticide.

Storage of Pesticides and Containers

Pesticides, excess pesticides, and pesticide containers, whose uncontrolled release into the environment would cause unreasonable adverse effects on the environment, should be stored only in facilities where due regard has been given to the hazardous nature of the pesticide.

Special storage procedures and criteria should be observed at sites and facilities where pesticides (and containers) that are classed as highly or moderately toxic and required to bear the signal words DANGER, POISON, or WARNING, or the skull and crossbones symbol, are stored.

Storage sites should be located where flooding is unlikely and where soil texture/structure, and geologic, hydrologic characteristics will prevent contamination of any water system by runoff or percolation.   Where warranted, drainage from the site should be contained by dikes or barriers.

Pesticides should be stored in a dry, well-ventilated, separate area where fire protection is provided.   Pesticides should be stored in original containers with labels in plain view. If original containers are damaged or in poor condition, contents should be transferred to a suitable, sound container and labeled clearly. The facility should be secured by a climb-proof fence, and doors and gates should be kept locked to prevent unauthorized entry. Signs should be posted advising of the contents and warning of the hazardous nature of the pesticides. Equipment used in handling pesticides at the storage site should be labeled "contaminated with pesticides" and should not be removed from the site unless thoroughly decontaminated. Provisions should be made for decontaminating personnel and equipment.

In addition to precautions specified on pesticide labels, rules for personal safety and accident prevention should be made available and followed at storage sites.   Protective clothing should be provided for workers. Procedures for fire control, fire hazard abatement, and fire fighting precautions should be developed.

If a large quantity of pesticides is stored in an area, or if the situation otherwise warrants it, the owner of the stored materials should inform local fire departments, hospitals, public health officials, and police in writing of the hazards which would be present in case of a fire.   He should also have the telephone numbers of the person responsible for the storage facility, the appropriate EPA Regional Administrator, United States Coast Guard, Pesticide Safety Team Network of the National Agricultural Chemicals Association, and the National Response Center. The National Agricultural Chemicals Association, (202) 296-1586, has an excellent free booklet entitled, *Pre-Fire Plan for Handling Agricultural Chemical Fires*. THE OWNER MAY DECIDE TO MAKE ARRANGEMENTS WITH THE FIRE DEPARTMENT TO LET A FIRE BURN WITHOUT ATTEMPTING TO PUT IT OUT, SINCE HIGHER TEMPERATURES

ADEQUATELY DESTROY MANY PESTICIDES AND BY-PRODUCTS.

Where applicable the outside of each storage area should be labeled with warning signs (DANGER, POISON, PESTICIDE STORAGE). An up-to-date list of types of chemicals should also be posted outside each storage area.

A number of special precautions should be taken when fighting fires involving pesticides:

- air-supplied breathing apparatus and rubber clothing should be worn
- avoid breathing or contacting toxic smoke or fumes,
- wash completely and as quickly as possible after contacting smoke and fumes,
- contain water used in firefighting within the drainage systems of the storage site,
- after fighting fire involving organophosphate or N-alkyl carbamate pesticides, cholinesterase tests should be taken,
- persons near pesticide fires should be evacuated.

It is advisable to monitor ground and surface water and plant and wildlife environments on a regular basis around pesticide storage facilities to assure minimal environmental damage.

PRE-FIRE PLAN for handling

AGRICULTURAL CHEMICAL FIRES

FACILITY NAME _____

LOCATION _____

PHONE NUMBER _____

EMERGENCY TELEPHONE NUMBERS: DAY   NIGHT

MANAGER'S NAME _____ _____ _____

ASST. MANAGER'S NAME _____ _____ _____

ALTERNATE _____ _____ _____

ALTERNATE _____ _____ _____

PHYSICIAN'S NAME _____ _____ _____

CHEMTREC (Chemical Transportation Emergency Center)   **(800) 424-9300** (TOLL FREE)
(For calls originating outside the continental U.S., call (202) 483-7616 collect.)

Most chemical manufacturers are equipped to provide *emergency* INFORMATION ON THEIR PRODUCTS. Manufacturers may be contacted through CHEMTREC.

Fires in agricultural chemical facilities can be dangerous—the possibility of poisoning must be considered in addition to the usual fire hazards. The general guidelines inside will help reduce these hazards. However, a specific plan should be developed for each facility as outlined in the instructions. Local fire departments should be invited to your facility at least annually. They should be thoroughly familiar with the contents of *your* Pre-Fire Plan. Special consideration should be given to providing them with relevant information **IN ADVANCE** as to anticipated quantities, locations and types of hazardous materials. The use of Material Safety Data Sheets (MSDSs), which are available from manufacturers, is encouraged.

PRE-FIRE PLAN UPDATE (Revise annually and after any important change):

FACILITY MANAGER _____
                              (signature)   *(date)*

FIRE DEPT. OFFICIAL _____
                              (signature)   *(date)*

NAME OF FIRE DEPT. _____

NEXT SCHEDULED REVIEW OR UPDATE _____
                                                              (date)

SKETCH OF FACILITY & IMMEDIATE SURROUNDINGS

Draw map showing the property site and immediate surroundings. Show outline of buildings, type of construction, permanent interior walls, building openings, and major fixed equipment. Provide elevation views if more than one story. Locate all fixed outside equipment. Show perimeter fences, gates, rail spurs, floor drains, etc.

Show access routes and approximate distances to important buildings. Select a suitable scale. *Identify areas of the facility committed to* **pesticides, flammables, oxidizers,** *etc. including bulk storage tanks.* Use symbols in legend below. Show North arrow.

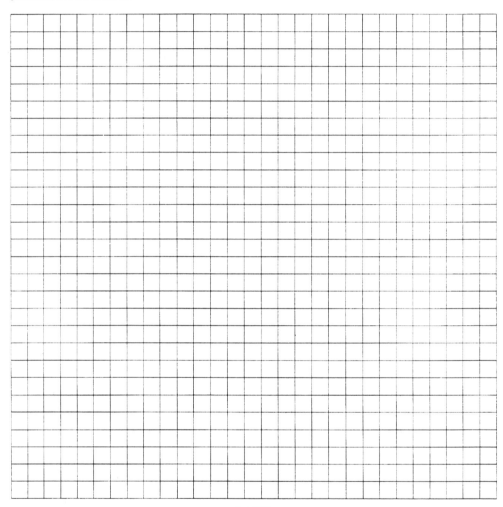

LEGEND

FIRE PROTECTION EQUIPMENT	WALL CONSTRUCTION —	BUILDING
Fire Hydrant .... Ⓗ	Concrete	Pedestrian Door ....
Sprinkler Booster Connection ..... Ⓑ	Masonry	Sliding Door ....
Main Gas Shutoff .... Ⓖ	Metal	Overhead Door ....
Main Electrical Shutoff .... Ⓔ	Wood	Fire Door (Add to door symbol) ..... ⒻⒹ
	Fire Wall (Add to wall symbol) ...... Ⓕⓦ	

244

SITE RUNOFF CONTROL

Draw map showing the surrounding area for about one mile in all directions. Extend the map in the direction of the site drainage so that drainage can be traced until it reaches the nearest large body of water. If runoff can be impounded on or off site show location and approximate number of gallons that can be contained. Locate where and how runoff may be blocked by dikes, dams, shutting off lift pumps, etc. Show surrounding land use (residential, cornfield, etc.). Show places of public assembly, such as schools, churches. Use symbols below. Show North arrow.

EXTERIOR

Fence . . . . **-*-*-*-*-*-**	Well . . . . ⓦ	Direction Ground Slopes . . . . ⟿
Gate . . . . ⌒⌐	Drain Lines or Culverts	Stream or Creek . . . . ➾
Railroad . . . . +++++++	(with direction of flow)	Impoundment Location . . . . . ⟨⟋⟋⟋⟩
Drain Inlet . . . . ⓓ	Surface . . . . ⟶ ⟶	Lift Pump . . . . ⓟ
Manhole . . . . ⓜ	Underground . . . . - ➔ - ➔ -	Proposed Dike or Berm . . . . . ▬▬

245

1. **AGENCY NOTIFICATION:** (List the names and telephone numbers of agencies that need to be notified should a spill or fire involving pesticides or fertilizers occur. Include railroads if rails may be blocked.)

NAME	PHONE NUMBER

2. **SURROUNDING OCCUPANCIES & LAND USE:** (Describe surrounding land use in all four directions for one mile radius. For example, north: grazing land to 1/4 mile, commercial district 1/4–1/2 mile, residential zone 1/2 to 1 mile. Hospital located at 5th and Main. Show as much as possible in sketch on page 3.)

NORTH _____

_____

SOUTH _____

_____

EAST _____

_____

WEST _____

_____

3. **LOCATION OF EMERGENCY EQUIPMENT & SUPPLIES:** (Available 24 hours a day. Include phone numbers.)

Self-contained breathing apparatus _____

Spare compressed breathing air tanks _____

Earth moving equipment _____

Portable water pumps _____

Street barriers _____

Sand bags _____

Other _____

4. **LOCATION & TYPES OF WATER SUPPLIES:** (Hydrants, ponds, irrigation canals, fresh or salt water, etc. Verify hydrant thread compatibility and water pressure and flow rates.)

_____

_____

_____

_____

FIRE FIGHTING TACTICS

FOR FIRE DEPARTMENTS FIGHTING FIRES INVOLVING PESTICIDES AND FERTILIZERS

 1 Contact facility operator. Determine type, quantity and hazards of products. Determine if fire should be fought after weighing fire fighting & postfire hazards vs. possible salvage.

 2 Notify physician to stand by. Physicians may obtain poison control information by contacting the manufacturer. (See Front Cover of Guide)

 3 Contact Chemical Manufacturer. Maintain liaison for specialized information, particularly during a large fire.

 4 Evacuate downwind & isolate area. Patrol area to keep out spectators.

 5 Wear personal protective equipment. Wear rubber or neoprene gloves, boots, turnouts & hat. If contact cannot be avoided (such as entering an unventilated building for rescue) also wear self-contained breathing apparatus (Air Paks).

 6 Attack fire from upwind & from a safe distance. Bottles, drums, metal & aerosol cans are not vented and may explode.

 7 Contain fire & protect surroundings. Prevent spread of fire by cooling nearby containers to prevent rupture (move vehicles & rail cars if possible). Burning chemicals cannot be salvaged.

 8 Use as little water as possible & contain runoff. Contaminated runoff can be the most serious problem. Water spreads contamination over a wide area. Construct dikes to prevent flow to lakes, streams, sewers, etc. Cooling effect of water retards high-temperature decomposition of the chemicals to less toxic compounds.

 9 Use water fog spray, not straight stream. Fog spray is more effective for control. Avoid breaking bottles and bags; adds fuel and contamination. Straight streams spread fire and contamination.

 10 Poisoning. Avoid product, smoke, mist and runoff. In case of contact or suspected poisoning, leave site immediately, follow instructions on back cover. Any feeling of discomfort or illness may be a symptom of poisoning. Symptoms may be delayed up to 12 hours. Chemicals may poison by ingestion, absorption through unbroken skin, or inhalation. Wash face and hands before eating, smoking or using toilet. Do not put fingers to mouth or rub eyes.

Post-Fire Clean-Up

- **FIRE FIGHTING PERSONNEL & EQUIPMENT**
  Remove protective clothing upon leaving site and impound with contaminated fire fighting equipment
- Upon return to fire station, shower & shampoo thoroughly with soap and water, change into clean clothing and wash inner clothing with detergent
- Watch for signs & symptoms of pesticide poisoning
- Put on coveralls and rubber or neoprene gloves and decontaminate protective clothing and equipment using a strong detergent solution. Decontaminate in an isolated area
- Contaminated cotton-jacketed hose may have to be destroyed; most are weakened by strong detergents

- **FIRE SITE** Isolate & secure scene to keep people away; waste and runoff may be toxic
- Contact federal, state, or local health authorities for disposal instructions and approval
- Handle waste & runoff same as for a product spill—Personal protective equipment is required
- If the amount of waste and/or run-off is significant or you have any doubts, contact the manufacturer.

247

FIRST AID — IN CASE OF ACCIDENTAL CONTACT

Flush with water for 15 minutes. Get medical attention immediately. Refer to product label for further instructions.

Wash thoroughly with soap & water. Refer to product label for further instructions. If in doubt about nature of material, get medical attention immediately.

Remove contaminated clothing & wash skin thoroughly with soap & water. Refer to product label for further instructions. If in doubt about nature of material, get medical attention immediately. Wash clothing in strong detergent before reusing.

NOTE: If medical attention is sought, take labeled container.

IMPORTANT NOTE

Should this facility become involved in fire, the Commanding Officer at the scene should be in position to let the facility burn if he determines that continued water application: 1) will result in extensive contaminated water runoff or, 2) could result in incomplete combustion of chemicals, resulting in a release of toxic compounds into the air. It would be desirable if he had advance written authority from the Facility Manager to do so if necessary or appropriate. This eventuality should be discussed with the insurers of the establishment.

This information is based on a pre-fire plan developed by Chevron Chemical Company and is reprinted by the National Agricultural Chemicals Association with permission.

NATIONAL AGRICULTURAL CHEMICALS ASSOCIATION

THE MADISON BUILDING
1155 Fifteenth Street, N.W., Washington, D. C. 20005
202 • 296-1585   *Cable: NAGRCHEM*

Revised 1985

248

TOXIC AIR POLLUTION CONTROL THROUGH THE CLEAN AIR ACT

Joseph W. Phillips, MPH, CHMM

and

Jack Don Lokey, P.E., CHMM
Tennessee Valley Authority

INTRODUCTION

The Clean Air Act (CAA) is just one among many laws and associated regulations that affect the hazardous materials managers job. Clean air legislation grew out of a public awareness of the effect of industrialization on air quality. Visible pollution from heavy industry was once viewed as a sign of progress. However, by the 1960's industrial emissions, as well as those from coal or wood-fired home heating equipment, had become a major problem in our towns and cities. Air pollution had grown to the point that many cities were characterized by the light-blocking overcast of particulate air pollution.

Early legislation to deal with this problem relied for the most part on voluntary compliance. Improvements were made in the area of home heating equipment, primarily due to changes in price and availability of alternate fuels. But it took new laws and specific regulations to spark the first major strides in reducing industrial air pollution.

The CAA of 1970 set definite goals for emissions reductions and ambient air quality improvement. National ambient air quality standards (NAAQS) were established to protect primarily public health and secondarily public

249

welfare (e.g., materials and vegetation). The new regulations required use of available control methods and development of new and innovative control technologies. Regulations were also enacted to require even more stringent control for new sources, as well as specific standards for hazardous pollutants. The requirements of the CAA bolstered by amendments passed in 1977 and most recently in 1990 have resulted in both direct and indirect control of toxic air pollutants. However, the Clean Air Act Amendments of 1990 contain the most comprehensive requirements yet regarding toxic air pollution.

THE CLEAN AIR ACT AMENDMENTS OF 1990

On October 26, 1990 the Congress passed and on November 15, 1990 the President signed the most comprehensive air pollution control legislation since the Clean Air Act of 1970. The Clean Air Act Amendments of 1990 is the culmination of 8 years of work to reauthorize the Clean Air Act and includes many new provisions of significant interest to the hazardous materials manager.

Although the legislation will be implemented through regulations yet to be promulgated by EPA, clear mandates are provided by Congress. Three titles are of particular interest to hazardous materials managers. Title III specifically addresses toxic air pollutants and mandates controls on emission sources of at least 189 toxic compounds. Title V mandates a new Federal/State permit system for all major sources of air pollution including toxic air pollution. Finally, Title VII radically changes enforcement provisions of the act.

Title III - Toxic Air Pollutants

Title III of the amendments gives a new approach to regulating hazardous air pollutants (HAP). The former requirement that emission standards protect health with an ample margin of safety has been replaced by a control-technology approach, with an evaluation of residual health risks to be done later. EPA must set maximum available control technology (MACT) emission standards for major source categories that emit any of the 189 HAP listed in the Act (table 1). MACT standards require the maximum degree of emission reduction that is economically achievable. MACT is defined differently for new sources than existing sources. MACT for new sources may not be less stringent than that achieved at the best controlled similar source. MACT for existing sources must be at least as stringent as the average of the best performing 12 percent of the existing sources (excluding recent BACT/LAER cases) for categories with many sources.

Major sources are nominally defined as a facility emitting more than 10 tons per year of any HAP, or 25 tons per year of any combination of HAP. However, EPA can set a lesser amount as the defining criteria for any category. It seems very likely that EPA will set lower criteria in some cases, based on the potency of the HAP and other factors. Chromium electroplating sources have been identified as a likely example for such a decision. EPA plans to propose by May 1991 and must finalize by November 1991 a list of all major source categories. A preliminary draft list contains 766 major source categories and subcategories in 18 broad industrial groups, with about 400 of them in the synthetic organic chemical manufacturing industry. EPA must publish by November 1992 a schedule for setting MACT emission standards for all the listed categories within the ensuing 8 years.

Area sources are defined as stationary sources with HAP emissions less than the major source criteria. Area source categories may be subject to emission standards if EPA judges the sources individually or in the aggregate to present a risk to health or the environment. These standards may require either MACT or a less stringent GACT (generally available control technology). A separate list of area sources subject to regulation under this title must be established by November 1995.

Section 112(g) requires MACT to be applied at any major source that is constructed or modified after the title V permit program begins (no later than November 1995). A source is modified when any physical or operational change increases net HAP emissions above a de minimis level. Any offsetting decreases must involve a HAP which is deemed more hazardous than the HAP being increased. This section was added in the conference committee, and many aspects are unclear. EPA must provide implementing guidance (e.g., determining de minimis levels and identifying relative hazard to human health for the 189 HAP listed in the Act) by May 1992.

New sources must comply with MACT after the effective date of an applicable standard. In general, existing sources must comply within 3 years, with a 1-year extension possible. Sources that have achieved (or committed to) significant HAP emission reductions prior to proposal of an MACT standard will receive 6 additional years' compliance extension. Emission reductions of at least 90 percent (or 95 percent for particulate HAP) will be required to participate in the early-reduction program. Issues such as source definition, enforceable commitments, reduction demonstrations, and high-risk pollutants are yet to be resolved. EPA plans to propose implementing regulations by the end of March 1991 and finalize them by November 1991.

Several National Emission Standards for Hazardous Air Pollutants (NESHAP) were under development prior to passage of the 1990 Clean Air Act Amendments (e.g., dry cleaning, ethylene oxide sterilizers, chromium electroplating, and chemical industry sources of hazardous organics). These will likely be the first categories regulated with MACT standards. Also, the New Source Performance Standards (NSPS) for municipal waste combustors (MWC) were addressed specifically in the 1990 amendments. The final standards were promulgated 11 February 1991 (56 FR 5488 and 5514) and regulate MWC emissions (metals, organics, and acid gases) and NO_x. Mercury was not regulated as a specific pollutant, and a proposed recyclable material separation requirement was deleted. Section 129 of the Act now requires that the MWC regulations be reexamined and MACT standards be promulgated by November 1991 for large MWC units to control several specific pollutants, including mercury, cadmium, and lead.

Electric utility steam generating units received special treatment in Section 112(n). Congress required EPA to study the hazards that remain after applying current controls to the HAP emissions from these sources. Based on the results of these studies, EPA may set MACT standards for utilities if appropriate and necessary.

Implementation of this legislation will result in new requirements for many sources that are not familiar with air pollution control regulations. Also, demand for state-of-the-art control technology will increase. This situation will be ripe for those pushing technology that has not yet been proven.

The hazardous materials manager should be wary of overly optimistic claims of control and carefully consider the new pollutant streams in non-air media that may be generated by controlling the toxic air pollutant.

Title V - Permits

The amendments create a new Federal/State permit system. Nearly all sources of significant air emissions will be required to apply for and obtain permits that will establish detailed requirements governing emissions from the source and related activities such as monitoring, record-keeping, and reporting.

Many sources for which permits will be required have permits under the State Implementation Plan. However, many new sources of toxic air pollutants regulated under Title III have not been regulated by the State, and the permit requirements will be new. The new requirements will be a different aspect of the hazardous materials manager's job.

The new permitting system will also implement a nationwide system of fees based on $25 per ton for each regulated pollutant emitted to the atmosphere. The new fees are designed to support the regulatory programs that implement the regulations.

Overall the new permit system will add lead time for major new projects or modifications. The hazardous materials manager should be aware of these requirements and the lead times they require so that major projects are not impacted.

Title VII - Enforcement

The amendments add a full array of tough new enforcement authorities including both civil and criminal sanctions. Civil sanctions include new administrative penalties that can be imposed by the Administrator for up to $25,000 per day for essentially any violation. The maximum administrative penalty is $200,000 in most cases.

EPA has increased inspection authority including the mandate to establish a field citation program for minor violations. Such a program will allow inspectors to issue "tickets" for up to $5000 per day for each violation. Also, private citizens are now authorized to seek civil penalties in citizen suits. This in combination with a new self-reporting mandate provides the potential for a vast increase in citizen suits.

Criminal prosecution of individuals who knowingly violate any provision now carries felony penalties of up to $250,000 and 5 years in prison for each count. Corporate fines are up to $500,000 for each violation. Maximum fines double for subsequent convictions. Record-keeping crimes now include failure to maintain required records or file required notifications.

Air toxics are specifically included in the definitions of negligent endangerment and knowing endangerment. Negligent endangerment is defined as the negligent release of air toxics which put another person in imminent danger of death or serious injury. Knowing endangerment is defined as knowingly releasing air toxics that put another person in imminent danger of serious injury. For knowing endangerment individuals can be fined up to $250,000 per day and imprisoned for up to 15 years. Businesses may be fined up to $1 million per violation.

Finally, Congress has authorized EPA to pay a bounty of up to $10,000 for information leading to a civil penalty or criminal conviction. The potential impact of these provisions on the hazardous materials manager is staggering. In addition to the potential for specific liability, the fate of entire corporations will rest on the competent handling of toxic air pollution issues.

The new amendments to the clean air act present the most specific requirements regarding the control of toxic air pollutants. However, the Clean Air Act contains unchanged many other provisions for both direct and indirect control of toxic air pollutants.

OTHER UNCHANGED PROVISIONS OF THE CLEAN AIR ACT

Existing provisions of the CAA have not been replaced by the 1990 amendments. Title III of the amendments in essence replaces the Section 112 program to establish National Emissions Standards for Hazardous Air Pollutants (NESHAP). The NESHAP program has faced many problems since its implementation. However, NESHAP standards for seven pollutants have been established. Arsenic, asbestos, benzene, beryllium, mercury, radionuclides, and vinyl chloride are all regulated under NESHAP. This directly reflects the difficulty that has been encountered in applying the NESHAP provision of the CAA that prompted the changes codified in the 1990 amendments.

The requirements for managing sources of the pollutants now being regulated under NESHAP vary across the range of control methodologies. Methods ranging from proper material handling to direct air pollution control technologies are required. Most of the regulated pollutants are industry specific. That is, they are not typical pollutants found among many types of industries. In these cases, companies which handle or emit these pollutants are usually aware of the applicable requirements and reiteration of these here would not be productive.

Those unsure of the specific requirements should consult the Background Information Document (BID) for the respective pollutant and the Code of Federal Regulations (Title 40, Part 61) for the specific standard.

The exception to the industry-specific NESHAP rules is asbestos. In years past, asbestos has been used very commonly as a building insulation material. As late as the 1960's newly constructed schools financed with Federal money were required to use asbestos insulation. Since its use was so wide and varied, all managers responsible for older buildings or heating equipment will be faced with a need to seal or remove and dispose of some asbestos material. Because of this, EPA publishes guidance for handling such problems (EPA 560/5-85-024). Asbestos is also regulated under the Toxic Substances Control Act, the Occupational Safety and Health Administration, and the Clean Water Act.

Indirect Control of Toxic Air Pollutants

Section 110 of the CAA requires all States to adopt State implementation plans (SIP) to attain and maintain any NAAQS. NAAQS have been set for six "criteria" pollutants that are emitted from widespread sources (e.g., motor vehicles and numerous stationary sources). Two of these, particulate matter and ozone, are especially relevant to control on toxic air pollutants. The limitation of particulate emissions simultaneously reduces toxic and hazardous pollutants which enter the atmosphere as particles. Similarly, the control strategy for ozone, which is a secondary pollutant formed by atmospheric reactions involving volatile organic compounds (VOC), has resulted in reductions of VOC emissions that may also be toxic. Thus, implementation plans have provided States with the means for enacting rules that indirectly limit some toxic pollutants.

Section 111 of the CAA requires EPA to establish rules for emissions from new sources. These new source performance standards (NSPS) reflect the demonstrated control level that is economically achievable at the time the standard is proposed or updated. These standards apply nationwide and require strict control regardless of the plant's location or stack heights. As such, the NSPS regulations are intended to discourage industrial facilities from moving to States with less stringent air pollution rules.

Just as with SIP standards, reductions in toxic air pollutant emissions occur indirectly as a result of NSPS rules for sources emitting particulates or VOC. In addition sometimes an NSPS for a source category will regulate specific pollutants that have toxic properties, such as acid mist from sulfuric acid plants. In all, about 60 NSPS rules have been finalized and are published in the Code of Federal Regulations (Title 40, Part 60). Most of these standards have some effect on toxic air pollution emissions.

State and Local Enforcement Responsibilities

The confusion associated with the regulation of air toxics should be improved by the implementation of Title III of the 1990 amendments. However, local air pollution control agencies will be delegated authority for implementing the new regulations. To obtain delegation, an agency must promulgate regulations at least as restrictive but not necessarily identical to EPA's.

Title III of the CAA amendments of 1990 will refocus the control strategy for toxic air pollutants. However, some states have already initiated toxic air pollutant control programs that regulate a much greater number of substances as toxic emissions. EPA has been supporting this effort since 1985 when a new strategy to reduce risks to public health from air toxics was announced (FR 50, No. 111, p. 24319) It is unclear how this program will be affected by the implementation of Title III. However, the hazardous materials manager should not assume that State specific standards do not or will not continue to apply in the wake of implementation of Title III.

More than three dozen state and local agencies have already established air toxics control programs, and others are considering a similar steps. Most of these agencies are setting emission limits only for new sources. These limits are intended to assure that the ambient impacts from the source do not exceed an adjusted workplace air standard. The adjustment consists of applying a safety factor to allow for increased hours of exposure and for more sensitive members of the general population. In most cases existing sources remain unregulated (a situation that will change with the implementation of Title III).

EPA and state cooperative programs to regulate air toxics not specifically targeted under Title III are likely to continue even with implementation of Title III. Locally applicable controls allow more precisely tailored requirements where relatively few sources of a specific toxic pollutant exist across the country. State control strategies can be targeted to solve geographically isolated problems without the problems caused by a single level of control applied throughout the nation.

Future Developments

EPA's strategy for controlling toxic air pollutants has been and continues to be concentrated on major industrial (point) source categories, especially the chemical industry. However, industrial sources may not be the major source of our national air-toxics problem. In a recent study of air toxics (EPA -450/1-85-001), EPA estimated that the chemical industry is responsible for about 10 percent of the cancer incidence from air toxics.

Point sources as a whole were estimated to account for less than 50 percent. By comparison, over 50 percent of national incidence was estimated to be due to area sources, which are smaller emission sources that may be widespread over a given area. Road vehicle emissions and home heating equipment (including woodstoves) account for a major portion of these area sources. In addition, as much as 3 percent of the cancer incidence has been estimated to result from publicly-owned wastewater treatment works. Fortunately, EPA has begun to take action on residential woodstoves in its recent approval of NSPS regulations (40 CFR Part 60).

In the area of toxic air pollution, public perception and demand for action has been followed by regulatory and legislative action.   Title III incorporating major new limits on emissions of toxic air pollutants was incorporated into the 1990 amendments with much less debate than other major provisions of the new legislation.

Table 1

HAZARDOUS AIR POLLUTANTS LISTED IN THE 1990 AMENDMENTS

CA number	Chemical name	CA Number	Chemical Name
75070	Acetaldehyde	105602	Caprolactam
60355	Acetamide	133062	Captan
75058	Acetonitrile	63252	Carbaryl
98862	Acetophenone	75150	Carbon disulfide
53963	2-Acetylamino-fluorene	56235	Carbon tetra-chloride
10702	Acrolein	463581	Carbonyl sulfide
79061	Acrylamide	120809	Catechol
79107	Acrylic acid	133904	Chloramben
107131	Acrylonitrile	57749	Chlordane
107051	Allyl chloride	7782505	Chlorine
92671	4-Aminobiphenyl	79118	Chloroacetic acid
62533	Aniline	532274	2-Chloroaceto-phenone
90040	o-Anisidine		
1332214	Asbestos	108907	Chlorobenzene
71432	Benzene (including benzene from gasoline)	510156	Chlorobenzilate
		67663	Chloroform
		107302	Chloromethyl methyl ether
92875	Benzidine		
98077	Benzotrichloride	126998	Chloroprene
100447	Benzyl chloride	1319773	Cresols/Cresylic acid(isomers and mixture)
92524	Biphenyl		
117817	Bis(2-ethyl-hexyl)phthal-ate (DEHP)		
		95487	o-Cresol
		108394	m-Cresol
542881	Bis(chloromethyl)-ether	106445	p-Cresol
		98828	Cumene
75252	Bromoform	94757	2,4-D, salts and esters
106990	1,3-Butadiene		
156627	Calcium cyanamide	3547044	DDE
		334883	Diazomethane

132649	Dibenzofurans	121142	2,4-Dinitro-
96128	1,2-Dibromo-3-		toluene
	chloropropane	123911	1,4-Dioxane
84742	Dibutylphthalate		(1,4-ethyl-
106467	1,4-Dichloro-		eneoxide)
	benzene(p)	122667	1,2-Diphenyl-
91941	3,3-Dichloro-		hydrazine
	benzidene	106898	Epichlorohydrin
111444	Dichloroethyl-		(l-Chloro-2,3-
	ether (Bis(2-		epoxypropane)
	chloroethyl)-	106887	1,2-Epoxybutane
	ether)	140885	Ethyl acrylate
542756	1,3-Dichloro-	100414	Ethyl benzene
	propene	51796	Ethyl carbamate
62737	Dichlorvos		(Urethane)
111422	Diethanolamine	75003	Ethyl chloride
121697	N,N-Diethyl		(Chloroethane)
	aniline (N,N-Di-	106934	Ethylene di-
	methylaniline)		bromide(Di-
64675	Diethyl sulfate		bromoethane)
119904	3,3-Dimethoxy-	107062	Ethylene di-
	benzidine		chloride
60117	Dimethyl amino-		(1,2-Dichloro
	azobenzene		ethane)
119937	3,3-Dimethyl	107211	Ethylene glycol
	benzidine	151564	Ethylene imine
79447	Dimethyl carba-		(Aziridine)
	moyl chloride	75218	Ethylene oxide
68122	Dimethyl	96457	Ethylene thiourea
	formamide	75343	Ethylidene
57147	1,1-Dimethyl		dichloride
	hydrazine		(1,1-Dichloro-
131113	Dimethyl phthalate		ethane)
77781	Dimethyl sulfate	50000	Formaldehyde
534521	4,6-Dinitro-	76448	Heptachlor
	o-cresol, and	118741	Hexachloro-
	salts		benzene
51285	2,4-Dinitrophenol		

87683	Hexachloro-butadiene
77474	Hexachlorocyclo-pentadiene
67721	Hexachloroethane
822060	Hexamethylene-1,6-diiso cyanate
680319	Hexamethyl phosphoramide
110543	Hexane
302012	Hydrazine
7647010	Hydrochloric acid
7664393	Hydrogen fluoride (Hydrofluoric acid)
7783064	Hydrogen sulfide
123319	Hydroquinone
78591	Isophorone
58899	Lindane (all isomers)
108316	Maleic anhydride
67561	Methanol
72435	Methoxychlor
74839	Methyl bromide (Bromomethane)
74873	Methyl chloride (Chloromethane)
71556	Methyl chloroform (1,1,1-Trichloro-ethane)
78933	Methyl ethyl ketone (2-Buta-none)
60344	Methyl hydrazine
74884	Methyl iodide (Iodomethane)

108101	Methyl isobutyl ketone (Hexone)
624839	Methyl iso-cyanate
80626	Methyl metha-crylate
1634044	Methyl tert butyl ether
101144	4,4-Methylene bis(2-chloro aniline)
75092	Methylene chlo-ride (Dichloro-methane)
101688	Methylene di-phenyl diiso-cyanate (MDI)
101779	4,4-Methyl-enedianiline
91203	Naphthalene
98953	Nitrobenzene
92933	4-Nitrobiphenyl
100027	4-Nitrophenol
79469	2-Nitropropane
684935	N-Nitroso-N-methylurea
62759	N-Nitrosodi-methylamine
59892	N-Nitrosomorpho line
56382	Parathion
82688	Pentachloro-nitrobenzene (Quinto-benzene)
87865	Pentachloro-phenol

108952	Phenol	108883	Toluene
106503	p-Phenyl-	95807	2,4-Toluene
	enediamine		diamine
75445	Phosgene	584849	2,4-Toluene
7803512	Phosphine		diisocyanate
7723140	Phosphorus	95534	o-Toluidine
85449	Phthalic	8001352	Toxaphene
	anhydride		(chlorinated
1336363	Polychlorinated		camphene)
	biphenyls	120821	1,2,4-Trichloro-
	(Aroclors)		benzene
1120714	1,3-Propane	79005	1,1,2-Trichloro-
	sultone		ethane
57578	beta-Propiolactone	79016	Trichloroethylene
123386	Propionaldehyde	95954	2,4,5-Trichloro-
114261	Propoxur (Baygon)		phenol
78875	Propylene	88062	2,4,6-Trichloro-
	dichloride		phenol
	(1,2-Dichloro-	121448	Triethylamine
	propane)	1582098	Trifluralin
75569	Propylene oxide	540841	2,2,4-Trimethyl-
75558	1,2-Propylenimine		pentane
	(2-Methyl	108054	Vinyl acetate
	aziridine)	593602	Vinyl bromide
91225	Quinoline	75014	Vinyl chloride
106514	Quinone	75354	Vinylidene
100425	Styrene		chloride
96093	Styrene oxide		(1,1-Dichloro-
1746016	2,3,7,8-Tetra		ethylene)
	chlorodibenzo	1330207	Xylenes (isomers
	-p-dioxin		and mixture)
79345	1,1,2,2-Tetrachloro	95476	o-Xylenes
	ethane	108383	m-Xylenes
127184	Tetrachloroethylene	106423	p-Xylenes
	(Perchloro		
	ethylene)		
7550450	Titanium tetra-		
	chloride		

0	Antimony Compounds
0	Arsenic Compounds (inorganic including arsine)
0	Beryllium Compounds
0	Cadmium Compounds
0	Chromium Compounds
0	Cobalt Compounds
0	Coke Oven Emissions
0	Cyanide Compounds (1)
0	Glycol ethers (2)
0	Lead Compounds
0	Manganese Compounds
0	Mercury Compounds
0	Fine mineral fibers (3)
0	Nickel Compounds
0	Polycylic Organic Matter (4)
0	Radionuclides (including radon) (5)
0	Selenium Compounds

NOTE: For all listings above which contain the word "compounds" and for glycol ethers, the following applies: Unless otherwise specified, these listings are defined as including any unique chemical substance that contains the named chemical (i.e., antimony, arsenic, etc.) as part of that chemical's infrastructure.

(1)   X'CN where X = H' or any other group where a formal dissociation may occur. For example KCN or Ca(CN)2

(2)   Includes mono- and di- ethers of ethylene glycol, diethylene glycol, and triethylene glycol R-(OCHCH)n-OR' where
       n = 1, 2, or 3
       R = alkyl or aryl groups
       R' = R, H, or groups which, when removed, yield glycol ethers with the structure: R-(OCHCH)n-OH. Polymers are excluded from the glycol category.

(3)   Includes mineral fiber emissions from facilities manufacturing or processing glass, rock, or slag fibers (or other mineral derived fibers) of average diameter 1 micrometer or less.

(4)   Includes organic compounds with more than one benzene ring, and which have a boiling point greater than or equal to 100C.

(5)   A type of atom which spontaneously undergoes radioactive decay.

CLEAN WATER ACT

Bruce A. Brye, PE, DEE, CHMM
Consulting Environmental Engineer

INTRODUCTION

In response to the growing National environmental awareness and the disappointment in the fragmented nature of the Nation's approach to the protection of the Nation's surface waters, the Federal Water Pollution Control Act (FWPCA) was passed in 1972. This Act completely rewrote all of the Federal water pollution laws and established a uniform approach for the enhancement and protection of the Nation's surface waters. The objective is to restore and maintain the chemical, physical, and biological integrity of the Nation's waters. The national goal is to eliminate the discharges of all pollutants into the navigable waters. An interim goal is to provide water quality for the protection and propagation of fish, shellfish, and wildlife and recreational use of all waters. The act also established a national policy that the discharge of toxic pollutants in toxic amounts be prohibited.

Subsequent to its initial passage on October 18, 1972, the Act has been amended a total of 23 times through August 18, 1990, and is now referred to as the Clean Water Act (CWA). The purpose of the frequent amendments was to correct deficiencies in the initial Act, to expand the requirements of the Act to be consistent with other environmental legislation, technology developments, and to adjust as appropriate certain dates and deadlines contained in the initial Act. The overall responsibility for the implementation of the requirements of the Act are vested with the United States Environmental Protection Agency (USEPA) although there are provisions for the individual states to be delegated responsibilities for

265

major portions of the Act subject to USEPA oversight. All such state-administered programs under the Act must be consistent with the Federal requirements as a minimum, but the Act does include provisions for individual States to establish more restrictive requirements as they may deem appropriate to protect the water resources within their State.

There are several sections of the CWA which include provisions or requirements which relate to the management of hazardous materials and wastes. The following summary discussions of these Sections reflect an overview summary of the requirements as currently incorporated into the Act and do not attempt to discuss the chronology of how these specific requirements evolved through the numerous amendments to the Act since 1972.

SECTION 303

Section 303 requires the development of water quality criteria and standards. EPA has the overall responsibility for the development of water quality criteria guidelines which will protect various stream uses (i.e. water contact recreation, water supply, and support of fish and aquatic life). EPA has promulgated water quality criteria for 126 pollutants under the CWA. The states are to establish water quality standards which consist of four distinct components: (1) use classifications for each water body; (2) water quality criteria which must be met to protect and maintain each use classification; (3) an anti-degradation statement ensuring that use classifications will not be downgraded; and (4) an implementation and enforcement plan. These state standards are subject to EPA's review and approval and must be updated on a triennial basis. The state standards serve as the basis for the acceptability of any subsequent permitted discharges to the streams and for the evaluating of any damages associated with spills under the CWA, and as the primary surface water related corrective action criteria for corrective action for solid waste management units at hazardous waste sites under the Resource Conservation and Recovery Act (RCRA). In many cases, the water quality criteria for the protection of aquatic life (including the toxic parameters) are much more stringent than those associated with the protection of human health.

At this time the protection of groundwater resources is provided under the provisions of the Safe Drinking Water Act. However, under certain circumstances, the CWA criteria could become applicable for the regulation of discharges (or spills) to groundwater if the groundwater subsequently contaminates the surface waters.

SECTIONS 301, 306, AND 307

Sections 301, 306 and 307 relate to the requirements for the establishment of effluent limitations for point source discharges from all sources except for Publicly Owned Treatment Works (POTWs -- i.e. municipal waste water plants). EPA has established specific effluent limitations for each waste stream for more than 50 categories of industrial operations (the initial list of categories is identified in Section 306). These effluent limitations reflect the maximum level of contamination which can be discharged from each industrial category. In general all effluent limitations are technologically based and are subject to future review and revision as advances in technology are developed. As additional industrial categories and processes evolve in the future, these operations will be reviewed and appropriate effluent limitations will be established. Section 301 also included provisions for the scheduled implementation of the technologically based effluent limitations on an orderly basis.

The CWA amendments of 1977 added a list of 126 toxic pollutants (commonly referred to as the priority pollutants) and required EPA to establish appropriate effluent limitations for each of these pollutants consistent with the other requirements of the CWA. EPA is also charged to periodically review the list to identify the need to add or delete parameters to the list and to review the effluent limitation for each parameter at least every three years. In addition, this section requires the establishment of appropriate effluent limitations for the discharge of industrial wastes to municipal waste water treatment systems. These limitations known as pretreatment standards must be met by each industrial discharger to a municipal treatment facility to ensure that the introduced industrial waste is compatible with both the treatment process and the effluent limitations for the municipal facility. While the primary concern with the industrial wastes in the municipal systems is toxicity to the biological treatment process, the pretreatment standards are also applicable to the conventional parameters of the waste discharge. Under these provisions, each municipal system receiving industrial process wastes for treatment is required to develop and implement a pretreatment program. It should be noted that the effluent limitations for municipal (publicly owned treatment works) are addressed in Section 304; however these waste discharges are usually considered beyond the scope of hazardous material and waste management activities.

SECTION 401 AND 402

The National Pollutant Discharge Elimination System (NPDES) is the permitting mechanism for the implementation of the effluent limitations for all point source discharges. A NPDES permit issued by either EPA or a delegated state is required for all point source discharges to surface waters. The discharge of effluents to the surface waters without a permit for the discharge or at pollutant levels exceeding those provided for in the permit is a violation of the CWA and is subject to civil or criminal penalties or both. The contents of an NPDES permit reflect three basic components. Part I identifies each facility wastewater stream and establishes the applicable effluent limitations and monitoring requirements for that wastewater stream. Part II contains the permit's boilerplate administrative requirements associated with the implementation of modifications, monitoring methods, and reporting requirements. Part III includes special provisions which are deemed to be applicable to the specific facility as determined usually by mutual agreement with the permittee. Examples of Part III conditions include instream monitoring programs, specific prohibitions with respect to the facility such as no discharge of PCB's, oils or other toxic or hazardous substances, the requirements for a Best Management Practices Program to prevent the spilling and subsequent discharge of any hazardous materials storage, for those materials identified in Section 307, the requirements for a SPCC plan may be reiterated, and usually most permits have a reopener clause with respect to the development by EPA of any new or revised criteria for toxic substances under Section 307.

Recent amendments to Section 402 have required the addition of stormwater runoff as a waste stream subject to regulation under the NPDES permit for industrial operations and designated major population centers. The final regulations implementing the provisions of these requirements were issued in November 1990, and the impacted facilities are now in the process of conducting the initial screening, monitoring and preparation of permit applications to determine the extent that the storm water runoff from their facilities will be subject to the requirements. The occurrence of toxic and hazardous materials in the runoff from such facilities is one of the major issues relating to the development of the requirements. Depending upon the results of the screening monitoring, these requirements could have a significant impact on industrial operations and larger metropolitan areas. The requirements would also be applicable to both RCRA and CERCLA sites.

Closely related to the NPDES permit under section 402 is the state certification process under Section 401 for Federally issued licenses or permits. The 401 certification is the vehicle by which a state certifies to a permitting agency that the action (or facility) for which it intends to issue a license or permit will be in compliance with the state water quality standards. Through the 401 certification the state may also establish requirements for the license or permit which it deems as necessary to ensure compliance with the state water quality standards. Examples of applicable permit actions which involve the state 401 certification process are NPDES permits issued by EPA, Section 404 permits issued by the Corps of Engineers, and RCRA permits.

SECTION 311

Section 311 establishes mechanisms for the prevention of spills and other releases of oil and hazardous substances to the surface waters. In addition to oil, EPA has designated almost 300 substances as hazardous when spilled and has identified minimum reportable quantities which if spilled in excess of these amounts must be reported through the National Response Center.

This section established a fund for the cleanup of discharges (spills) of oils and other hazardous materials, the initiation of planning for the prevention of such discharges and the development of a National Contingency Plan which outlines the powers and responsibilities for cleanup efforts. The individual discharger can be held liable for the costs of removal and cleanup of the discharges as well as being subject to civil fines of up to $250,000. The cleanup fund was initially established under the CWA, but because of the similarity of the CWA requirements to those included under

CERCLA, the two funds and cleanup plans have been combined under CERCLA to address all sites and not just those spills to surface waters. The CWA does still regulate the spills of oil to surface waters and includes provisions for the recovery of cleanup costs, environmental damages, as well as substantial civil and criminal penalties. Section 311 requires that anyone storing oil (in excess of 1,320 gallons above ground or 42,000 below ground) develop a spill prevention, control and countermeasure (SPCC) plan. This plan must address those engineered provisions which have been included in the design and construction of the storage facilities, to prevent the spill of oil, the identification of control measures to be implemented to control a spill onsite and the countermeasures to be undertaken in the event a spill should extend offsite to surface waters. Although the SPCC plan does not have to be submitted to the regulatory agencies for prior approval it must be available onsite and is subject to review by the agencies during regular inspections. In the event of an oil spill the regulatory agencies may call for the submission of the plan for review and approval. The SPCC plan must be updated every three years and must be certified by a registered engineer to be valid. Although the development of a SPCC plan may be expensive, especially if extensive facility modifications are required to satisfy the engineered design provisions of the regulations, the consequences of failing to have a SPCC plan if called for by the agencies is a fine of up to $5,000 per day.

One of the requirements usually under Part III of the NPDES permits is that the facility develop a best management practices program for the storage of any Section 311 hazardous materials identified as toxic under Section 307. Rather than develop two separate plans, a combined BMP/SPCC plan can be developed for each facility as a step toward the development of an overall facility management plan. In addition, because of the potential consequences and liabilities associated with a spill it is recommended that a BMP/SPCC plan be developed for each facility even if the onsite quantities of hazardous or potentially hazardous materials are less than the reportable quantities. In the event of a spill, the availability of such a plan to guide cleanup efforts would be good insurance.

SECTION 404

Section 404 regulates the discharge of dredged or fill material to the surface waters including those materials disposed of in wetlands. The permit program for the discharges (or disposal) of material is administered by the Corps of Engineers and is commonly referred to as the 404 dredging permit. Contrary to popular understanding these permits are for the disposal of materials and do not regulate the actual dredging action associated with the removal of material. The actual dredging activities are subject to regulation under Section 10 of the Rivers and Harbors Act which is also administered by the Corps.

Aside from the much publicized issues associated with wetlands, the major issues associated with the Section 404 permits is the impact the disposal and final placement of material will have on water quality and designated stream uses. The discharge of toxic and hazardous constituents contained in the material is one of the major environmental concerns. At this time there are no specific numerical criteria for contaminated sediments, however in 1990 EPA announced its intent to pursue the development of such criteria. These criteria would be applicable to both the Section 404 permitting actions as well as any RI/FS and corrective actions evaluations of contaminated sediments associated with RCRA and CERCLA sites. As with the water quality criteria it is reasonable to expect that many of the final sediment criteria for the protection of aquatic life will be much more restrictive than those associated with the protection of human health.

SECTION 405

Under Section 405 the disposal of sewage sludge is regulated to ensure the protection of public health and the environment from such practices. EPA is to develop regulations which identify alternative uses of sludge and alternative disposal methods as well as criteria for characterizing the sludge including the occurrence of toxic components. These requirements are primarily related to public owned treatment works, and will be reflected in the renewal of the NPDES permits for these facilities. However there is a potential for some liability for the industrial operations which discharge to POTWs if it is determined that their discharges have contaminated or are contaminating the sludge of the POTW with toxic or hazardous materials. These sludge disposal requirements are just now beginning to be implemented and it may be some time before the full impact of these requirements can be determined.

MIXED WASTE: GENERATION, REGULATION AND DISPOSAL

James T. McVey, CHMM, CHCM, REP
Diversified Scientific Services, Inc.

INTRODUCTION

In the truest of definitions, mixed waste is, at the same time, both hazardous and radioactive in nature. This co-mingling of the two categories of hazardous substances has unknowingly occurred, most likely, since the discovery and increasing use of radioactive materials. It is inevitable that some of these radioisotopes would come in contact with other hazardous substances. As radioactive and hazardous substances or wastes become co-mingled either chemically or physically, various handling concerns arise.

This paper presents an overview of the typical types of mixed wastes generated as well as the methods for its proper handling and disposal. Most generators of mixed wastes are not required to obtain all of the complicated licenses and permits discussed below. The degree of licensing required for the generator is dependent upon several factors, the most important of which are type of waste, duration of storage and method of disposal. Those generators who can merely produce mixed wastes and quickly transfer the mixed waste to a totally permitted disposal facility will have less permitting needs, for instance. As a matter of general protection from the generator's standpoint with regard to long term liabilities, it is important to completely understand all of your responsibilities. Likewise, it is important to verify that any facility receiving your wastes also has the correct permits and operates in accordance with them.

DESCRIPTION OF MIXED WASTE

Mixed wastes can exhibit a variety of characteristics and often present some unusually cumbersome handling and health hazard concerns. The co-mingling of radioactive materials with solely hazardous materials can be of a physical, a chemical or a combined nature. To understand these different natures of co-mingling it is first important to understand the physical nature of radioactive materials. The greatest misunderstanding by most people is that radioactive material is not present in a supernatural nor undefinable physical state, by itself.

Radioactive material can exist as a solid (particulate, lump, item), a liquid (aqueous, organic, inorganic) and as a gas (naturally occuring, inert, vapor, etc.). Radioactive materials can be simplistically thought of just as any other compound, substance, chemical or material with regard to its physical nature. In this respect, radioactive material could be weighed, pumped, poured, stirred, swept-up, compressed as a gas, boiled, burned, etc. The difference between a radioactive material and its counterpart non-radioactive version exists in a temporary state of atomic imbalance or an excited state. As the radioactive atom attempts to attain, through decay, a stable atomic balance of charge between the nucleus and the surrounding electrons, it will emit a characteristic form of radiation. The unstable atom can gain or lose atomic components and emit alphas or betas (an electron) or gammas (electromagnetic energy similar to light waves) or neutrons. It is these emissions of atomic components that gives radioactive material its publicly perceived "mystical" and "super dangerous" context. In reality radioactive material is often more easily detectable at high and low concentrations and easier to prescribe protective or corrective measures for because of its ready awareness when monitoring.

From a strict physical standpoint many radioactive materials can not be casually differentiated from a non-radioactive counterpart. Diagram 1 depicts tritiated water in comparison to normal water. The only major difference between the two is the fact that tritiated water has hydrogens with two too many electrons. As these electrons are expelled a beta particle is produced (radioactive hazard) which can interact with things around and near to it (skin cell, lung cell, other water molecules, etc.). Tritiated water can be held, boiled, drunk, and breathed as a vapor just like its counterpart. Likewise, most other radioactive materials can be thought of physically as being similar to its non-radioactive counterpart. Still keeping this physical relationship in mind, radioactive lead, as an example, could be produced. The physical hazard and consequences of being hit with a 500 pound slab of lead will probably hurt you faster than the radioactive hazard present in the lead. However, if you are merely pinned down by the radioactive lead for an extended period of time, then the radioactive emissions of lead would begin to present a more dangerous hazard. Likewise, a very safe and common item of use such as a screwdriver, pencil, coffee, etc., could be coated physically with or mixed with a radioactive material version of grease, dust or sugar, respectively, and physically become a radioactive hazard.

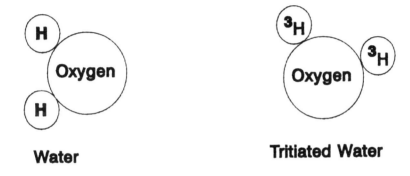

Water   **Tritiated Water**

Diagram 1

This physical co-mingling of hazardous radioactive materials, as for instance in Cobalt-60 particulates with benzene, produces a mixed waste which possesses both a radioactive and a chemical (RCRA) regulated hazard. If the two could be unequivocally reseparated into their two individual components, then technically the individual hazards should follow each component and be handled accordingly. From a regulatory standpoint this concept of physical repartitioning is not understood. Consequently, the regulators tend to quote *adnausium*, "Once a mixed waste always a mixed waste."

Now turning to mixed waste from a chemical standpoint one finds a very different perspective. When chemically hazardous and radioactively hazardous materials chemically bond or mix in a nature that they are physically inseparable, then the term *mixed waste* takes on its truly intended definition. As seen in Diagram 2, by chemically combining sodium with radioactive chlorine we now have radioactive salt. Likewise if the same radioactive chlorine were used in making PCB's, then a TSCA regulated and radioactively regulated material would be encountered. The material possesses both hazards in a simultaneous and inseparable nature.

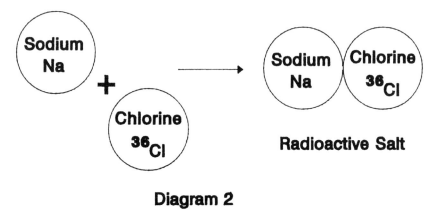

Diagram 2

Therefore, from a generator's viewpoint when dealing with or in a nuclear or radioactive environment, it is important to consider what end products might result. If a substance that is regulated by the Nuclear Regulatory Commission (NRC) comes in contact with an Environmental Protection Agency (EPA) regulated material, then most likely a mixed waste could result. Care should be exercised in the selection of chemicals used and the total quantity utilized. In other words, is there a better selection of materials and do you really need as much as you think to do a particular task? Care must be used to reduce the overall resultant volume and the relative combined hazard because the regulations and disposal options for such mixed wastes become complicated issues to deal with.

Currently in the United States there are several classes of mixed wastes which are prevalent:

a. RCRA Solvents -- D001, F001 through F005
b. TSCA fluids -- PCB's

c.   Heavy metal materials -- mercury, lead, beryllium, cadmium
d.   Caustics
e.   Toxic materials

Disposal methodologies exist for each of these.   However, the actual
disposal sites and facilities are few due to the extensive health and
environmental precautions required for protection against the combined
"mixed waste" hazards and due to the overwhelming regulatory permitting
necessary as discussed in the next section.

MIXED WASTE REGULATIONS

Two primary agencies regulate the handling, storage, and disposal of
mixed wastes. These are the NRC and the EPA. Each of these agencies
has delegated most of their licensing and day to day regulatory control and
enforcement to those states which elect to and have demonstrated their
own ability to do so. Under the NRC these are known as agreement states
while under the EPA they are authorized states. Not all states have full
mixed waste regulatory capabilities. Table 1 illustrates those states with
part or full regulatory authorities. When a generator or potential disposal
site begins to first explore their regulatory requirements associated with
mixed wastes it is crucial to know which agencies to deal with. Even if
a state has dual regulatory authority over mixed wastes, there are certain
regulatory aspects which have not yet been granted to the states. Such
aspects include:

a.   Nuclear Power Plant licensing -- NRC
b.   Import/Export Regulations -- NRC
c.   Major Quantity licenses such as fuel reprocessing, with SNM
     -- NRC
d.   NESHAP -- EPA
e.   BIF -- EPA
f.   TSCA -- EPA
g.   Others -- EPA

Before discussing the permits in greater detail for a mixed waste facility
it should also be noted that on both sides of the regulatory coin (NRC

State	NRC Agreement	EPA Authorized	Full Regulatory Authority
Alabama	X		
Arizona	X		
Arkansas	X	X	X
California	X		
Colorado	X	X	X
Florida	X		
Georgia	X	X	X
Guam		X	
Idaho	X	X	X
Illinois	X	X	X
Iowa	X		
Kansas	X	X	X
Kentucky	X	X	X
Louisiana	X		
Maryland	X		
Michigan		X	
Minnesota		X	
Mississippi	X		
Nebraska	X	X	X
Nevada	X		
New Hampshire	X		
New Mexico	X	X	X
New York	X	X	X
New York City	X		
North Carolina	X	X	X
North Dakota	X	X	X
Ohio		X	
Oklahoma		X	
Oregon	X	X	X
Rhode Island	X		
South Carolina	X	X	X
Tennessee	X	X	X
Texas	X	X	X
Utah	X	X	X
Washington	X	X	X
TOTALS	80	23	18

Table 1 -- States with part or full regulatory authorities

and EPA) there are regionalized working groups. The "Compacts" within the radioactive community are groups of states organized together to help plan and assure uniform regulations and disposal capacities. Likewise certain states have formed working groups to cooperate in the logical development and availability of hazardous materials disposal capacities.

When considering which set of licensing and permitting regulations to apply to a particular facility it is crucial that an accurate accounting of the types and quantities of potential mixed waste be obtained. From this understanding of the mixed wastes and what is going to be done with it, it will become more obvious as to which agencies need to be contacted. Considerations:

A.   Radioactive Materials

1.   Agreement State -- Y/N
2.   If No, contact the regional NRC office
3.   Large quantities of Special Nuclear materials and source materials require NRC permits
4.   All applications must thoroughly consider and provide protection for or procedures for:

     a.   Inventory control and storage safety
     b.   Personnel training
     c.   Exposure controls and monitoring
     d.   Health physics expertise and safeguards
     e.   Environmental and general public protection from direct exposures and releases
     f.   Proper handling, area posting/security and records/notifications
     g.   Many other issues such as emergency notices

B.   RCRA Treatment, Storage and Disposal Permit

1.   Authorized State -- Y/N
2.   If No, contact the regional EPA office
3.   All applications must present information about and procedures for such things as:
     a.   Types and quantities of materials to be received, stored and/or disposed of.

b. Manifesting and inventory control and recordkeeping
c. Physical protection and security of the materials
d. Personnel, environment and general public exposure protection
e. Waste analysis plans
f. Emergency Contingency Plan
g. Spill Prevention Plan
h. Effluent Monitoring
i. Closure Plan and financial assurance and many more

C.   NPDES Permit

Any liquid waste discharge which might be both radioactive and hazardous must meet the Clean Water Act with regard to release levels. This can include releases to the obvious receiving locations as rivers, lakes and streams as well as groundwater, waters of the state, sanitary sewer systems and subsurface aquifers. The newest permit addition for mixed waste facilities to consider and almost definitely apply for is the Storm Water Runoff permit. This permit considers the potential effluents from the facility, its gutters, parking lots, and other land associated with the site. Some releases associated with these just mentioned sites could also classify as a reportable spill under the RCRA or TSCA permits if they occur.

The NRC also has very strict release limitations for radioactivity in liquid effluents.

D.   Clean Air Act

This particular set of EPA regulations can have at least two significant segments to comply with if any mixed waste is volatilized, burned or otherwise released into the air.

1.   National Emissions Standards for Hazardous Air Pollutants (NESHAP) -- Regulations govern the release of not only some hazardous substances such as beryllium, asbestos and mercury but also the release of radioactive materials. The EPA regulations pertaining to NESHAP permits and radioactive materials can be found in 40 CFR 61 Subpart I. These regulations limit the total dose to the most likely individual from all radioactivity released in

a year's time to less than 25 mRem. Recent revisions or proposed revisions have made the NESHAP permit unnecessary for nuclear power plants and may reduce the allowable exposure for other licenses to 10 mRem per year.

The Clean Air Act also is applied through the EPA or authorized state's Air Pollution Control Programs. This separate permit regulates the other effluents such as particulates, volatile organic compounds (VOC) and all other possible air pollutants. Emission limits, feed ratio limitation, combustion or effluent release sources may be limited. It is also very probable that accurate inventories, air treatment devices and detailed records of monitoring data will be required of a permittee.

Also, as with the water discharge limitations, the NRC has very restrictive limitations established for the release of radioactive materials into the air. These can be found in 10 CFR 20.

E.   Toxic Substances Control Act (TSCA)

If the generator is unlucky enough to have mixed wastes which fall within the regulatory purview of EPA's TSCA program, another set of permits would be required. The most likely mixed waste materials to fall under the TSCA provisions are polychlorinated biphenyl (PCB's). These materials normally result from older electrical transformers, heat exchangers, and hydraulic systems. Only a few methods of disposing of PCB's are recognized and approved. The only site able to deal with PCB type mixed waste is operated by the Department of Energy.

F.   Boiler and Industrial Furnace Laws (BIF)

This new set of EPA regulations pertains to the combustion of RCRA regulated materials in systems other than true incinerators. This includes boilers, rotary kiln, and industrial furnaces. These regulations require the BIF type combustion systems to meet stringent feed, safeguard, effluent and monitoring criteria similar to incinerators.

To obtain these various permits can require from four months to as much as three years. Estimates on the costs to obtain a full complement of permits can range from one to ten million dollars and involve numerous public meetings and hearings.

DISPOSAL CAPACITIES -- TODAY

Currently there are only a very few sites which have attained some or various combinations of the permits listed above. No facility available to the commercial mixed waste generators has all of the permits listed above. Two facilities are capable of receiving solvents. One of these facilities has on-site burning capabilities while the second has limited off-site burning arrangements. Another mixed waste facility is licensed for primarily long term storage and limited physical treatments. A final facility is currently licensed to receive non-land ban and TCLP passable solid wastes for land burial. The Department of Energy has a mixed waste TSCA incinerator which is currently unavailable to the commercial mixed waste generators. Less than a handful of additional facilities are in various stages of permitting. Therefore, the disposal options available to mixed waste generators is not currently totally able to handle all mixed wastes generated.

CONCLUSION

Mixed wastes have been generated for well over fifty years. It wasn't until the 1980s that the term mixed waste became a reality and the generators were required to consider both radioactive and hazardous materials concerns. The required permits and licenses to enable mixed waste storage and/or disposal is a tedious, complicated, time consuming, overlapping and very costly process.

MANAGEMENT

LIABILITY AND COMPLIANCE

Colonel William F. Brandes, Ph.D., P.E.
Chemical and Environmental Services, Inc.

and

James M. Weaver, Esq.
Waller, Lansden, Dortch, & Davis

INTRODUCTION

This chapter addresses the complex legal concepts of liability and compliance. A person can spend his whole lifetime studying this subject. We can only cover the broad topics. If you have serious real life questions about these matters, seek the advice of counsel. It is a very old saying, "He who would be his own lawyer has a fool for a client." Even competent attorneys hire another lawyer to represent them when they get into trouble. It helps to be able to recognize when you have a problem.

Legal System

The subject can be divided into two components: common law and statutory law. Common law is a body of rules and procedures designed to govern and protect persons and properties. It originated in the customs and practices of the Anglo-Saxon people of England. (The major exception is Louisiana, where the code is founded on French law). These practices and traditions evolved into a set of laws affirmed by the courts through judicial decisions. The common law is flexible and adapts to change. It is sometimes referred to as "court-made law" or "case law," but it is just as real as any law passed by the United States Congress or any other legislative body. Since State court systems operate independently and are subject to Federal review only on federal constitutional issues and in certain prescribed situations, the common law may differ in its interpretation from State to State. If a person is involved in litigation under the common law, he should obviously retain an attorney familiar with common law practices in that State. It has recently been affirmed that there is a Federal common law, though this is invoked much less frequently. Some States have codified parts of the common law, making it very important to seek the advice of an attorney familiar with the laws of the jurisdiction where one is involved. Statutory law is the result of enactments by a legislative body and it forms the basic part of the jurisprudence of most of the States.

Common Law

The class of common law actions commonly encountered in environmental cases is called Tort Law. Environmental or "toxic" torts are civil wrongs that do not arise from a specific and explicit agreement between parties such as in a contract, but from a generalized duty of any citizen to avoid harming his neighbor. These actions can arise from injury or damage to property and from injury to a person including not only his body, but also his reputation or sensibilities.

Violations of these private rights can be abated by award of monetary damages, injunctive relief, or a combination of the two. Monetary damages can be actual, punitive or exemplary.

An injunction is an order of the court to do or refrain from doing a certain act. Injunctions can be temporary or permanent. Generally, temporary injunctions are issued to provide time for a case to be litigated. Permanent injunctions are intended to provide permanent relief, and are normally issued as part of the outcome of a trial. Courts have great flexibility in determining whether to issue injunctions, but they generally follow certain rules. In making this determination, the court will examine whether the plaintiff appears to have a complaint that would prevail when and if the case came to trial. Second, the court would examine whether the alleged injury is of such a nature to be irreparable or, probably more importantly, whether the alleged injury is incapable of abatement by later award of monetary damages. The court would next examine whether granting the injunction would be an unreasonable present burden to the defendant. And, lastly, the court would review the public interest involved. For example, would granting an injunction provide relief to a few, while throwing many out of work? There are other rules as well, but again the practices in a local jurisdiction must be studied in an actual case.

The types of torts encountered in the environmental field are: (1) nuisance, (2) trespass, (3) negligence, and (4) strict liability. Long before the enactment of current environmental statutes, tort actions have afforded remedies to private individuals harmed by exposure to hazardous wastes.

The most common of the environmental torts is nuisance. Nuisance is "the class of wrongs that arise from the unreasonable, unwarrantable, or unlawful use by a person of his own property, either real or personal, or from his own lawful personal conduct working an obstruction or injury to the right of another, or of the public and producing material annoyance, inconvenience, discomfort, or hurt." By and large, a person may act as he sees fit or use his property as he sees fit. The limitation is that the person must act in a reasonable manner avoiding material injury or annoyance to another. The injury or annoyance must be material, such that it tangibly affects the physical comfort of ordinary people under normal circumstances.

Nuisances may be private or public. A private nuisance affects a limited number of people while a public nuisance affects the community as a whole. Private citizens bring private nuisance suits, but a public official normally abates a public nuisance. Public nuisances are generally defined by statute or ordinance and are customarily criminal acts. A public nuisance, though a crime, may also be a tort and a private nuisance if the plaintiff can show that he has suffered special damages. The damages must be individual to the plaintiff and not those which he shares with the rest of the public. Nuisances can rise from noise, smoke, dust, odors, and especially in this day and age, hazardous substances.

For example, the Earthline Corporation was licensed and began to operate a hazardous waste recovery, treatment, storage, and disposal site, near the town of Wilsonville, Illinois. Wilsonville sued Earthline to stop the operation and remove all hazardous wastes and toxic substances from the site. The Court ruled that the site was a public/private nuisance and issued an injunction not only against further operation of the site but also requiring Earthline to remove all wastes and contaminated soil. This brings up a very important point. Possession of a properly issued permit in full compliance with all government regulations is not a defense against a common law tort action. Negligence is not a material element in a cause of action for nuisance. Negligence and nuisance are separate torts. Nuisance is a condition and not a negligent act or failure to act.

Trespass is wrongful interference with the plaintiff's possessory interest in land, personal property, or his own person. Traditionally, the cause of action for trespass arises when the defendant unlawfully enters upon another's land. Trespass may also occur when the plaintiff's land is invaded by some instrumentality or object under defendant's control. An owner of land may recover where the intrusion of hazardous waste on or under his property impairs his legal interests.

Negligence is conduct that "falls below the standard established by law for the protection of others against unreasonable risk or harm." There are generally four elements of proof in an environmental tort case. Strictly speaking, these apply to negligence, but they are rather effective standards for any environmental tort. First, the defendant did or failed to do an act which, second, he owed to the plaintiff by virtue of a legal duty. Third, this act caused material injury to the plaintiff or his property. And, fourth, the act was the proximate cause of the injury. Proximate cause is that which forms a natural and continuous sequence and which, if unbroken by an intervening act, produces the injury and without which the injury would not have occurred. The standard of care required by law is that degree which would be exercised by a person of ordinary prudence under the same circumstances. This is often related to the famous "reasonable man" rule; namely, what a reasonable person would have done. Persons harmed as a result of careless and improper disposal or handling of hazardous waste can recover for their losses under a negligence cause of action. Both State and Federal courts have long recognized recovery against defendants who engage in the negligent disposal of pollutants such as hazardous wastes. While having an appropriate permit and being in full compliance with all government regulations is not a defense against negligence, noncompliance with regulations or permit conditions may be *prima facie* evidence (proof without any more evidence) of liability under a negligence cause of action. This theory is commonly referred to as negligence *"per se."*

Strict liability differs from negligence in that the defendant may be liable even though he may have exercised reasonable care. Not all States have applied the doctrine of strict liability to hazardous waste disposal actions, but certainly the overwhelming trend is toward broadening of this application. Certain courts have already ruled that a person who keeps a potentially dangerous substance which, if permitted to escape, is certain to injure others, must make good the damage caused by the escape of the substance regardless of negligence on the defendant's part. The theory is that a person engaged in an ultra-hazardous or dangerous activity for profit should bear the burden of compensating others who are harmed by his activities.

With regard to hazardous wastes, there has been a judicial expansion of the common law concerning liability. Plaintiffs injured by hazardous wastes have often found it difficult to establish common law liability against individuals and companies who may have managed or disposed of those wastes. At abandoned disposal sites, records are scanty or nonexistent. Many different generators may have used a particular disposal site, and the plaintiff generally has the burden of proving which of the multiple defendants caused his injury in order to establish liability. Damage to human health from exposure of hazardous wastes often involves long latency periods which make it difficult for a plaintiff to prove his case.

Recently, courts and legislatures have taken steps to ease these burdens. Most States now delay commencement of the statute of limitations until the injury has been discovered (the "discovery" rule). Several alternative theories of liability have also been developed to alleviate the plaintiff's burden of proof on identifying a proper defendant. At least four theories have evolved: concert of action, enterprise liability, alternative liability, and market share liability.

Under the concert of action theory, a defendant may be held liable if he negligently or intentionally harms someone in concert with others who all have a common design. There need not have been an express agreement.

All defendants properly joined in such a case are held jointly and severally liable for injuries to plaintiffs. Thus, each defendant is potentially liable for the damage caused by all defendants.

Under the enterprise liability theory, a similar rationale is applied on an industry-wide level. A plaintiff must establish that his injuries were caused by members of a class of defendants engaged in a particular enterprise or industry. Once this showing has been made, enterprise liability shifts the burden of proof to the individual class members to show that they did not cause the plaintiff's injury.

Alternative liability allows a plaintiff to recover against several nonconcerting defendants where only one committed the wrongful act, but where it is extremely difficult to ascertain which defendant was responsible. The plaintiff must prove that he suffered injury and that he has joined in the lawsuit all potential defendants. The burden then shifts to the defendants who must each prove that they did not harm the plaintiff.

Market share liability relieves the plaintiff's burden of having to join all potential defendants in the lawsuit as a prerequisite to shifting the burden of proving causation; joinder of all defendants is not necessary as liability is apportioned by the court on an industry-wide basis in accordance with the market share held by each manufacturer. This theory of apportionment has not yet been specifically applied in the context of hazardous waste management, but it does represent a mood of judicial expression in the broad field of toxic tort litigation.

Insurability

The common law is undergoing considerable expansion in the field of toxic and hazardous waste management. Many courts appear to be easing the burden of proof for plaintiffs and imposing broader liability on those who handle hazardous wastes. Expanded common law tort liability poses added risks and costs of doing business for any company handling hazardous substances.

One of the most significant problems in this entire field is the matter of insurance protection. Hazardous substance liability insurance is disappearing or becoming prohibitively expensive. Liability faced by owners and operators of hazardous waste facilities under current law is too uncertain for traditional underwriting practices.   It is extremely difficult to assess the potential risks when liability is so strict that even careful hazardous waste management practices will not prevent liability. Liability may be "joint and several," resulting in the need for duplicative and wasteful insurance coverage. Liability may also be retroactive in that past practices may cause harm at some indefinite time in the future, further complicating and overlapping statutes and common law liabilities.

Because of liability, insurability in the hazardous waste management field is in a state of chaos.   Perhaps, like flood insurance, the Federal Government will have to take it over.   An association of waste handlers is proposing a joint self-insurance scheme.   One thing is certain, costs will be very high.   Even so, this may not be enough.   The lessons are too clear.   Literally tens of thousands of asbestos-related tort suits were instituted against Johns Manville. This major corporation simply collapsed under the pressure. Thus far, EPA and the Federal Government generally have been far from helpful. The attitude seems to be, "We set the rules, you worry about whether you can do business under them."

Environmental Liability

The matter of environmental liability should be of interest to all of you. The environmental laws and regulations provide for a wide range of civil and criminal penalties for failure to comply. The courts are no longer holding only a corporation liable under the statutes for a fine, but are holding individuals personally liable, even for imprisonment, in their corporate roles.

Most Federal environmental statutes make knowing violations a crime: e.g., RCRA (42 U.S.C. 6928(b)(e)); CERCLA (42 U.S.C. 9603 (b)). The same is true for State environmental laws: e.g., Tennessee Air Quality Act (Tenn. Code Ann. 68-25-112 (a)); Tennessee Petroleum Underground Storage Tank Act (Tenn. Code Ann. 68-53-120(a)). During 1990, over 100 federal indictments were returned against top corporate officials under these and other similar statutory schemes.

These prosecutions resulted from a myriad of activities, most of which were unrelated to what is normally thought of as "traditional" environmental crimes -- illegal dumping, false statements, etc. Indicative of this type enforcement activity is the case of *U.S. v. Haynes International Corp.*, 786 F. 2d 1499 (11th Cir. 1986). In *Haynes*, the company and one of its employees were convicted of causing the transportation of a hazardous waste to a facility which did not have a RCRA permit. The corporation was in the business of airplane refurbishing. As a by-product of its operation, it generated fuel, paint waste and spent solvents. A Haynes employee contracted with a third-party to remove the jet fuel drained from the planes Haynes was refurbishing. The third-party would pay Haynes $.20 per gallon for the fuel. The contractor would also remove the "other wastes" [paint and solvents] for no charge. The paint and solvent wastes were disposed of in an illegal landfill. Although a RCRA permit was not needed for the fuel recycling, the paint waste and spent solvents, as hazardous wastes, were required to be transported to a RCRA approved facility. The 11th Circuit held that:

(1)   A mistake of law -- that defendants had no knowledge that the wastes were "hazardous" or that the waste needed to be transported to a permitted facility -- is not a defense to an action of this type. The Court states, "It is completely fair and reasonable to charge those who choose to operate in such areas [hazardous waste] with knowledge of the regulatory provisions; and

(2)   The government need not prove a defendant's actual state of mind in order to establish knowledge of a statutory requirement. The intent necessary for a criminal conviction can be successfully proven by a showing that the defendant willfully failed to make the inquiry necessary to avail herself of the available knowledge.

Based upon these holdings, the Court upheld a jury verdict of guilty on eight counts of violations of 42 U.S.C. 6928(d)(1).

Another possible tool for criminal enforcement of environmental laws is the Racketeer Influence Corrupt Organizations Act (RICO), 18 U.S.C. 1962. In *U.S. v. Paccione*, the defendants, two individuals and six companies, were convicted under RICO for illegal storing and transportation of infectious medical waste and for operating an illegal garbage dump. Although the defendant alleged violation of environmental laws were at the heart of this case, the prosecution used the federal mail and wire fraud statutes, 18 U.S.C. 1314 and 1343, to "trigger" RICO's provisions. The sentences imposed in this action were extremely stiff; twelve years and seven months imprisonment for the individuals and $22,000,000 in forfeitures, fines and restitution for the companies involved.

There is no doubt that there also will be an increased emphasis on civil enforcement in the 1990s. According to EPA Administrator Reilly:

> A strong enforcement program is one of our highest priorities for the agency. Progressive enforcement is the key to effective EPA, state, local, and international programs and a clean environment. We take pride in our recent enforcement and accomplishments. As our regulatory responsibilities grow, we must maintain an enforcement program that will protect human health and the environment, as well as promote pollution prevention and waste minimization on the part of the regulated community.

The heightened emphasis on enforcement programs will be maintained through the use of the EPA's increasingly sophisticated data tracking systems. These systems will be used to focus enforcement activities on areas where the EPA perceives they can have the greatest immediate impact. To that end, according to its strategic plan*, EPA's enforcement activities will focus in three distinct areas:

(1)   *Targeting* -- focusing compliance monitoring and enforcement resources to achieve environmental results in a manner both consistent with national priorities and sensitive to regional and state needs;

(2)   *Screening* -- reviewing possible enforcement actions for enforcement response and realizing the full potential of environmental authorities and addressing environmental problems;

(3)   *Leverage* -- gaining the maximum leverage from each individual enforcement action, both in terms of general and specific deterrents

---

Enforcement Four-Year Strategic Plan: Enhanced Environmental Enforcement for the 1990's, U.S. Environmental Protection Agency, Sept. 1990.

and incentives for the regulatory community to prevent pollution and minimize waste.

In the enforcement plan, EPA sets out seven goals for its enforcement activities in the 1990s. These goals are as follows:

I.   Strengthening the institutional enforcement voice.
II.   Targeting for maximum environmental results.
III. Screening violations for appropriate enforcement response.
IV.   Improving EPA relationships with other units of government.
V.   Creative use of environmental authorities.
VI.   Expansion of enforcement communications efforts.
VII. Improving the infrastructure/training.

EPA believes that the key to moving its enforcement program towards these goals is flexibility in the use of its regulatory programs for enforcement purposes and decentralization of enforcement activities through greater use of its regional offices and the states. The impact on this new emphasis on civil enforcement is already apparent to the regulated community. See *U.S. v. Zimmer Paper Prods.*, (S.D. Ind. Feb. 22, 1991) (CAA defendant must pay $500,000 civil penalty); *U.S. v. Elken Metals Co.*, (S.D. W.Va. Jan. 29, 1991) (CWA defendant must pay $130,000 penalty for NPDES permit violations); *U.S. v. Huron Dressed Beef Co.*, (D. S.D. Feb. 22, 1991) (CWA defendant must pay $125,000 civil penalty for unpermitted wastewater discharges).

We will not attempt to go through the provisions of the dozen or more Federal statutes which cover toxic and hazardous substance control, nor the reams of implementing regulations having the "force and effect of law." In discussing liability and compliance in the statutory sense, it is essential to broaden these considerations to include inspection, reports and enforcement. It is under all of these subject headings that one must diligently study the provisions of any particular enactment such as RCRA, CERCLA or TSCA. There are similarities between the separate provisions of the various environmental statutes, but one needs to study each act to be certain. The best solution is to do some reading and then, if there are any questions that arise, retain the services of a competent environmental lawyer.

Environmental violations may result in reactions by more than one governmental body under more than one provision of more than one statute. Since the environmental laws, generally, are framed for delegation to the States, there may be concurrent violations of both State and Federal law. Some States are more diligent even than the Federal Government in enforcing environmental requirements. Indeed, some States have more resources to devote to this activity than does the Federal Government. This means that differences in enforcement practices from one State to another can be substantial. It is important to study the enforcement attitudes and the abilities of a State as well as the written laws on the State's books.

Second, one must recognize that the Federal Government is not a monolithic structure. Though the enforcement scheme for Federal laws is intended to be set by EPA, that agency itself is made up of a number of different offices in its own headquarters and ten regional offices across the country. Attitudes and interpretation of policy may differ substantially between offices and between regions. Some regions may have written policies for specific issues, others will rely on "case by case" analysis. EPA has stated that it encourages the use of persuasion, administrative action and other alternatives before going to court for judicial action. The practice and the announced policy may not always coincide.

Cases referred for trial in Federal Court by EPA are actually handled by the United States Department of Justice. This provides another possibility for differences in interpretation and action. Program offices within EPA, legal offices in EPA, the headquarters of the Department of Justice, and the various Unites States Attorneys (who are the local representatives of the Department of Justice) may all have vastly different ideas of appropriate measures to force compliance. One must be aware of all these potential variations.

Even beyond the environmental statutes, one must be aware of possible violations of such laws as those covering mail and wire fraud. Liability may be established simply by mailing a false report. Other statutes, for example, cover making false official statements to Federal officials.

Most environmental statutes permit citizen suits. Citizens may act even as "Private Attorney Generals" to allege violations of Federal law and go to court even if EPA does not agree. Some State laws also permit citizen suits. In some cases, the government may investigate a situation and decide to pursue some alternative correction mechanism instead of a law suit. Private citizens can gain access to the government's reports and go directly to court rather than having to wait for the government's action.

SUMMARY

The complexities of common law liability added to the incredible array of statutory laws and regulations existing through multiple government agencies at Federal and State levels, plus the complications of possible citizen suits under statutory law, should make any individual dealing with hazardous substances take a realistic look not only at his company's liabilities, but also at his own personal concerns. What is your company's policy on defense of individuals and what is the extent of the company's insurance coverage for damage actions? The best advice to protect your company and yourself is to be familiar with the legal requirements and never knowingly violate them. Study the statutes and the regulations, talk to people who are knowledgeable and experienced in compliance matters, and try to anticipate problems as they arise. Finally, if you think you have a problem, consult a capable lawyer.

ETHICS FOR CERTIFIED HAZARDOUS MATERIALS MANAGERS

Richard T. Cartwright, P.E., CHMM
Metcalf & Eddy Technologies, Inc.

and

Brian Thomas
Signal Environmental Services, Inc.

INTRODUCTION

Society, through elected government officials, controls the activities of both barbers and florists by regulating the process of granting individuals licenses to provide a service to the public. In the field of hazardous materials management, where the public is at a much greater risk, the activities of individual professionals are not regulated by either a licensing or a government-endorsed certification process. Anyone can fill out a manifest or claim to be an environmental consultant!

Recent highly publicized news reports regarding unethical practices by several environmental professionals at hazardous waste disposal facilities are eroding the public's trust and confidence in our profession. In order to help restore the public's trust, a code of ethics describing personal standards and convictions for environmental professionals has been established by a group of professionals who have been certified by the Institute of Hazardous Materials Management (IHMM) and are members of the Academy of Certified Hazardous Materials Managers (ACHMM).

The IHMM is a private not-for-profit corporation with educational status. The ACHMM is incorporated as a professional society within the IHMM.

DEFINITIONS OF THE CHMM

The IHMM defines hazardous materials management as "the application of scientific, engineering, and managerial technology to identify, evaluate, and eliminate or reduce risks involving conditions and practices related to hazardous materials over their total life cycles, including ultimate disposal." The word *hazardous* itself has many definitions: the Department of Transportation (DOT) and the National Fire Protection Association (NFPA) define hazardous materials; the Comprehensive Environmental Response, Compensation, and Liability Act (CERCLA) defines hazardous substances; the Resource Conservation and Recovery Act (RCRA) defines hazardous waste; and the Occupational Safety and Health Administration (OSHA) defines hazardous chemicals. There is no universally accepted definition of the term *hazardous*.

The Institute of Hazardous Materials Management has initiated the Certified Hazardous Materials Managers (CHMM) program. It establishes the qualification requirements of the CHMM, develops the CHMM examination, approves the examination administrators, and publishes books and magazines for use by CHMMs. After becoming certified by the IHMM as a CHMM, the hazardous materials professional is eligible to maintain his or her certification through peer interaction and periodic evaluation as a qualified member of the ACHMM.

DUTIES OF THE CHMM

A CHMM must be familiar with civil, criminal and common law principles, as well as government regulations based on statutes such as the National Environmental Policy Act (NEPA), the Clean Water Act (CWA), and Resource Conservation and Recovery Act (RCRA). A CHMM must also be aware of scientific and technological advances. This technical background covers a wide area, including chemistry; public health and safety; collection, analysis, interpretation, and presentation of data; engineering; information resources; and economics. A CHMM must possess sound management principles, such as abilities of policy making, decision making, negotiation, and public speaking. A CHMM must be familiar with hazardous materials management skills, waste minimization, waste generation management, and TSD facility management. All of these fundamental skills, along with a mature judgment acquired through years of practical "hands-on" experience, are essential to solving the tasks that a CHMM must face.

RESPONSIBILITIES OF THE CHMM[1]

The primary responsibility of the CHMM is the protection of public health. The voice of the public is heard through government regulations. Compliance with these regulations, then, is a CHMM responsibility to the general public.

CHMM's are also responsible for the protection of the environment: plants and animals, natural resources, and the overall quality of life within the biosphere that we share.

CHMM's are responsible to their employers and clients. Every CHMM owes them thorough, objective investigation and reporting, consideration of possible alternatives, diligent pursuit of knowledge in regulations, technology and business, mature judgment, insurance of safe practices, timely response, and cost control. CHMM's must write reports that present data clearly and objectively, and must protect the safety of colleagues, clients, and others in the work site area.

To meet these responsibilities, CHMM's must thoroughly study the regulations and keep track of any changes; study current technology; consult with specialists when necessary; avoid speculation by concentrating on facts; and develop personal standards. These personal standards are expressed in the CHMM Code of Ethics.

CHMM CODE OF ETHICS[2]

Professionalism requires a public commitment, a realization that this competence has significant social value. Society turns to its professionals

---

[1]Adapted from "Ethics of an Environmental Professional," Hal Taback and Douglas Hileman, October 1989.

[2]ACHMM, "Ethics Committee Paper," 1990.

for guidance and judgments in eradicating and rectifying its problems. There is clearly a relationship between the professional and society; this relationship is based on public trust and confidence. Confidence is acquired through experience, but trust is more subjective. In order to deal with trust in a more objective manner, a code of ethics is established. This code of ethics is a clear message from the ACHMM which states what kind of person the CHMM is and how to serve his clients or employers. The code of ethics sets an example for all CHMMs to follow.

(1)   *A CHMM shall be a judge of his or her own competence and not attempt a function beyond his or her own level.*

There is no excuse for the CHMM that attempts a task beyond his or her own abilities. Such an act could endanger the public or the environment, and the acquisition of expertise in any given area is always achievable.

(2)   *A CHMM shall never compromise the public welfare.*

Because of the position of the CHMM, one wrong action could result in irreparable damage to the environment as well as long-lasting damage to the general public. The CHMM must never put his own interest above that of the public at large.

(3)   *A CHMM shall be involved in a program of continued learning and education.*

Hazardous materials management is a rapidly growing and changing field, and the CHMM must keep up with the scientific and technological advances. Decisions must be made based on facts and knowledge; without this continued education, sound, mature judgments can not be made.

(4)   *A CHMM shall act as an agent or trustee in any relationship that involves an employer or client.*

The relationship between a CHMM and his or her client should remain strictly professional. The CHMM must avoid potential conflicts of interest with his or her client, and all information that the CHMM receives from the client should remain confidential.

(5)   *A CHMM shall hold only the highest standard of integrity and virtue.*

Trust in the professional is mandatory.   If integrity or virtue is missing from the professional, then mistrust results.   This mistrust is not only mistrust of the individual, but of the industry as a whole. Each individual must maintain these standards in order for the industry to maintain community trust.

(6)   *A CHMM shall seek opportunities to be active in civic affairs.*

The CHMM holds a very important place in this society as a controller of hazardous waste; only through interaction with the public can the public understand the duties, responsibilities, and actions of the CHMM. Understanding of these traits leads to better communication between the CHMM and society and to better solutions to the problems that both parties face.

(7)   *A CHMM shall not malign, damage, indiscriminately criticize, injure or degrade another individual without proper justification.*

Because of the visibility of hazardous materials and wastes in the media, it is much easier to damage the reputation of a CHMM than that of any other professional.   This type of action results in no gain for either side, and in the end damages the industry as a whole.   The professional should handle any situation as a professional.   A productive, civilized manner is desired over mudslinging through the media.

(8)   *A CHMM will attempt to contribute to the furthering of his profession, by disseminating acquired knowledge and skill to others, and upholding the moral precepts of this profession.*

Individual growth and knowledge is useless without the growth of the Academy as a whole.   Discussion between members results in acquired knowledge in all who are involved.

Also, morality is the basis of an ethical code.   The morality of an individual contributes to the morality of the whole; the individual who performs his or her duties in an ethical manner provides an example for others to follow.

THE ETHICS CHECK QUESTIONS[3]

When faced with an ethical dilemma, the CHMM may ask himself the following ethics check questions. The ethics check questions are three questions that help one to decide if a certain option is ethical or not. It helps sort the grayness of each situation encountered into black and white.

(1)   *Is it legal?*

This question includes not only civil and criminal laws but company laws as well. Some people say that if the answer to this question is, "No," then the other two questions are irrelevant. However, it could be a good idea to answer all three questions before making a final decision.

(2)   *Is it balanced? Will the decision be fair, or will it heavily favor one party over another?*

If the decision results in a big winner and a big loser, the loser will often find ways of getting even with the winner. The winner may eventually become the loser. On top of this, a third party may surpass the first two while they are embroiled in competition. Any such fighting between parties can reflect negatively on the industry as a whole.

(3)   *How will it make me feel about myself? Would I feel good if my family or fellow CHMM's knew about it?*

This question is possibly the most important of the three. If the CHMM would be ashamed of his actions, then the actions are probably ethically wrong and should not be made.

---

[3]Adapted from Kenneth Blanchard and Norman Vincent Peale, The Power of Ethical Management, Morrow and Co. Inc., 1988.

CONCLUSION

As qualified members of the ACHMM, we are individually and collectively building up a profession of certified hazardous materials managers serving the public's environmental needs. We are faced with the clear choice of developing the source of our professional livelihood in the same manner successfully advanced by doctors, accountants, and engineers, or we can watch our profession drift away into oblivion. Unprofessional acts based on questionable ethics by any individual CHMM will hurt all of us as a group. We need to stay in touch with our peers and uphold our standards. Unfortunately, every barrel can have at least one rotten apple. We must have the fortitude to enforce discipline within our membership including, if necessary, revocation of certification by the IHMM and membership in the ACHMM.

ENVIRONMENTAL MANAGEMENT

Kenneth L. Manchen, PE, CHMM
Groundwater Technology, Inc.

INTRODUCTION

Companies today spend considerable time and money complying with environmental laws. Their actions are scrutinized by employees, government regulators, and environmental groups. Firms that are known to behave in a less than concerned manner face a crisis in public confidence that can harm and even bankrupt their businesses. This chapter discusses how we got to this point, what actions responsible companies are taking, and finally how to select and manage environmental consultants.

HISTORICAL PERSPECTIVE ON THE ENVIRONMENTAL MOVEMENT

Relative to other national issues, the environmental movement is rather new. It is generally considered to have begun in the 1960s. A chronology of the movement follows:

1962 Rachel Carson published a book (*Silent Spring*) that became a symbol of the environmental movement. Carson warned that the misuse of pesticides threatened to upset the balance of nature. She presented case after case of pesticide disaster. She was the first to suggest that pesticides could climb the food chain and become more concentrated as they ascended. She related how insecticides were killing insect-eating birds, squirrels, rabbits and muskrats, and warned of a silent spring to follow. The Audubon Society took notice and the U.S. Department of Agriculture was besieged with calls. President Kennedy set up a pesticides committee, and congressional hearings were held. The environmental movement was born.

1970 *Time* magazine named "environment" the issue of the year. The first Earth Day followed. President Nixon established the U.S. Environmental Protection Agency. The nations first clean air act was passed. This act would ultimately require industries to obtain air emission permits and to curb emissions. Industries were similarly required to apply for water pollution discharge permits (according to the 1899 Refuse Act). Industrial environmental regulations had begun.

1972 A comprehensive federal water pollution control act was passed. It regulated the discharge of liquid industrial waste.

1976 A federal waste disposal act was passed. It was called the Resource Conservation and Recovery Act (RCRA). The major goal of the act was to regulate industrial waste disposal.

1978 The nation was shocked by the hazardous waste contamination of the Love Canal neighborhood in New York State. The tragedy was highlighted on national news broadcasts. President Carter found himself in a perplexing situation because there was no mechanism in place for the federal government to help people displaced from their homes by toxic chemical contamination.

This incident ultimately lead to the enactment of the Comprehensive Environmental Responsibility, Compensation and Liability Act (CERCLA) in 1980. This act, better known as Superfund, empowered the federal government to assist in clean-ups, and to recover costs from responsible industries. It also required industrial officials to report environmental spills to the government.

1979 The Three Mile Island nuclear accident occurred. The outgrowth was a rash of anti-nuclear sentiment. The anti-nuclear movement spurred more regulation and, coupled with the scrutiny of a protesting public, served to drive up costs and adversely affect the economies of nuclear power. For the first time a pollution related incident was featured as a *Time* magazine cover story.

1980 *Time* magazine featured its second environmental cover story entitled the "Poisoning of America". The article described the problem of improper disposal of toxic chemicals. It highlighted major problem areas across the country. The article appeared just two months before the long awaited federal hazardous waste disposal (RCRA) regulations took effect. The regulations required industries to send their hazardous wastes to federally permitted disposal sites.

1984 The world was shocked by the gas release and associated deaths of over 2,500 people in Bhopal, India. Government officials realized that an accident of this type could occur in the United States. Debate began on regulations to address this potential problem.

1985 *Time* magazine updated and repeated its cover story from 1980 and titled it "The Poisoning of America '85". The story described the failure of the Superfund program to clean-up toxic waste sites. The artist preparing the 1985 cover took the original one from 1980 and made the contamination depicted worse. This was to signify a lack of progress and a continued deterioration of the environment.

1986 Congress passed the Superfund Amendment and Reauthorization Act (SARA). Where Superfund was short, vague, and general, SARA was specific. The amendments included a section titled the Emergency Planning and Community Right to Know Act (EPCRA). This section was enacted to address the concerns raised by the Bhopal gas leak. Companies were now required to notify local communities of the names and amounts of toxic chemicals on-site, and of the amount released annually to the environment. Local communities were required to prepare emergency response plans to deal with chemical accidents.

1988 Global warming (the greenhouse effect), improper medical waste disposal, and a major oil spill dominated environmental discussions. The greenhouse effect was featured in a cover story in *Newsweek* magazine. Concerns over the greenhouse effect became a topic of international discussion. The problem of medical wastes washing up on our shores was also featured in a *Newsweek* cover story. Debate began on medical waste disposal regulations. A non-cover story concerned the spill of a million gallons of oil from an Ashland Oil Company aboveground storage tank into the Monongahela and Ohio Rivers. This spill led some states to enact rules governing aboveground storage tanks.

1989   A major oil spill, discussions of a nationwide garbage glut, the danger of Alar sprayed on apples, and the worldwide emergence of environmental advocate groups dominated environmental news in 1989. The major oil spill was the Exxon Valdez disaster. The Exxon Valdez tanker released 11 million gallons of crude oil into the waters off Alaska. Debate began over requiring double hulled oil tankers. Damage lawsuits abounded. The discussions of a garbage glut called attention to a nationwide shortage of landfill space. Major recycling efforts began. The use of Alar on apples was banned because of alleged threats to human health. Leading the debate on environmental issues was Greenpeace, the National Defense Council, and the World Wildlife Fund. A Gallup poll showed that 75% of Americans now considered themselves environmentalists.

1990   The twentieth anniversary of Earth Day occurred. It was similar in spirit to Earth Day 1970, but much different in scope. Earth Day 1990 was a worldwide event. An estimated 200 million people representing all sectors of society participated. Revisions to the Clean Air Act were enacted by Congress. The idea of using health risk assessment studies to set clean-up and regulatory standards became more prominent. An intriguing article on the wasteful pursuit of zero risk appeared in the 4/30/90 issue of Forbes magazine. It warned that emotional reactions were causing environmental misspending that could ultimately threaten support of the environmental movement.

ENVIRONMENTAL STRATEGIES FOR THE 1990s

Corporate America is not only feeling pressure from environmental advocacy groups, regulators, and consumers. They are also feeling pressure from their stockholders. Doug Cogan of The Investor Responsibility Research Center, a group that follows shareholder proxy submissions, reports that the environment may be the shareholder proxy issue of the 1990s. The implications for industry are clear. Stockholders are concerned about environmental liabilities and many are willing to vote their stock in support of environmental initiatives.

Successful companies have developed proactive strategies for dealing with environmental pressures and liabilities. The most common actions that have been taken and are recommended to be taken are as follows:

1. Adopt a company environmental policy. Environmental advocacy groups recommend companies adopt the Valdez Principles. These principles were formulated by an environmental advocacy group following the Exxon Valdez oil spill. These principles call for the naming of an environmental advocate to the company's Board of Directors. The principles also call for programs assuring responsible environmental actions. The Valdez Principles have not been embraced by American industry. Alternative principles proposed by other groups have experienced much more acceptance. A list of groups that have proposed company principles is given in Table 1. At the very least, companies should formulate their own environmental policy.

2. Establish a committee of senior managers to meet periodically and coordinate company environmental activities. Attempt to name at least one person to the committee that serves on the company Board of Directors.

3. Establish a high level environmental management position (i.e. V.P. of Environmental Affairs). The purpose of this position is to coordinate company environmental efforts and to assume overall responsibility for compliance with the company's environmental policy. As much as possible, consolidate safety and environmental activities under this position.

4. Assure top management support of environmental efforts, and make employees aware of this support.

5.   Conduct regular environmental compliance audits of company facilities. Require immediate correction of problems.

6.   Require an environmental survey of any facility earmarked for acquisition or divestiture, and correct any problems found.

7.   Establish an on-going training program for employees with environmental responsibilities. Bring these people together for periodic (at least annual) briefings/meetings.

8.   Prepare a written environmental procedures manual and distribute it throughout the company. Let employees with environmental responsibilities clearly know what is expected of them.

9.   Require the company environmental department to annually inspect and approve of all hazardous waste disposers and consultants. Restrict the number and require the use of high quality disposers and consultants.

10.   Require the company environmental department to approve significant environmental capital expenditure requests. Assure that the right equipment is being purchased.

11.   Establish company waste minimization and emission reduction goals. Strive to save money and reduce environmental liabilities.

12.   Communicate what you are doing to your employees. Make sure they know the company's commitment and progress. If appropriate, inform your shareholders and the public at large.

SELECTING AND MANAGING ENVIRONMENTAL CONSULTANTS

Trends in the Environmental Consulting Business

Changing regulations and increasing demands on American industry have resulted in a booming business for environmental consultants. The environmental consulting industry grew at an explosive rate in the 1980s and is expected to grow at a 15-20% annual rate in the 1990s. Firms employing environmental consultants need to understand the pressures high growth has put on consultants. They also need to know how to intelligently select and manage consultants.

Today 20-30 large consulting firms dominate the market. The high growth rate among these firms has caused a tug-of-war for experienced employees. All are struggling to come up with qualified people to manage expanding businesses. Turnover is high and the tug-of-war for employees is expected to become even more intense.

Most industrial firms have begun to limit the number of consultants they employ. This makes it easier for them to manage their consultants, and puts the industrial firm in a position of strength when dealing with their consultant(s).

Selecting a Consultant

There are many questions that should be asked of a prospective consultant. It is important to understand the capabilities of the consultant being considered, and to determine whether that firm is right for the job. A prequalification interview is recommended. The following questions should be asked:

1. What is the technical focus of the consulting firm? Is it a full service or specialty firm? Where are their offices and do all offices have similar capabilities?
2. Can the consulting firm do what is needed?
3. How long has the consulting firm done this type of work?
4. How many similar jobs have been done? What is the largest job of this type done?
5. What are the qualifications and expertise of the proposed project team?
6. What is the consulting firm's applicable regulatory experience? What experience do they have with the local regulators that will be involved?
7. Can they handle worst-case findings (i.e., perform needed remediation)?
8. Is a list of client references available?
9. What are the limits of the firm's insurance coverage? Do they have environmental impairment liability (EIL) insurance?
10. Can a visit be arranged to the local office that will perform the proposed work? What is the age of the office and current staffing? What senior level technical support is available to this office?
11. What services are typically subcontracted? What subcontractor prescreening/prequalifications are required by the consulting firm?

12.   What consultant billing rates and subcontractor mark-up rates apply?

13.   What is the workload of the local office?

14.   What invoice format is used and what are the proposed payment terms?

15.   Does the firm provide expert testimony? At what billing rate?

16.   What contract terms and conditions are needed to perform the work? Is the industrial firm's standard contract acceptable? If not, what changes are needed?

17.   Does the consultant:

- separate his quote into tasks
- give costs for each task
- provide a detailed project flowchart and timeline
- provide invoices with costs shown for each task
- provide estimates (by task) of percent of work completed with each invoice
- provide monthly project status reports?

Managing Consultants

The most important duty of an industrial client is to insist that all of the project management controls stated in point 17 are provided. Monitor project progress and do not allow the consultant to deviate from the agreed upon plan without an explanation. Consultants frequently take on more work than they can handle and must be held accountable for their projections and cost estimates. Devise a change order process and insist that change orders be approved before any additional work is performed. Actions like these will ensure that work is performed to your satisfaction.

ENVIRONMENTAL POLLUTION CONTROL

Nic E. Korte
Chemical Projects Manager
Environmental Sciences Division
Oak Ridge National Laboratory

Environmental pollution control in the industrial environment is challenging, time-consuming, and usually expensive. Being responsible for pollution control matters, however, is more than saving money and doing it right for the company. The pollution control manager must also protect himself because the current laws may make him personally liable for any wrong-doing, even if there is no malicious intent.

Pollution control generally means preventing or mitigating harm to the environment. Harm to the environment can be difficult to prove so regulations are increasingly designed to eliminate contamination. For example, effluent standards are based on health effects studies; but because of factors such as cancer's long latency period, and the lack of human exposure data, standards generally include a large safety factor. Indeed, the standards may be based on the health effects observed from force-feeding susceptible rats. This discussion is not meant to denigrate the regulatory or standard-setting process; rather it is meant to convey the idea that present regulations are stringent and allow little margin for error.

---

*Operated by Martin Marietta Energy Systems, Inc. under contract No. DE-AC05-8421400 with the U.S. Department of Energy

The following example further illustrates the status of pollution control issues. An industry group challenged the Government's standard for benzene in the workplace. The group's defense was that research had shown benzene was harmless at concentrations above the Government's standards. In finding for the Government, the court held that if the Government had a reputable study to support its position, equally reputable studies by other groups that resulted in an opposite view could not overturn the original standard. In other words, as long as a body of evidence existed to support the more strict standard, OSHA was free to err on the side of safety. This case has significant implications for the pollution control professional because it illustrates the prevailing regulatory mind set.

Erring on the side of safety will be the least expensive and most legally defensible option. Taking that position will lead the company to more efficient use of raw materials, recycling, and other waste minimization tactics. A chief difficulty, however, is that regulatory personnel freqently request a greater margin of safety than manufacturing personnel feel is necessary. The pollution control professional is called on to balance the needs of both sides while ensuring that the margin of safety remains adequate.

Ensuring that the company embarks on a serious waste minimization program is the safest, most cost-effective pollution control program that can be conducted. Indeed, waste minimization is not just a catch word for a good business practice. It is required by RCRA. Even if disposal costs are not yet a problem, those costs are increasing dramatically. The only prudent approach to waste disposal is to include a program of waste minimization.

Controlling waste generally involves the following four major issues: identification (air and water emissions, rinsewaters, spent raw materials, etc.), storage and handling, disposal and shipping, and recordkeeping. If an industrial operation has any waste it should have a program for each of these items.

The pollution control manager must know what his plant is purchasing, generating, and storing in order to have an effective program. Such recordkeeping and communication are essential because they lead directly to some key elements of any pollution control program: emergency procedures, contingency plans, and employee training. For example, if a caustic line from a plating building breaks, how is the waste material kept out of the storm sewer in order to prevent a National Pollutant Discharge Elimination System (NPDES) violation? Contingency plans must describe actions the facility will take to minimize hazards in case of a release, and employees must be trained to respond appropriately. RCRA permits six months to complete the training of new hires. OSHA may not allow this for newly hired spill responders. Although on-the-job training is acceptable, a written training program is necessary. Fines may result if the training is not properly documented.

It is best to establish a Hazardous Materials Management Program. This formal program will encompass all of the pertinent aspects of OSHA, TSCA, CERCLA (and SARA), RCRA, and DOT. The need for an integrated program can be demonstrated by considering what happens if a hazardous material is purchased or generated without the knowledge of the pollution control manager: OSHA could be violated because proper precautions for employee exposure are not taken, SARA could be violated because the proper notifications concerning the presence of the material are not made, and RCRA could be violated if the material is not stored or disposed of properly. These are only part of the story. There are also potential violations of other laws such as the Clean Air Act and Clean Water Act.

Thus, a pollution control manager must be involved with all aspects of a plant's processes. A properly informed pollution control manager can help limit the amount of a hazardous material stored on-site, he can monitor the location of the material so that right-to-know regulations are not violated, and he can assess the rate at which a waste is generated to minimize storage and disposal difficulties.

Disposal issues are increasingly important because the regulations are changing rapidly under HSWA (amendments to RCRA in 1984). A company can easily accumulate too much waste or have to contend with unexpectedly high disposal costs unless allowances are made for the changing regulations.

On-site management of hazardous waste is another critical issue. Storage locations must be specific. There must be spill containment, supplies for clean-up, controlled access, and prohibition of incompatible materials. In addition, the law holds that the storage area cannot be subject to a 100-year flood.

Storage issues include satellite accumulation. Up to 55 gallons of hazardous waste (or one quart of acutely hazardous waste) can be accumulated in containers at or near the point of generation if the area is under the control of the operator of the waste generation process.

Underground storage tanks pose additional problems. EPA has proposed extensive regulations that include among other things a schedule for additional regulations; therefore, if a facility has underground tanks, some combination of testing, retrofitting, and replacement will probably be required.

A pollution control manager must also concern himself with problems of acquisition and divestiture. A company cannot transfer its responsibilities by selling contaminated land to someone else, but it can add to its liabilities by purchasing contaminated property. Thus, a pollution control manager is often required to conduct or participate in property transaction site assessments. These assessments include both on and off-site investigations and include reviews of property and tax records and historical aerial photos. Typically a thorough review of the facility's waste management practices and limited field sampling is also required. Often, in order to minimize liabilities, environmental consultants will refuse to certify a site as clean. Consequently, the judgment of the corporate pollution control manager is often the final word in a property transaction.

Unfortunately, many companies already own contaminated property with projected remedial actions that may cost millions of dollars. A pollution control manager may be called upon to plan, negotiate, and manage these expensive and complicated hazardous waste cleanups. If activities are not managed properly, cost overruns and disputes can be expected. Bidders must be prequalified. Contract documents must be precise and accurate. There must be a management plan that includes numerous inspections and thorough documentation including photographs and videotape. There must also be emergency plans in case of spills or fire.

How does a pollution control manager keep track of all of this? First, he needs access to information. Subscriptions to one of a number, or perhaps several, of the newsletters describing the latest congressional, EPA, and state decisions are an excellent means of keeping up with changing regulations. The *Environmental Reporter*, which updates the Code of Federal Regulations, is one of the most useful publications of this type. There are also a number of other publications such as the *Environmental Manager's Compliance Adviser, Hazardous Waste News,* and *Inside EPA.* These newsletters allow one to determine at a glance if there are recent developments that affect the plant's operations.

It is also useful to belong to technical associations. Urban areas will have local chapters of the Air and Waste Management Association or of Certified Hazardous Materials Manager. It is important to be on the mailing lists of the local EPA region and appropriate state agencies. New practitioners in the field are often surprised to hear that each EPA region behaves differently. For example, a recent published review demonstrated that chemical fixation remedial action programs had been approved in all regions but one. Likewise, the quantity of documentation support required for various permits and reports varies significantly. It is highly important, therefore, to understand how the local region applies the regulations.

Finally, effective communication and support throughout the plant and among all organizational units is essential. Successful pollution control programs only result from a total commitment of management and staff.

Additional Reading or Reference Materials:

Environmental Protection -- Law and Policy -- 2nd Edition, F.R. Anderson, D.R. Mandelker, A.D. Tarlock, published by Little, Brown, and Company.

Hazardous Wastes Handbook -- published by Government Institutes, Inc., Rockville, MD.

How to Manage Workplace Hazards and Avoid Liability -- C.K. Wang. Published by Noyes Publications, Park Ridge, New Jersey.

Prudent Practices for Disposal of Chemicals from Laboratories -- published by National Academy Press, Washington, D.C.

RCRA Orientation Manual -- EPA Office of Solid Waste, EPA 530--SW-86-001, January 1986.

Numerous publications from EPA and other governmental sources:

1.   ORD (Office of Research and Development) Publications USEPA, Cincinnati, Ohio 45268 (513-569-7562).

2.   RCRA/Superfund Hotline -- 800-424-9346.

3.   Safe Drinking Water Act -- 800-426-4791.

4.   Chemical Energy Preparedness -- 800-535-0202.

5.   Pesticides -- 703-557-7090.

6.   Air -- 919-541-2777.

7.   Water -- 202-382-5400.

8.   OSHA -- 202-523-9667.

9.   TSCA Hotline -- 1-800-835-6700.

MOTIVATION OF EMPLOYEES WITH RESPECT TO ENVIRONMENTAL MATTERS

Jerry M. Loftin, CHMM
Alcoa Fujikura, Ltd.

Motivation of employees is critical to any organization if it is to be successful and competitive in today's society. Motivation is particularly critical to the environmental manager. The consequences which follow when an employee through disinterest, ignorance, oversight, or defiance creates a situation where his company is threatened by regulatory intervention are potentially disastrous. Citations and fines, possible criminal penalties, and adverse publicity which accompany mismanagement of hazardous materials and hazardous wastes have effects potentially far more devastating than the average employee can imagine. As society becomes more aware of the problems that come with environmental mismanagement it becomes less tolerant of "polluters." This environmental awareness translates into an additional consequence other than legal sanctions -- LOST BUSINESS. An informed public is unwilling to do business with companies perceived as having no respect for our national resources. How then, through motivational techniques, does the environmental manager stimulate the employee to ensure compliance and concern in the organization's environmental programs?

Motivational techniques are as varied as the personalities of employees the manager seeks to motivate. Managers must deal effectively with persons that behavioral scientists define as failure-type, happiness-prone, unhappiness-prone, type-A, type-B, and so forth. There are no specific management or motivational techniques for environmental programs. Basic, conventional techniques can be applied. Before these methods are discussed, a discussion of a person's self image as it relates to how he or she may be effectively managed and motivated is appropriate.

There is a relationship between a person's self image and his level of motivation. One of management's greatest problems is how to provide a climate that will motivate employees toward company (environmental) goals when, because of their self image, the employee is intrinsically motivated in another direction ("I've always thrown this in the dumpster," "We've mixed this stuff together for years," "I've never had to put a label on this junk."), or is not motivated at all. The first step in creating a desirable climate is understanding how the self image is formed, how it is maintained, and how it can be changed.

An examination of the physiology of the brain illustrates how self image is formed, maintained, and changed. The human brain is a library of past experiences and feelings, both failures and successes. Much like inactive recordings on tape, feelings and experiences are recorded on neural engrams. All these impressions are equally real and accessible.

The important fact about these engrams or impressions is that they can be changed or modified. Impressions tend to change each time they are retrieved from memory. They take on some of the tone and temper of our present mood. Each impression or thought can become part of more than one memory. Not only does the past influence the present, but the present influences the past. Patterns of behavior are not set, predetermined, or unchangeable ("You know I could pour this trichlor in with the waste oil, but it's really not right.")

The more a given memory is recalled, the more potent it becomes and conversely lack of activation decreases memory potency. This means good habits can be developed and reinforced, bad habits can be suppressed or forgotten, and one's self image changed accordingly. An adult can learn to be happy or motivated.

Approximately ninety-five percent of our behavior, feeling, and response is habitual. One's self image and habits tend to come together. So a person is highly motivated or unmotivated as a matter of habit because it is consistent with his self image. Habits, responses which are performed automatically without thought, are learned. We all learn that certain attitudes, ways of feeling and thinking, are appropriate in certain situations. We tend to think, feel, and act the same way whenever we encounter what we interpret as the same sort of situation that has previously been encountered.

The relationship between habits and self image and perhaps motivation is clarified by experiments conducted by Prescott Lecky, a pioneer in self image psychology. Lecky conceived of the personality as a system of ideas, all of which must be consistent with each other. Ideas which are inconsistent with the system are rejected, not believed, and not acted upon. The converse is also true. At the center of this system of ideas is the keystone or base upon which all else is built. This is the individual's "ego ideal" or his self-image. It can be inferred from this theory that if an individual's motivation is poor it is because the individual believes that it would be inconsistent with his self image to be motivated. As Lecky said, "the same attitudes will be maintained in spite of environmental changes." Lecky believed that if you could change a person's self-conception, his attitude toward things (and being motivated) would change accordingly. Lecky found that there were two powerful levers for changing beliefs and concepts. There are standard convictions which are strongly held by nearly everyone. These are:

1.   The feeling or belief that one is capable of doing his share and can exert a certain amount of independence.
2.   The belief that there is something inside you which should not be allowed to suffer indignities.

The inference here is that levels of motivation are intrinsic to the individual and motivation cannot be forced or achieved through directive styles of management. Also, changes in an individual's external environment do not affect his level of motivation.

Another important point, which gives an indication that management can develop motivated employees, is made by Dr. John A. Schindler. Dr. Schindler relates that "regardless of the individual's past, a person has to start in the present to acquire some maturity so that the future may be better than the past. The present and future depend on learning new habits (a new self image) and new ways of looking at old problems." Put another way, it can be said that most people have not learned to control present thinking to remain motivated in their job. Again it is important for managers to realize that such behavior can be learned.

How does all this relate to the environmental manager? Simply put, it is physiologically and practically possible to change a person's self image or attitudes (attitudes toward the company's environmental goals).

What can the environmental manager do to assist employees in developing a self image of which motivation toward environmental goals is a consistent part? First the environmental manager must become a good leader. Some of the characteristics of a good leader are:

1. Being people-oriented versus task oriented (as mentioned earlier, directive styles of management are not effective in motivating employees; participative management is effective).
2. Recognizing the need for outcomes over which the leader has some control (recognizing what will and won't work with certain employees with respect to their motivation).
3. Increasing personnel payoffs for (environmental) goals attainment (positive reinforcement).
4. Helping employees clarify what is expected of them in environmental programs.
5. Reducing barriers which prevent effective environmental management.
6. Increasing opportunities for employee satisfaction depending on performance.

A good leader and environmental manager is someone who understands that, under proper conditions, people will seek organizational (environmental) objectives and that rewarding people for a good job is a more effective motivational technique than penalizing people for doing no job or a poor job. The environmental manager may take some simple steps to bring his company closer to its environmental goals:

1. Start with yourself. Are you really motivated toward all your environmental responsibilities? If not, admit it and find someone who would like these responsibilities.

2. Look for employees who are intrinsically motivated toward environmental concerns. Fit the task to the employee, not vice-versa.

3. Motivate them by allowing them to participate in environmental planning. Get people involved. They may have some good practical ideas to make reaching company environmental goals easier.

4. Reward good environmental efforts through recognition, status (job title change to reflect increased responsibility), and financial rewards.

The good environmental manager must provide environmental goals for the employee which will not only satisfy the organization, but the individual as well. This is best done through participative management where goals and ideas come from the individual with direction from management.

Make your subordinates feel good about themselves and their environmental responsibilities, and improve their self image.

SAFETY OVERVIEW OF HAZARDOUS MATERIALS MANAGEMENT ACTIVITIES

Patricia Mahoney, CHMM, CSP
Los Alamos National Laboratory

INTRODUCTION

To the safety professional, activities in the hazardous materials management (HMM) field, such as those involved in pollution prevention, control, and environmental regulation compliance, are in many ways similar to those encountered in general industry and construction. One major difference is the potential for facing substances of unknown identity in remedial or emergency response situations. Another difference is that the zeal often displayed in the performance of HMM tasks may lead the employee to take chances or encounter hazards in a manner unacceptable in management. These differences mean that a safety and health program must be carefully designed to address actual hazards, be explicitly communicated to workers, and be rigidly enforced -- just like any other industry policy.

In this overview, the term "safety" shall be understood to include concerns for worker health (as reflected in occupational injuries and illnesses), and the term "safety professional" shall include persons engaged in the profession of safety management and engineering, industrial hygiene, and occupational medicine.

The safety professional's main tool is information -- both for himself and for those he seeks to protect. Those responsible for development of safety programs in an HMM activity must acquaint themselves with good safety management standards and practices as outlined in literature such as the OSHA regulations -- both those in 29 CFR 1910 (General Industry) and in 29 CFR 1926 (Construction). Other useful sources include Department of Transportation (DOT) regulations, publications of the National Institute of Occupational Safety and Health (NIOSH), the National Safety Council (NSC), American Society of Safety Engineers (ASSE), American Conference of Governmental Industrial Hygienists (ACGIH), American Industrial Hygiene Association, American Occupational Medicine Association, National Fire Protection Association (NFPA), and the American National Standards Institute (ANSI).

Safety Program

Every organization needs to define how its safety program will be implemented. This definition will provide the framework within which safety, health, and loss concerns can be addressed. Whether the program is to be implemented by a person with part-time responsibilities for safety or by a staff of several safety professionals, the plan must be developed to reflect and acknowledge the organizational culture which it supports.

Elements of a safety program include: a corporate safety policy, which will provide the charter or establish the mission of the program; an organization plan, reflecting that the safety officer has access to top management; assignment of responsibilities for inspections, safety committees and recognition of the roles played by different levels of management and supervision. Once these elements have been defined and set in place, then the program can be reviewed internally and revised to provide the best fit for the needs of the organization.

Risk Assessment

A proper assessment of a site or facility's real safety needs must be performed. The safety program must be developed around the real risks faced by workers if it is to have acceptance by both employees and upper management, fulfill regulatory requirements, and protect workers and company assets.

Two elements must be present for a risk to be "real": (1) a hazard; and (2) exposure of people, equipment or facilities to that hazard. Following determination of hazards, proper barriers and controls can be devised. These may include engineering controls (such as ventilation systems, interlocks, shielding, etc.), work practice controls (such as training, written procedures), personal protective equipment use, medical surveillance, preventive maintenance programs, equipment and facility inspections, and emergency plans. An experienced safety professional may be required at this stage to assure that the assessment is comprehensive and accurately reflects real hazards and real exposures. Consultation with a local professional safety chapter can provide names of people who would be able to provide this service. It may be that the company's insurance carrier will have professional safety, fire, and health people on its staff that can assist with various aspects of a safety program.

Attention should be given to all employees and their respective risks, not just risks associated with exotic hazards. Much attention is presently being paid to hazards faced at Superfund-type sites and those faced in emergency response activities. Without ignoring these, attention must also be given to tasks involving risks such as driving hazards, heavy equipment usage, climbing of meteorological towers, drum handling, custodial and maintenance operations, field work, safety/wilderness survival, wild and domestic animal handling methods, medical activities, protective garment laundering, and office tasks (See Table 1). All situations in which an employee is expected to work alone must be carefully examined to determine if use of a team of workers or a monitoring device would reduce the risk.

Table 1

EXAMPLES OF TASK ASSESSMENTS

Driving	--	does employee have a valid driver's license?
	--	has employee's driving record been checked?
	--	has the employee received driver training?

Heavy Equipment	--	is employee experienced in specific pieces of equipment?
	--	has employee been trained/certified?
	--	is noise protection required?
Climbing	--	is fall protection provided, used?
	--	have prohibitions been developed against climbing in bad weather conditions?
Drum Handling	--	are hand trucks, dollies, forklifts used to move drums?
Laboratory Work	--	has education/training of all employees been assessed?
	--	have spill cleanup materials been provided?
	--	are employees aware of how to dispose of contaminated glassware and equipment?
	--	is personal protective equipment provided and used?
Sampling	--	do water sampling activities use boats?
	--	do boats meet Coast Guard regulations?
	--	can employees swim?
	--	have life jackets been provided and are they used?
	--	do air sampling activities require climbing buildings?
Custodial/ Maintenance	--	have special training/procedures been provided for activities in restricted areas?
	--	have these people been included in evacuation plans/drills for the facility?
	--	have personal protective equipment needs been established for this group?

Field/Wilderness	--	do employees working at remote sites understand basic survival techniques appropriate for the climate/location?
	--	has a system been established to determine when workers at remote sites are overdue to return?
	--	are vehicles equipped with radios/CBs/first aid kits?
Animal Handling	--	have employees been trained in procedures for environmental sampling of domestic animals or wildlife?
	--	are proper cages/restraints provided/used?
	--	is personal protective equipment provided/used?
Medical	--	are medical personnel expected to respond to accidents?
	--	are medical personnel properly trained/equipped to respond to accidents involving hazardous materials?
Laundering	--	has the laundry been informed of potential contamination of garments?
	--	has a survey of the laundry's procedures been performed?
	--	are garments with different types of contamination segregated from one another?
Office	--	are samples left with secretaries/clerks?
	--	are they trained to deal with hazardous materials?
	--	is a proper storage area provided/used?
	--	have procedures for leaking samples been established?

--   are office personnel included in
      evacuation plans/drills?

A system must be developed for accumulating information on all accidents
and incidents.   Injuries/illnesses must be evaluated and recorded in
accordance with OSHA requirements.   Losses due to fire, vehicle
accidents, or other causes must be carefully evaluated. A documentation
system capable of capturing this information provides the opportunity to
establish corrective or preventive action.

Once the safety assessment is complete and management has been advised
of its recommendations, it should be repeated at intervals consistent with
changes in operation and activities. This will assure that money spent to
support the safety program will be most effective in preventing
injuries/illnesses and protecting assets. It may be part of each assessment
to establish the frequency for this update, but, as a minimum, it should be
repeated every five years.

Controls

Once hazards and exposures have been identified and evaluated, a
determination of appropriate controls and barriers can be made.
Elimination of hazard or exposure is always the best control, but that
option is often not available.   A control serves to prevent an incident
and/or diminish the consequences by separating the hazard from the
exposure. Three general categories of controls are available -- engineering
controls, work practice (administrative) controls, and personal protective
equipment.

Engineering controls are preferred as they operate with a minimum of
worker input.   Sprinkler systems, ventilation systems, interlocks,
permanent shielding, remote controls, machine guards, etc., are
engineering controls. A control requiring input from a worker is less
desirable because it is subject to the worker's initiative in using it
properly.

Work practice controls include procedures and training. Anything which
influences how a worker performs his tasks is subject to work practice
control. Written procedures are essential. If a step-by-step instruction

cannot be used because of procedural uncertainty, a written description of the hazards and their controls should be provided instead.

Personal protective equipment (PPE) is the last line of defense. The use of glasses, goggles, respirators, gloves, protective clothing, etc., means that the hazard is present right at the worker's body, and distance from the hazard is no longer an ally. Training and procedures for the use of PPE must be rigorously followed as there is often a reluctance to use the device provided because of inconvenience. An all-too-common example is the resistance of some male employees to the requirement for shaving of facial hair in order to obtain a good seal with a half- or full-face respirator.

Training

Training is a key element of any safety program. Even a casual glance at OSHA regulations will underscore this. Regulations (29 CFR 1910.120) outlining training requirements of hazardous waste workers have inspired a new industry providing "canned" courses emphasizing provisions of RCRA, CWA, CAA, SARA, emergency response, and notification. These courses should be carefully reviewed before being used to be sure they are consistent with the organization's policies and address the actual hazards faced.

Actual training programs must reflect not only operational concerns but those of safety and health as well. This training must be in response to the actual workplace risk assessment. It must be tied to the evaluation of worker backgrounds of education and experience. For instance, a degreed chemist understands that bases are hazardous, as are acids. Chemical technicians are not always aware of this and may be sometimes observed handling dilute acids with great care but casually exposing themselves to harm from concentrated bases.

Following the training assessment portion of a risk assessment process, needs should be developed for which a schedule of training can be established to assure that workers receive the information they need to appropriately and safely perform their jobs. This assessment may be performed for each individual worker but it is probably more practical to key it to a job category. Thus, drivers will receive different training than that appropriate for geologists. It should not be assumed that workers who are more formally educated in their specialty have necessarily received the information they need to participate in the assurance of their own workplace safety and health.

The training schedule should include a safety and health orientation of new workers, workers transferred from other departments or facilities, summer students, consultants, and contractors (see Table 2). The orientation should include, as a minimum, review of the organization's safety policy, safety organization (including where to go for specific safety information), facility lay-out (including restricted areas), hazards at facility or associated with various processes, controls, emergency response procedures, Safety Manual or Handbook, procedures to be followed in case of injuries or exposures, and peculiarities of the organization or location, such as neighborhood crime, high altitude sickness, endemic wildlife diseases, etc. An introduction to the organization's Hazard Communication program may be included.

Table 2

Safety Briefing for Contractors

Prior to starting work on your site, contractors should be provided a briefing which consists of the following, as a minimum:

A. Disclosure of potential hazards.
B. Procedures for clearance into restricted areas. (An alternative may be to provide escorts).
C. How emergencies should be handled.
D. Vehicle rules/requirements. (Contractors may be required to use your vehicles).
E. Equipment to be used. (If contaminated, who will take care of it?)
F. Restrictions on handling of materials or articles to be encountered in working areas.
G. Rules for storage and transportation of hazardous materials.
H. Personal protective equipment. (Need to review to be sure it is adequate/appropriate for anticipated hazards).
I. Applicable operating procedures which may affect tasks.

Further safety and health training is usually comprised of two phases --
classroom and on-the-job training (OJT). Classroom training is often
employed to communicate regulatory, theoretical, or technical information,
where on-the-job training may be used for operational or equipment-related
tasks.

Documentation of each kind of training is essential for two primary
reasons: as proof or evidence that training actually did take place, and
as a tool to ensure that each employee so trained received the same basic
foundation of information. Classroom training is easily documented by the
lesson outlines, handouts or manuals, exams or quizzes used. OJT must
also be documented -- an acceptable and relatively easy way is through
checklist on which each operational or safety point covered is checked off
or initialed by the instructor. Such a checklist may include an item for the
instructor demonstrating how a particular task is to be performed, followed
by another item where the student-employee performs the task while being
observed by the instructor. Copies of the OJT checklist can then be
provided to the employee and to the employee's training file.

A means of providing OJT particularly suitable for emergency response
teams is in the performance of accident response drills using a variety of
scenarios. After a team receives applicable classroom training and OJT,
it is important that their skills be practiced under adrenalin-producing
conditions. A review session after each response allows personnel to
discuss successes and problems, and it is a valuable adjunct to the training
program. It may be useful in this post-drill review to videotape the
exercise, giving participants an opportunity to review their own part of the
action plus the overall response.

Medical Surveillance

Medical surveillance on personnel exposed above the general population
level to hazardous materials is appropriate, and for some materials is
legally required.

A minimum program would provide for an incoming (baseline) medical
evaluation (physical) to assure a worker's fitness to assume the duties of
a new job or task and identify any previous work-related problems. A
termination (outgoing) evaluation assures that no work-related

injuries/illnesses have been incurred during the course of employment. The frequency of clinical testing or performance of other evaluations in between is driven by the type of work being performed, the exposures expected, and the general health status of the worker. A physician trained in the practice of occupational medicine may be consulted to establish the program and review results of tests. The tests themselves may be performed by occupational health nurses or technicians, as appropriate.

Equipment and Facility Inspections

Although there are various regulatory requirements for specific types of inspections, this section will discuss inspections to be performed for the purpose of protecting personnel and facilities from hazards and loss. While it is impossible to itemize each and every thing to be observed, a means will be described by which an in-depth inspection may be performed.

First, a preventive inspection and maintenance program should be in place -- not only for fixed equipment but for portable articles and vehicles. This pays dividends not only in increased quality and quantity of work able to be produced but also in safety. Records of maintenance performed, discovery and disposition of problems, and identity of the worker performing the inspection/maintenance activity must be retained.

A regular cycle of safety inspections should be performed on facilities and on pieces of equipment. The inspections team should consist, as a minimum, of a safety professional, a worker familiar with the area who will be able to answer questions about practices and usage, and the unfamiliar worker who will spot conditions overlooked by those closer to operational practices.

The frequency of facility inspections should be established by the risk assessment. One guideline which may be adopted would be to inspect office areas annually, laboratories and warehouses quarterly, and field sites monthly or weekly.

Facility and equipment inspections should be documented to reflect the areas reviewed, problems found, disposition of those problems, and the identity of the inspectors. If identified risks are deemed acceptable by upper management, that acceptance should be documented in writing along with the reasons or justification. Manufacturer's guideline for equipment inspections and checklists can be used to document inspections. Vehicles should be checked before use and problems promptly reported and fixed. More extensive safety checks should be performed on a monthly, quarterly, or semiannual frequency based on the service in which vehicle is used. (Specific requirements for special vehicles and equipment such as forklifts and cranes may be found in the OSHA regulations and ANSI standards).

Following up on problems discovered is as important as the discovery itself. Before initiating an inspection, previous reports should be reviewed to assure that all items were corrected or the associated risk accepted in writing by management.

The risk assessment should determine if operational reviews are to be included in the safety program. Operational reviews are inspections that focus on worker activities rather than facilities/equipment. Activities are observed by a team to assure that procedures are being followed completely and accurately. If steps are omitted or added, then a determination must be made whether the activity or the procedure requires revision. If a procedure is not available, the training checklist may be consulted by the team. Documentation of the operational review is necessary.

Emergency Response

To prepare workers to respond in emergencies, it is necessary to assess the most likely emergency situations. Proper equipping and training is necessary to assure the First Rule of emergency response (Don't make more victims) is observed. Many employees involved in emergency response will respond like fire horses to the sound of the bell, charging in to assist the victims at hand. This may also be a response observed in management personnel who wish to be part of the emergency management activities but who have not or will not participate in training. This inclination must be rigorously controlled to conform with the organizational policy on risk taking.

The most basic emergency response is evacuation -- of a building, a site, or a region. It should be remembered that the school fire drill is often the average employee's most recent training in evacuations. A plan should be developed that instructs the employee in proper evacuation behavior (see Table 3). Evacuation drills should be held annually as a minimum. Spotters are useful to identify problems and to review these findings with the employees. If a video camera is available, taping the drill allows employee behavior to be reviewed at leisure. Although it is the most basic emergency response, it is not a simple operation and should not be lightly dismissed.

Table 3

ELEMENTS OF EVACUATIONS/DRILLS TO BE CONSIDERED

When to evacuate -- sound of alarm, more than one kind of alarm, different responses to different alarms

How to evacuate -- run, fast walk, use of nearest exit (not necessarily the front door), no coffee or soft drinks (to spill on floors)

Where to go -- assembly areas (out of traffic pattern, away from building), accountability of personnel

Behavior -- business-like, no smoking (may be flammable vapor, dried grass in area), stay together for instructions

Re-entry -- based on release of area by incident Coordinator

Operational response to an onsite emergency begins when the written procedures are generated. The operational procedures and training should communicate instructions well in advance of their being needed. These include whether to shut down equipment, turn off ventilation, etc.

If a contaminant or suppression response is to be made, the First Rule must always be observed. For a team response above the "first-aid" level, a specific individual should be designated the safety officer, charged with the safety of responders. For a small scale response, this may be Incident (coordinator or equivalent). For a larger response, a separate individual should be identified as safety officer and be given sufficient authority that any proposed activity can be stopped. Any decision of the safety officer should only be reversed if the IC determines acceptable risk. These lines of authority will be established during the planning process and reinforced in appropriate drills.

SUMMARY

To establish a safety program which will protect hazardous material workers, an assessment should be performed which will evaluate risks faced by all employees, not just those performing exotic tasks such as at a Superfund-type site. As a result of the assessment a plan can be developed specifying appropriate training for each category of worker, frequency and type of inspection for facilities and equipment, establish pertinent medical surveillance for specified workers, provide for preventive maintenance programs, establish criteria for use of engineering controls, work practice controls, and personal protective equipment, and assign responsibility for development of written procedures and maintenance of emergency response capability. By keying each of these elements to real risks, management will be encouraged that their financial support has maximum effectiveness. The program can be audited by review of the accidents and incidents encountered to identify concerns overlooked or inadequately evaluated in the assessment. Appropriate action can then be taken, if needed, to improve the program.

REFERENCES

Below is a list of references. It is not complete but certainly provides a starting point for anyone concerned with safety programs in an HMM context. Many of the listed references also include their own list of reference documents.

OSHA Regulations

29 CFR 1910.22	Access to employee exposure and medical records
1910.120	Hazardous waste operations and emergency response
1910.132	Personal protective equipment

1910.157	Portable fire extinguishers
1910.178	Powered industrial trucks (forklift)
1910.179	(also 1926.55) Cranes
1910.251	Welding, cutting and brazing
1910.1000	Toxic and hazardous substances
1910.1200	Hazard communications
1926.300	Tools, hand and power
1926.650	Excavations, trenching and shoring

DOT Regulations

| 49 CFR 177.816 | Training |
| 391 | Qualification of drivers |

NIOSH Publications The Industrial Environment -- Its Evaluation and Control

Occupational Safety and Health Guidance Manual for Hazardous Waste Site Activities

ACGIH Publications Fire Protection Guide on Hazardous (1-800-344-3555) Materials

NFPA Publications Accident Prevention Manual for (1-800-621-7619) Industrial Operations: Administration and Programs, Engineering and Technology

Fundamentals of Industrial Hygiene

Introduction to Occupational Health and Safety

PERSONAL PROTECTIVE EQUIPMENT FOR HAZARDOUS MATERIALS OPERATIONS

Prepared by Charles J. Caudill, CSP, CHMM
Science Applications International Corporation
Oak Ridge, Tennessee

INTRODUCTION

Activities which involve hazardous materials will require the use of personal protective equipment to prevent harmful exposures of chemicals from contacting and being absorbed through the skin, and from being inhaled, ingested, or injected. The need for proper personal protective equipment (PPE) has received much attention in recent years with the increase of work activities under CERCLA and RCRA; and more recently the accompanying OSHA regulations for hazardous waste operations (29 CFR 1910.120).

This material has been developed for persons preparing for the hazardous materials management certification examination. It is intended as an overview of a complex subject. More detailed information to aid in the selection of protective clothing can be obtained from such sources that are listed as references to this article.

Preliminary Activities

It can be safely assumed that any work activity which exposes, or potentially exposes, persons to harmful concentrations of hazardous materials will require some level of PPE.

The key words to the above statement are "harmful" and "potentially harmful" concentrations of hazardous materials, and "level" of PPE. Before any PPE is selected, some preliminary work is essential. For hazardous waste sites, the preliminary site characterization and/or the preliminary survey will help identify "what" might be encountered, as well as the existing conditions. Remember, potential exposures must always be considered. Once the potentially harmful material(s) is identified and the concentration(s) (and potential concentration) is known, a decision as to whether this is a harmful level of exposure must be made. For this decision, the current revision of 29 CFR 1910.120. Hazardous Waste Operations and Emergency Response, directs persons to the following:

- 29 CFR 1910 Subpart Z.
- "NIOSH Recommendations for Occupational Health Standards" (Sept. 1986), or
- American Conference of Governmental Industrial Hygienist (ACGIH) "Threshold Limit Values and Biological Exposure Indices for 1986-1987"

The NIOSH and ACGIH documents are incorporated by reference into the OSHA standard. Where differences in acceptable exposure levels exist, the lesser levels should always be used. In the absence of data from OSHA, NIOSH, or the ACGIH, the chemical manufacturer's MSDS should be consulted.

Before PPE is selected, certain pieces of key information must be obtained. This information includes:

- Contaminant(s),
- Concentration(s) or potential concentrations,
- Harmful concentrations levels,
- Immediately dangerous to life or health (IDLH) conditions,
- Potential skin absorption and irritation sources,
- Potential eye irritation sources, and
- Explosive sensitivity and flammability ranges.

Add to this information such as:

- Physical hazards peculiar to the site,
- Engineering controls in use,
- Work to be performed,
- Duration of work, and
- Climatic conditions.

It is apparent there is more to the selection of PPE than chemical resistance alone. Personal protective equipment, fabricated from a wide variety of synthetics and natural materials, is commercially available from literally hundreds of sources in the United States. The "right" PPE for the job is a judgment call usually made by the site safety and health officer and based on many variables. The PPE used at a specific site may be increased or decreased as these variables change.

In the selection and use of PPE there are some constants. For example:

- If IDLH conditions are encountered, a SCBA respirator, or an airline respirator with an escape bottle, must be used,
- Level A protection must be used if the IDLH condition can result from skin contact, and
- Level B protection is normally used during the initial site survey to identify the hazards.

Caveats

Persons who select and provide PPE to others should compare their program to OSHA (29 CFR 1910, Subpart I) to ensure all the appropriate requirements are met.

While much attention is focused on the potential safety and health hazards from hazardous materials, the person selecting PPE should always consider the "greater hazard" paradox. By protecting persons from the potential harm of the hazardous material we have placed individuals in an environment of:

- Reduced visibility
- Reduced dexterity

- Reduced ability to communicate, and
- Increased stress (physical and emotional)

Thus increasing the likelihood of other injuries.

Personal Protective Equipment Selection

The January 1989 edition of Applied Industrial Hygiene carried an article entitled "Chemical Protective Clothing Selection." This article was excerpted from Volume I of the Guidelines for the Selection of Chemical Protective Clothing (3rd Edition) developed by A.D. Schwope and P.O. Costas of Arthur D. Little, Inc. and J.O. Jackson of Los Alamos National Laboratory; J.O. Stull of the U.S. Coast Guard, and D.J. Weitzman of the U.S. Environmental Protection Agency. The following information has been extracted from that article to provide guidance to the selection of protective equipment.

CPC Limitations

The use of chemical protective clothing is but one component of the overall program for maintaining the health and safety of workers. It compliments (and is not a substitute for) good planning, work practices, engineering and administrative controls, or personal hygiene. Factors which should be considered in the specification and selection of CPC are the following:

Chemical Resistance

The performance of CPC as a barrier to chemicals is determined by the materials and quality of its construction. Typically, each chemical interacts with a given plastic or elastomer in a relatively unique manner. This situation becomes complex when multi-component solutions are involved. Four important factors to bear in mind when considering CPC are:

- In general there is no such thing as "impermeable" plastic or rubber clothing.
- No one clothing material will be a barrier to all chemicals.

- For a given clothing material type, chemical resistance can vary significantly from product to product. For example, not all brands of nitrile gloves provide equivalent protection.
- For certain chemicals or combinations of chemicals, there is no commercially available glove or clothing that will provide more than an hour's protection following contact. In these cases, it is recommended that clothing be changed as soon as it is safely possible after any contact with the chemical or chemical mixture.

(See Attachments 1 and 2).

Design and Construction

Design and construction factors that can influence performance:

- Stitched seams of clothing may be highly penetrable by chemicals if not overlayed with tape or sealed with a coating.
- Lot-to-lot variations do occur and may have a significant effect on the barrier effectiveness of the CPC. They may go undetected due to quality control procedures insensitive to chemical resistance issues.
- Pinholes may exist in elastomeric or plastic products due to deficiencies or poor quality control in the formulation or in the manufacturing processes.
- Thickness may vary from point to point on the clothing item. Depending on the manufacturing process, the finger crotch area of the glove is particularly susceptible to thin coverage.
- Garment closures differ significantly from manufacturer to manufacturer and within one manufacturer's product line. Attention should be paid to button and zipper areas and the number of fabric overlaps in these areas.

Gloves are typically produced by one of two principal processes -- latex-dipping and solvent (cement) dipping. Latex gloves predominate the market. Researches have speculated, however, that the chemical resistance of a solvent-dipped glove may be greater than that of a latex-dipped glove of the same generic material. The principal reason for this is that the solvent-dipped glove is produced by a multiple-dip process while the latex process is a single-dip operation. In a multiple-dip process, imperfections in any one layer are covered by subsequent layers. Since the solvent-dip process is more involved, these products are generally more expensive. Consequently, the manufacturers of such gloves typically highlight the fact that gloves are solvent-dipped in justifying the increased cost.

Application

The degree of protection provided by an item of clothing is also a function of the application. For example, a less durable piece of clothing may be more than adequate for a moderate duration, mild activity (e.g., sampling), whereas it would not endure more than 5 minutes of a vigorous, emergency response activity. Factors such as abrasion, puncture and tear resistance, and reaction to perspiration and crumpling should be considered. Temperature and, to some extent, humidity have significant influences on the performance of elastomeric and plastic CPC. Also with regard to application, it is important to recognize that protective clothing can be cumbersome and restrictive and thereby hasten the onset of worker fatigue. A result is that the period of safe and effective worker activity may be reduced.

Reuse

Protective clothing decontamination and reuse are controversial and unresolved issues at this time. Often, surface contamination can be removed by scrubbing with soap and water. In other cases, especially with highly viscous liquids, surface decontamination may be practically impossible, and the CPC should be discarded. A more subtle problem arises with regard to the detection and removal of a chemical that has been absorbed into the elastomer or plastic. Once absorbed, some of this chemical will continue to diffuse through the material towards the inside surface even after the surface has been decontaminated.

For highly resistant clothing, the amount of chemical reaching the inside may be insignificant. However, for moderately performing materials, significant amounts of chemical may reach the inside. This may not occur during the work shift but can take place while, for example, a glove is stored overnight. The next morning when the worker dons the glove, the skin may be placed in direct contact with a hazardous chemical. In addition to chemical resistance, which is a function of temperature, both duration and the surface area exposed affect the amount of chemical that may reach the inside surface.

Reuse decisions must consider these factors as well as the toxicity of the involved chemical(s). Unless extreme care is taken to ensure decontamination, the reuse of CPC which has been contacted with highly toxic chemicals is not advisable.

Substitution of CPC

Particular caution is required when substituting clothing from one manufacturer for that of another manufacturer. Clothing performance is determined by the type of plastic or elastomer, the specific formulation of that plastic or elastomer, and the clothing manufacturing process. For example, materials classified generically as nitrile rubber can differ significantly in composition and, therefore, chemical resistance. Testing is the only means for identifying the superior products for a particular application.

Cost

Cost is an important consideration in the selection and utilization of clothing, especially where clothing is likely to be damaged (e.g., tear, puncture, etc.). In some cases, it may be more cost-effective to adopt the practice of using multiple changes of less expensive but relatively poorer performing clothing than to attempt to extend the use of better performing but more expensive clothing.

Permeation Theory

An important aspect of selecting the most appropriate CPC for situations where human exposure to potentially hazardous chemicals is possible is the effectiveness of the CPC as a barrier to the chemicals. Permeation may occur with little or no visible or physical effect on clothing materials.

Permeation Theory Concepts

Permeation of a liquid or vapor through a rubber or plastic material is a three-step process involving:

- Absorption of the chemical at the outside surface of the CPC.
- Diffusion of the chemical through the CPC material.
- Desorption of the chemical from the inside surface (i.e., towards the wearer) of the CPC.

Of principal importance in selecting CPC for protection from chemicals is the rate at which chemicals permeate the clothing materials and the time elapsed between the contact with the chemical and the appearance of the chemical on the inside of the CPC.

Permeation Rate

Permeation rate is often expressed in terms of the amount of a chemical which passes through a given area of clothing per unit time. (Common units are micrograms per square centimeter per minute). Thus, the total amount of chemical permeating an article of clothing increases as the area exposed to the chemical is increased and also as the duration of exposure is lengthened. For a given chemical/material pair, the permeation rate decreases as the material thickness is increased.

Breakthrough Time

Breakthrough time is defined as the elapsed time from initial contact of the outside surface of the CPC with chemical to the first detection of chemical on the inside surface. In some cases (e.g., when handling suspect carcinogens), breakthrough time may be the single most important criterion for CPC selection.

Influencing Factors

Temperature -- Most CPC permeation data and other chemical resistance information are performed at 20°-25°C. Permeation rates increase and breakthrough times decrease with increasing temperatures. The extent of the reduction in barrier performance with increasing temperature is dependent on the chemical/material pair.

CPC Thickness

For a given chemical/clothing material pair:

- Permeation is inversely proportional to thickness. Thus, doubling the thickness will theoretically halve the permeation rate.
- Breakthrough time increases with thickness.

Solubility Effect

Permeation rate is a direct function of the solubility of the chemical in the CPC material. Solubility is the amount of chemical that can be absorbed by a given amount of CPC material (i.e., grams liquid per gram material); absorption may be accompanied by swelling. In general, chemicals having high solubilities will rapidly permeate the CPC material in question.

It is important to remember that permeation rate is a function of both solubility and diffusion coefficients. Gases, for example, have low solubilities but high diffusion coefficients and may permeate CPC materials at rates several times greater than a liquid with moderate to high solubility in the material.

Multicomponent Liquids

Multi-component liquids represent a difficult problem relative to the selection of the most appropriate CPC. Rarely is there any prior CPC experience with the particular solution of concern, and often the components of the solution are not known. Furthermore, mixtures of chemicals can be significantly more aggressive towards plastics and rubbers than any one of the components alone. Finally, the presence of a small fraction of a rapidly permeating component may carry a chemical that would permeate at a slower rate if in pure form.

Persistent Permeation

Once a chemical has begun to diffuse into a plastic/rubber material, it will continue to diffuse even after the chemical on the outside has been removed from the material, and there is a natural tendency for the chemical to move towards areas of lower concentration. This phenomenon has significant implications relative to the reuse of CPC. For example, a possible field scenario is:

- Chemical contacts and absorbs into a glove.
- Breakthrough does not occur during the workday since the glove has low permeability to the chemical.
- Prior to removal, the glove is washed to remove surface chemical, but
- The next morning some fraction of the absorbed chemical has reached the inside surface of the glove due to continued diffusion.

Of course, similar scenarios could occur over both shorter and longer time frames, for example, morning to afternoon or over a weekend. The user must take this possibility into account when reuse is considered.

CPC Use Procedures

Purchase

Protective clothing is purchased either directly from the manufacturer or through a CPC distributor. Virtually every manufacturer has a catalogue of its products which describes each product as to the sizes available, thickness of the rubber or plastic barrier, and the materials of construction.

Many of the catalogues also contain chemical resistance ratings charts for the products. The reliability of the ratings varies from vendor to vendor.

Pre-use Inspection:

- Each item of clothing should be inspected immediately upon removing it from the package.
- Determine that the material of construction is that which was ordered.
- This may involve comparing the item number with the catalogue number. Items of different materials should be kept separated (See: Storage and Reuse).
- Visually inspect the items for defects such as imperfect seams, non-uniform coatings, pinholes, malfunctioning closures, and

tears. Some flexible materials may stiffen during extended storage periods: flex the product and observe for surface cracks or other signs of shelf-life deterioration. Pinholes may be detectable by holding the garment up to a light in a dark room. Gloves with holes can be identified by pressurizing the glove. This can be accomplished by blowing into the glove and then tightly rolling the gauntlet towards the fingers (thereby reducing volume and increasing pressure) while observing that the glove holds pressure. Alternatively, the glove could be inflated and then held under water and examined for the presence of air bubbles. Full-body encapsulating ensembles should be checked for the operation of pressure relief valves and the fittings at the wrists, ankles, and neck.

Donning

Each worker should thoroughly inspect the clothing to be worn immediately before donning. Of principal concern are cuts, tears, punctures, and discoloration or stiffness which may be indicative of chemical attack resulting from previous use of nonuniformities in the rubber or plastic. The wearer should understand all aspects of the clothing operation and its limitations, especially important to full-body encapsulating ensembles where misuse could potentially result in exposure to an IDLH condition. Note: some materials may have temperature limitations; for example, some CPC become stiff and unusable at low temperatures. Once the clothing is on, all closures should be secured and checked. Use the "buddy system." Finally, the fit of the clothing should be evaluated. Improperly fitting protective clothing represents a severe potential hazard. Where clothing is too small, worker movement is restricted, likelihood for tear is increased, and the dexterity and coordination of the worker may be compromised.

In-Use

During the course of the work task, each worker should periodically inspect the protective clothing. Of principle concern are tears, punctures, seam discontinuities, or closure failure that may have developed while working. Evidence of chemical attack such as discoloration, swelling, stiffening, or softening should also be noted

(Note: Permeation can occur without any visible effects on the clothing material). Any item of clothing that has been physically damaged or chemically degraded should be removed and replaced as soon as safely possible.

Doffing

A principal objective of the doffing process is to restrict the transfer of chemicals from the work area. A second objective is to avoid contact of the person doffing the garment as well as others with chemical on the outside of the garment.

Detailed doffing procedures have been developed by the Environmental Protection Agency (EPA) and are contained in the *Interim Standard Operating Safety Procedures* of the Office of Emergency and Remedial Response, Hazardous Response Support Division. They address: doffing site location, decontamination, and disposal of contaminated garments.

Storage and Reuse

Several considerations relative to the storage and reuse of protective clothing primarily focus on hazards that could potentially develop upon the storage of contaminated clothing. Briefly, in cases where a chemical is absorbed by the clothing, the chemical begins to permeate into the clothing. Short duration washing of the clothing with soap and water removes surface contamination but not absorbed chemical. After surface decontamination, some of the absorbed chemical will continue to permeate the clothing material and may ultimately appear on the inside surface. This can happen during periods of overnight or weekend storage. Where such potential hazards may develop, clothing can be checked inside and out for discoloration or, if possible, by wipe testing for suspect chemicals prior to reuse. This is particularly important for full-body encapsulating ensembles which are generally subject to extensive reuse due to their cost. Note, however, that negative (i.e., no chemical found) test results do not necessarily preclude the possibility that some absorbed chemical will be released to the inside of the CPC during reuse.

At the present time, there is very little documentation regarding clothing reuse. Where reusable CPC is required, however, the type of problem discussed above can best be minimized by selecting the most resistance clothing for the chemical at hand; such clothing will absorb little or no chemical. Furthermore, used clothing should be stored in well-ventilated areas. Ideally, there should be good air flow around each item of clothing.

Reuse of face shields and lenses is a particularly important issue. Good vision is required of both safety and efficiency on the work site. All such items should be inspected for crazing, cracks, and fogginess prior to use.

Finally, in storing protective clothing, different types of materials of clothing should not be mixed. For example, gloves which are black in color and virtually indistinguishable from one another may be made from nitrile, neoprene, Viton, polyvinyl chloride, butyl, etc., materials. Each material has unique chemical barrier properties. Mixing the gloves significantly increases the chance that a worker will be wearing the wrong clothing for the chemical of concern. It may be possible to separate mixed gloves by using the manufacturer's product number that is often found in the gauntlet area.

CPC Vendor Literature

The most widely available sources of information on CPC are the product catalogues of the CPC manufacturers and vendors. These booklets contain descriptions of the types, sizes and varieties of CPC produced by each manufacturer. In most cases, the basic materials of construction of the CPC are also included in the product descriptions. Many manufacturers also include information pertinent to the chemical resistance of their products or of the materials from which the products are fabricated. This information is often in the form of tables of qualitative chemical resistance ratings or use recommendations for the products/materials and particular chemicals. However, the leading manufacturers are increasingly providing information from permeation testing. A few vendors also provide information pertinent to abrasion, tear, etc., resistance but in general most catalogues do not address such application-related issues.

Information contained in typical CPC catalogues is both qualitative and quantitative. The qualitative ratings/recommendations are often on a four-grade scale of "excellent," "good," "fair," and either "poor" or "not recommended." In a small number of cases, five- or six-grade scales are used. With the exception of data based on permeation testing, the catalogues generally do not include information as to the basis for the recommendations. It would appear that, at present, most do not have (or at least are unwilling to share) performance specifications or quantitative test data for their products. The ratings/recommendations for a particular type of product (for example, nitrile gloves) for a particular chemical may vary from vendor to vendor. Both of these factors -- little or no test data and inconsistencies among recommendation tables -- make the selection of the best CPC for a given application a difficult and uncertain task.

The most important consideration to keep in mind when using vendor recommendation tables, including those based on permeation tests, is that the tables are intended to provide guidance in the selection of CPC. That is, the tables are meant as a place to start the CPC selection process. The tables are meant for identifying candidate CPC for further evaluation and are particularly useful for identifying CPC from which poor performance would be expected and, therefore, which can be dropped from consideration. In no way do the recommendations address the wide variety of uses, challenges, and care to which the CPC may be subjected. Most vendors strongly emphasize this point in the descriptive text which accompanies the tables. In conclusion, the principal purpose of the catalogues is to provide information about products in terms of the sizes, styles, and materials of construction. The ratings charts should be used as a starting point for further evaluation if chemical resistance is an issue.

Levels of Protection

Personal protective equipment must be selected to protect individuals from the specific hazards they are likely to encounter onsite. As already discussed, this is a complex process that can be eased somewhat by obtaining as much information as possible about both the hazards and the performance of protective equipment.

Appendix B of OSHA's Hazardous Waste Operations and Emergency Response Standard (1010.120) divides protective equipment into four categories (A,B,C, and D) based on the degree of protection they afford. These levels are described below.

Level A -- To be selected when the greatest level of skin, respiratory, and eye protection is required. Level A equipment, used as appropriate, includes the following:

- Pressure-demand full face-piece self contained breathing apparatus (SCBA), or pressure-demand supplied air respirator with escape SCBA approved by the National Institute for Occupational Safety and Health (NIOSH).
- Totally-encapsulating chemical-protective suit.
- Coveralls*
- Long underwear*
- Gloves, outer, chemical-resistant
- Gloves, inner, chemical-resistant
- Boots, chemical-resistant, steel toe and shank
- Hard hat (under suit)*
- Disposable protective suit, gloves and boots (Depending on suit construction, may be worn over totally-encapsulating suit)
- Two-way radios (worn inside encapsulating suit)

See Figure 3.

Level A protection should be used when:

- The hazardous substance has been identified and requires the highest level of protection for skin, eyes, and the respiratory system based on either the measured (or potential for) high concentration of atmospheric vapors, gases, or particulates; or the site operations and work functions involve a high potential for splash, immersion, or exposure to unexpected vapors, gases, or particulates of materials that are harmful to skin or capable of being absorbed through the intact skin.

---

*Denotes Optional Equipment

- Substances with a high degree of hazard to the skin are known or suspected to be present, and the skin contact is possible, or
- Operations must be conducted in confined, poorly ventilated areas and the absence of conditions requiring Level A have not yet been determined.

Level B -- The highest level of respiratory protection is necessary but a lesser level of skin protection is needed. Level B equipment, used as appropriate, includes:

- Pressure-demand, full face-piece self-contained breathing apparatus (SCBA), or pressure-demand supplied air respirator with escape SCBA (NIOSH approved)
- Hooded chemical-resistance clothing (overalls and long-sleeved jacket coveralls; one- or two-piece chemical-splash suit, disposable chemical resistant coveralls)
- Coveralls*
- Gloves, outer, chemical resistant
- Gloves, inner, chemical resistant
- Boots, outer, chemical-resistant steel toe and shank
- Boot-covers, outer, chemical-resistant (disposable)*
- Hard hat
- Two-way radios (worn inside encapsulating suit)
- Face shield*

See Figure 4.

Level B protection should be used when:

- The type and atmospheric concentrations of substances have been identified and require a high level of respiratory protection, but less skin protection.

---

*Denotes Optional Equipment

Note -- This involves atmospheres with IDLH concentrations of specific substances that do not represent a severe skin hazard, or that do not meet the criteria for use of air-purifying respirators.

- The atmosphere contains less than 19.5 percent oxygen, or
- The presence of incompletely identified vapors or gases is indicated by a direct-reading organic vapor detection instrument, but vapors and gases are not suspected of containing high levels of chemicals harmful to skin or capable of being absorbed through the intact skin.

Level C -- The concentration(s) and type(s) of airborne substance(s) is known and the criteria for using air purifying respirators are met. Level C equipment, used as appropriate, includes:

- Full-face or half-mask, air purifying, canister-equipped respirators (NIOSH approved)
- Hooded chemical-resistant clothing (overalls, two-piece chemical-splash suit, disposable chemical-resistant overalls)
- Coveralls*
- Gloves, outer, chemical-resistant
- Gloves, inner, chemical-resistant
- Boots (outer), chemical-resistant steel toe and shank
- Boot-covers, outer, chemical-resistant (disposable)
- Hard hat
- Escape mask*
- Two-way radios (worn under outside protective clothing)
- Face shield*

Level C protection should be used when:

- The atmospheric contaminants, liquid splashes, or other direct contact will not adversely affect or be absorbed through any exposed skin.
- The types of air contaminants have been identified, concentrations measured, and a canister respirator is available that can remove the contaminants, and

---

*Denotes Optional Equipment

- All criteria for the use of air-purifying respirators are met.

Level D -- A work uniform affording minimal protection; used for nuisance contamination only. Level D equipment, used as appropriate, includes:

- Coveralls
- Gloves*
- Boots/shoes, chemical-resistant steel toe and shank
- Boots, outer, chemical-resistant (disposable)*
- Safety glasses or chemical splash goggles*
- Hard hat
- Escape mask
- Face shield*

Level D protection should be used when:

- The atmosphere contains no known hazard, and
- Work functions preclude splashes, immersion, or the potential for unexpected inhalation of or contact with hazardous level of any chemicals.

Note: As stated before, combinations of personal protective equipment other than those described for Levels A, B, C, and D protection may be more appropriate and may be used to provide the proper level of protection.

---

*Denotes Optional Equipment

PROTECTIVE CLOTHING COMPATABILITY GUIDE

Hazardous Chemical	Uncoated TYVEK® 1422A		TYVEK® 1.25 mil Polyethylene		TYVEK® SARANEX® 23-P Single Ply		CHEMREL™	
Acetone, 99%	nt	(nt)	nt	(nt)	33	(3.3)	>1440	(nd)
Acetonitrile, 99+%	nt	(nt)	nt	(nt)	97	(.09)	>1440	(nd)
Acrylonitrile	nt	(nt)	5	(0.00012)	23	(0.00022)	nt	(nt)
Ammonium hydroxide, 28.8%	nt	(nt)	<1	(10.3)	nt	(nt)	nt	(nt)
Carbon disulfide	nt	(nt)	nt	(nt)	nt	(nt)	5	(0.6)
Chlorine gas, 99+%	nt	(nt)	1	(3)	>480	(nd)	>1440	(nd)
Chloroform	nt	(nt)	<1	(58)	<1	(33.5)	4	(0.3)
Cresols	nt	(nt)	40-60	(0.0667)	>120	(<0.0233)	nt	(nt)
Cyanide salt soln., 45%, 70°C	nt	(nt)	<240	(0.001)	nt	(nt)	nt	(nt)
Cyanide salt soln., 10%, 60°C	nt	(nt)	<360	(0.0015)	nt	(nt)	nt	(nt)
Diethylamine	nt	(nt)	nt	(nt)	44	(6.3)	110	(2.0)
Dioxane	nt	(nt)	nt	(nt)	50	(2.9)	>1440	(nd)
Ethoxyethyl acetate, 98%	nt	(nt)	nt	(nt)	39	(0.3)	nt	(nt)
Ethyl acetate, 99%	nt	(nt)	nt	(nt)	36	(1.1)	55	(0.0002)
Ethylene oxide gas, 98%	nt	(nt)	0.3	(18)	8	(7)	>1440	(0.0)
Formaldehyde, 37%	nt	(nt)	>480	(nd)	nt	(nt)	>480	(nd)
n-Hexane, 99+%	nt	(nt)	nt	(nt)	2	(0.005)	>1440	(nd)
Hydrochloric acid, 37%	nt	(nt)	35	(—)	>2880	(—)	>1440	(nd)
Hydrofluoric acid, 50%	nt	(nt)	>30	(<0.0005)	>30	(<0.0005)	>1440	(nd)
Methanol	nt	(nt)	nt	(nt)	>480	(nd)	136	(0.06)
Methyl bromide	nt	(nt)	nt	(nt)	47	(0.000047)	nt	(nt)
Methyl ethyl ketone	nt	(nt)	nt	(nt)	29	(1.3)	>1440	(nd)
Methyl parathion, 57%	nt	(nt)	15	(0.015)	120-180	(0.0017)	nt	(nt)
Methyl parathion, 10%	<5	(7.5)	30-45	(0.033)	>240	(<0.0003)	nt	(nt)
Methylene chloride, 99+%	nt	(nt)	nt	(nt)	2	(53)	5	(0.5)
Mineral spirits	nt	(nt)	<5	(1.167)	480	(nd)	nt	(nt)
Nitric acid, 90%	nt	(nt)	nt	(nt)	107	(—)	nt	(nt)
Nitric acid, 70%	nt	(nt)	50	(—)	>2880	(—)	>1440	(nd)
Nitrobenzene	nt	(nt)	nt	(nt)	165	(0.1)	>1440	(nd)
Oleum, 65%	nt	(nt)	<1	(—)	37	(—)	nt	(nt)
Oleum, 20%	nt	(nt)	120	(—)	nt	(nt)	nt	(nt)
50% PCB, 50% mineral oil	nt	(nt)	nt	(nt)	>480	(—)	>480	(nt)
Sodium hydroxide, 40%	<10	(0.016)	>480	(nd)	>480	(nd)	nt	(nt)
Sodium hydroxide, 50%	nt	(nt)	nt	(nt)	nt	(nt)	>1440	(nd)
Sulfuric acid, 98%	immed.	(8.333)	>480	(nd)	>480	(nd)	>1440	(nd)
Sulfuric acid, 96%, 65°C	nt	(nt)	>120	(—)	330	(—)	nt	(nt)
Sulfuric acid, 90%	immed.	(6.389)	>480	(nd)	>480	(nd)	nt	(nt)
Sulfuric acid, 50%	6	(0.75)	>480	(nd)	>480	(nd)	nt	(nt)
Sulfuric acid, 16%	30	(0.153)	>480	(nd)	>480	(nd)	nt	(nt)
Tetrachloroethylene, 99%	nt	(nt)	nt	(nt)	13	(0.19)	26	(0.1)
Tetrahydrofuran	nt	(nt)	nt	(nt)	nt	(nt)	7	(2.0)
Titanium tetrachloride	nt	(nt)	nt	(nt)	>1000	(nd)	nt	(nt)
Toluene	nt	(nt)	<5	(27.5)	<5	(3.33)	>142	(0.003)
o-Toluidine	nt	(nt)	<5	(0.167)	>120	(<0.005)	nt	(nt)
Trichlorobenzene	nt	(nt)	<15	(0.833)	15-60	(<0.0167)	nt	(nt)
2,2,2-Trifluoroethanol, 99%	nt	(nt)	6	(—)	nt	(nt)	nt	(nt)

Bold number indicates breakthrough time in minutes

Second number indicates permeation rate in mg/m²/Sec.

(—) = not measured   nd = none detected   nt = not tested

Figure 1: Protective Clothing Compatibility Guide (reference: *Lab Safety Supply -- 1989 General Catalog*)

CHEMICAL	VITON® (10 mil)		BUTYL (17 mil)		SILVER SHIELD™ (3 mil)		NITRILE (22 mil)		PVA		NEOPRENE UNSUPPORTED		NEOPRENE SUPPORTED	
	Breakthrough Time (Hrs.)	Permeation mg/m²/sec	Breakthrough Time (Hrs.)	Permeation mg/m²/sec	Breakthrough Time (Hrs.)	Permeation mg/m²/sec	Breakthrough Time (Hrs.)	Permeation mg/m²/sec	Breakthrough Time (Hrs.)	Permeation mg/m²/sec	Breakthrough Time (Hrs.)	Permeation mg/m²/sec	Breakthrough Time (Hrs.)	Permeation mg/m²/sec
Acetaldehyde	NR	—	9.6 hrs.	0.066	>6 hrs	ND	NT	—	—	—	10 min.	<9000	17 min.	<9000
Acetic Acid (Glacial)	NT	—	NT	—	NT	—	1.9 hrs	221	—	—	7 hrs.	—	>6 hrs.	—
Acetic Acid (50%)	NT	—	NT	—	NT	—	>8 hrs	ND	—	—	—	—	—	—
Acetone	NR	—	>17 hrs	ND	>6 hrs	ND	NT	—	—	—	5 min.	<900	10 min.	<900
Acetonitrile	NT	—	>8 hrs	ND	>8 hrs	ND	NT	—	1 hr.	<0.9	30 min.	<9	1½ hrs.	<0.9
Ammonium Hydroxide (29%)	NT	—	NT	—	NT	—	>8 hrs	ND	—	—	>6 hrs	—	>6 hrs.	—
Aniline	NR	—	>8 hrs	ND	>8 hrs	ND	1.2 hrs	3	1½ hrs.	<9	35 min.	<9	3 hrs.	<9
Benzene	6 hrs	.012	NR	—	>8 hrs	ND	27 min	97	7 min	<0.9	—	—	—	—
Butyl Acetate	NR	—	1.9 hrs.	7.61	>6 hrs	ND	1.7 hrs.	24	ND	<0.9	—	—	—	—
p-t Butyltoluene	>8 hrs	ND	1.7 hrs.	8	>8 hrs	ND	NT	—	—	—	—	—	—	—
Carbon Disulfide	>16 hrs	ND	NR	—	RD	—	20 min	86	ND	<0.9	—	—	—	—
Carbon Tetrachloride	>13 hrs	ND	NR	—	>6 hrs	ND	5.7 hrs	8	ND	<0.9	—	—	—	—
Chloroform	9.5 hrs.	0.46	NR	—	NR	—	NT	—	ND	<0.9	—	—	—	—
Chloronaphthalene	>16 hrs	ND	NR	—	>8 hrs	ND	NT	—	ND	<0.9	—	—	—	—
Cyclohexane	>7 hrs	ND	1.1 hrs	20.3	>6 hrs.	ND	>8 hrs	ND	—	—	—	—	—	—
Cyclohexanol	>8 hrs	ND	>11 hrs.	ND	>6 hrs	ND	NT	—	6 hrs.	<0.9	2½ hrs.	<9	3 hrs.	<0.9
Cyclohexanone	NR	—	>16 hrs.	ND	>8 hrs.	ND	NT	—	—	—	—	—	—	—
Dibutyl Phthalate	>8 hrs.	ND	>16 hrs.	ND	>6 hrs.	ND	NT	—	ND	<0.9	2 hrs.	<0.9	5 hrs.	<9
1,2 Dichloroethane	6.9 hrs.	.81	2.9 hrs.	53	>8 hrs.	ND	16 min.	292	—	—	—	—	—	—
Diisobutyl Ketone (80%)	1.2 hrs.	90.6	3.3 hrs.	41.2	>6 hrs.	ND	NT	—	ND	<0.9	—	—	—	—
Dimethyl Formamide	NR	—	>8 hrs.	ND	>8 hrs.	ND	35 min.	41	—	—	10 min.	<90	1 hr.	<90
Dioxane	NR	—	>20 hrs.	ND	>8 hrs.	ND	NT	—	—	—	—	—	—	—
Divinyl Benzene	>17 hrs	ND	2.2 hrs.	238	>8 hrs	ND	NT	—	—	—	—	—	—	—
Ethyl Acetate	NR	—	7.6 hrs.	3.4	>6 hrs	ND	NT	—	ND	<0.9	15 min.	<90	20 min.	<90
Ethylamine (70% in water)	NR	—	>12 hrs.	ND	NR	—	NT	—	—	—	—	—	—	—
Ethyl Alcohol	NT	—	NT	—	NT	—	>8 hrs.	ND	—	—	1½ hrs.	<9	3 hrs.	<9
Ethyl Ether	NR	—	NR	—	>6 hrs	ND	NT	—	>6 hrs.	<0.9	10 min.	<90	10 min.	<90
Formaldehyde (37% in water)	>16 hrs	ND	>16 hrs.	ND	>6 hrs	ND	>8 hrs.	ND	—	—	2 hrs.	<0.9	2 hrs.	<9
Furfural	3.6 hrs.	14.8	>16 hrs.	ND	>8 hrs.	ND	NT	—	ND	<0.9	20 min.	<90	2 hrs.	<90
n-hexane	>11 hrs	ND	NR	—	>6 hrs.	ND	>8 hrs	ND	ND	<0.9	45 min.	<900	1½ hrs.	<90
Hydrazine (70% in water)	NR	—	>8 hrs.	ND	2.1 hrs.	1.0	>8 hrs	ND	—	—	ND	—	ND	—
Hydrochloric Acid (37%)	RD	—	RD	—	>6 hrs	ND	>8 hrs.	ND	—	—	ND	—	ND	—
Methylamine (40% in water)	>16 hrs.	ND	>15 hrs.	ND	1.9 hrs	2.0	NT	—	—	—	4½ hrs.	<90	6 hrs.	<0.9
Methylene Chloride	1 hr.	7.32	NR	—	1.9 hrs.	0.002	NT	—	17 min.	<0.9	—	—	—	—
Morpholine	1.9 hrs.	97	>16 hrs.	ND	>8 hrs.	ND	NT	—	3 hrs.	<0.9	—	—	—	—
Nitrobenzene	>8 hrs.	ND	>23 hrs.	ND	>8 hrs.	ND	1 hr	15	>8 hrs.	<0.9	—	—	—	—
Nitropropane	NR	—	>8 hrs.	ND	>8 hrs.	ND	NT	—	>6 hrs.	<0.9	5 min.	<900	1 hr.	<90
Pentachlorophenol (1% in kerosene)	>13 hrs.	ND	NR	—	>8 hrs.	ND	NT	—	7 min.	<900	6 min.	<0.9	6 min.	<0.9
n-Pentane	>8 hrs.	ND	NR	—	>6 hrs.	ND	NT	—	ND	<0.9	30 min.	<900	45 min.	<9
Phenol (85% in water)	>15 hrs.	ND	>20 hrs.	ND	NT	—	>8 hrs.	ND	30 min.	<90	3 hrs.	<90	>6½ hrs.	<0.9
Propyl Acetate	NR	—	2.7 hrs.	2.86	>6 hrs.	ND	NT	—	2 hrs.	<9	—	—	—	—
Sodium Hydroxide (50%)	RD	—	RD	—	>6 hrs.	ND	>8 hrs.	ND	—	—	ND	—	ND	—
Sulfuric Acid (3 molar)	RD	—	RD	—	>6 hrs.	ND	>8 hrs.	ND	—	—	3 hrs.	—	>6 hrs.	—
Tetrachloroethylene	>17 hrs	ND	NR	—	>6 hrs.	ND	NT	—	—	—	—	—	—	—
Toluene	>16 hrs.	ND	NR	—	>6 hrs	ND	28 min.	25	15 min.	<9	—	—	—	—
Toluene Diisocyanate	>16 hrs.	ND	>8 hrs.	ND	>8 hrs.	ND	>8 hrs.	ND	ND	<0.9	—	—	—	—
1,1,1-Trichloroethane	>15 hrs.	ND	NR	—	>6 hrs.	ND	2.2 hrs.	44	1 hr.	<0.9	—	—	—	—
Trichloroethylene	7.4 hrs.	0.24	NR	—	>6 hrs.	ND	9 min.	62	30 min.	<0.9	—	—	—	—
Vinyl Chloride	4.4 hrs.	0.098	NR	—	>8 hrs.	ND	NT	—	—	—	—	—	—	—

NR = Not Recommended
NT = Not Tested
RD = Resists Degradation; not tested for permeation.

ND = None Detected
> = Greater Than
< = Less Than
— = Data not available

Figure 2: Glove Compatibility Guide (reference: *Lab Safety Supply -- 1989 General Catalog*)

Figure 3: Level A Protection -- Full Body Encapsulating Suit (reference: *Guidelines for the Selection of Chemical Protective Clothing*)

Figure 4: Level B Protection -- Splash Suit (reference: *Guidelines for the Selection of Chemical Protective Clothing*)

ACCIDENT SCENARIO TRAINING

George L. Kramer, Ph.D.
Analysas Corporation

INTRODUCTION

Accidents involving chemical substances have the potential to cause great loss of property and lives (e.g., the Bhopal, India methyl isocyanate disaster and the Mexico City, Mexico natural gas explosion). Even where no direct injury is caused, the costs may be enormous in terms of environmental insult, cleanup, fines, litigation, productivity, and public relations (e.g. the Alaskan oil spill). Naturally, the most effective method for coping with such a threat is to prevent accidents. Training of personnel, good safety programs, effective preventive maintenance, and strict compliance with codes and statutes are among the measures which will help to ensure accident free operations. Unfortunately, prevention programs cannot always be 100 percent effective. Human error, equipment failure, and "acts of God" are possible despite the best efforts to reduce their probability. Facility managers must be prepared to mitigate the effects of an accidental chemical release.

Planning and preparation will largely determine the effectiveness of response to a chemical accident. "Worst case scenarios" must be envisioned and used as a basis for planning. Where it appears that mitigation would be inadequate, efforts must be made to further enhance prevention and safety systems. For example, train derailments before the early 1980s involving liquified petroleum gas (LPG or propane) shipments often resulted in punctured tank cars and fires which ultimately led to disastrous Boiling Liquid Expanding Vapor Explosions (BLEVE). In response to this situation, flammable gas cars were fitted with head shields, shelf couplers and thermal protection. With the completion of this program, the BLEVE virtually ceased to be a problem in rail transportation. In fact, so effective have these measures been, they are now contemplated or required for tank cars carrying many other hazard classes.

When accidents take place, successful mitigation will often depend upon close coordination of a number of public and private organizations. Many experienced incident managers feel that this coordination is both the most critical and the most neglected aspect of hazardous materials emergency response. This presentation is intended to clarify the role of the facility manager in the mitigation process and suggest some actions which can help minimize the impact of chemical spills.

Fixed Facility Incidents

Planning and preparation for airborne toxic releases from fixed facilities is required by the provisions of SARA Title III. A cooperative effort between facility management and the emergency response community is required and this approach should also be used for other chemical threats. Experience has shown that cooperation between the private and public sectors in planning, training, and exercises leads to much more effective response. This process not only helps to insure that the proper actions are taken in an emergency, but also establishes an atmosphere of trust, realistic expectations, and an understanding of roles and responsibilities.

Each facility must realistically determine the kinds of incidents that can be handled by facility personnel and when outside emergency responders should become involved. It is a common complaint of the fire service that they are called or allowed to become involved only after the situation is too far advanced to be controlled. Whether or not this criticism is justified, it reflects a lack of understanding and cooperation. The local fire department is usually the key organization when help from outside the facility is needed. It is most important that facility managers assist them, both in preparing for incidents and when an incident takes place. Once the planning process is finished, facility personnel should assist in the training of emergency responders and, most importantly, should conduct facility tours and emergency exercises. In doing this, it is important to know that, because firefighters work in shifts, most cities in effect have three fire departments. This may mean that activities must be carried out in triplicate.

Both in training and during an incident the first issue to be addressed is *where*. Where can responders enter the facility? Time has often been wasted when responders arrived at the wrong gate and found it locked and unattended. Once on site, responders must know where the problem is and the location of "exposures" (sources of potential problems should fire, toxic cloud or other hazards spread). A readily available facility map is invaluable for this purpose. This map should be clear and simple showing facility entrances, building locations and other landmarks, location of chemicals and other hazards within buildings, emergency resources such as water connections and any other important items. Blueprints and technical drawings are usually too complex and cluttered for this purpose. It may be helpful to provide emergency responders with a map during the planning process but it is usually unrealistic to expect them to carry it with them and arrive with it. Provisions must be made to get the map to responders immediately upon arrival, either from personnel at the gate or, if the facility may be unattended, from some predetermined repository such as a lock-box at the entrance. Even with a map, it is usually best if someone familiar with the facility is prepared to accompany and direct responders.

The foremost concern when an incident occurs will be for the rescue of any accident victims. It is of the utmost importance that there be a system for accounting for all facility personnel on-site. Responders must immediately be told if any persons are not accounted for and where they might be found. Responders are willing to risk their lives in a rescue attempt but are understandably upset if it later turns out that the person they looked for had called in sick or was out to lunch.

Following *where*, the next issue to be addressed is *what*. What materials are involved, or may become involved, and what are their hazards and unusual characteristics. Again, this information should be provided during planning, but it should not be expected that responders will arrive with it. Material safety data sheets (MSDS) for each product are most helpful but information must be stated in clear and simple language and a technical expert should be provided to interpret data. Written information should accompany the facility map. It should include not only technical information but guidance on necessary protective gear, protective actions, and mitigation techniques.

After the problem has been identified, responders should be assisted in determining *how* they should respond. Emergency response personnel should only be expected to take action where there is an immediate threat to human life. Maintenance, repair and clean-up should be left to facility personnel, clean-up contractors or other persons specifically trained and equipped as well as ways to carry them out should be discussed. Emergency responders may assume a lead role in mitigation activities or may provide support. Response roles, options and techniques must be learned in training and practiced during exercises. During an actual incident any aggressive action will be accompanied by risk, no matter how well trained and equipped responders might be. This means that the option chosen must be fitted to the situation so that risks are not taken unnecessarily.

Facilities should be prepared to provide emergency responders with any specialized resources that might be necessary. This might take the form of foams for fire or vapor suppression, protective clothing and gear, repair tools or materials, absorbents, or neutralizing agents, to name a few. Keep in mind that training is required if such resources are to be utilized safely and effectively. If very specialized equipment and techniques are required it may be better to train facility personnel in their use and utilize emergency responders in a back-up role.

Emergency responders are required to use an Incident Command System (ICS) to manage hazardous materials emergencies. Drills and exercises will help to familiarize facility managers with the local ICS but some classroom training and instruction may be helpful as well. Two important components of an ICS are a "command post" and a "staging area." The command post provides a common location from which all involved organizations can direct operations. The location of a command post should take a number of factors into account and, if possible, the facility should attempt to provide a suitable site. The command post should be located away from danger but, if possible, positioned so that the accident scene is within sight. One of the most important features of a command post is communications facilities. Most emergency response organizations have radio communications but telephones are usually more reliable, versatile and secure (remember that the news media almost invariably monitor emergency radio frequencies). The command post should also be identified in some way that allows arriving representatives to find it easily. Keep in mind that in many cases at serious incidents, more than one-hundred different organizations have sent one or more persons to the scene. Such a crowd would place a strain on even the best Emergency Operations Center and could easily overwhelm a command post but the problem will be even worse if they are wandering about at random. A staging area is a location where personnel, equipment and other resources are gathered to be utilized as needed. It should be located away from danger but convenient to the scene. Possible locations should be considered in planning and utilized in exercises.

Remember that, while the facility manager is responsible for facility property and personnel, the emergency response Incident Commander is responsible for the safety of the community and will base decisions on that consideration. The quickest way to lose cooperation and confidence is to appear to be basing decisions and recommendations on some other factor such as profit or public relations. For many reasons, it is a good idea to keep records of everything that is done including recommendations, notifications, response actions, etc. Some use a tape recorder to preserve conversations.

The Incident Commander should appoint a Public Information Officer (PIO) to deal with the media and the dissemination of announcements, warnings and the like. Facility personnel must be prepared to deal with the press and should coordinate their efforts through the PIO. There are many training programs available on the subject of press relations and it is beyond the scope of this presentation. There are, however, a few important guidelines that have been learned in the all too familiar "school of hard knocks":

- TELL THE TRUTH.
- Don't speculate -- especially about "worst case" scenarios.
- Tell only what you *know*. If you don't know -- say so.
- Don't discuss blame.

- Don't say "No comment." If you can't answer, explain why.

It may be worthwhile to include the media in the planning, training and exercise processes, especially if they would have a function in calling for an evacuation.

After an incident has been brought to a conclusion, it should be reviewed in a meeting with representatives of all involved organizations (with the exception of the media).   This review should be for the purpose of praising jobs well done as well as identifying mistakes and problem areas and converting them into lessons learned. It should not be concerned with placing blame.   The result should be the modification of plans and procedures.

Transportation Incidents

Transportation accidents are particularly difficult to deal with, primarily because of the inevitable time lag before the shipper is notified. This means that facility personnel (with the possible exception of the vehicle operator) are usually not present during the critical initial phases of an incident.   Again, accident prevention is the most productive form of preparation. Proper maintenance of equipment, training of personnel, care in loading, and adherence to transportation regulations will greatly reduce the occurrence of transportation accidents. Proper placarding of vehicles, marking and labeling of packages, and shipping paper preparation can greatly assist emergency responders. Regulations now require a 24 hour emergency telephone number on the shipping papers. Conscientious compliance with this regulation will be of great benefit to both responders and your company in the event of an accident. It will also be very helpful if printed, product specific, emergency response information accompanies the shipping papers.   Emergency responders should have the DOT Emergency Response Guidebook and, while the information in that book can be very helpful, it is quite general.

Planning and preparation for transportation incidents is usually more difficult than for fixed facility incidents, primarily because it is more difficult to predict where accidents might take place. However, commonly used routes should be investigated for vulnerable points such as areas of high population density, long tunnels, and places with a history of high accident frequency. Where such points can not be avoided, it is advisable to carry out planning activities with local authorities and responders. Since local emergency responders may be the only ones available to carry out emergency repairs or containment, they should be advised concerning necessary equipment and protective gear. Where such gear and equipment is not available, or responders are not trained in their use, they cannot be expected to take action. Responders are generally trained and oriented to act aggressively in emergency situations. Unless they are warned in advance of the consequences of their actions, and/or trained and equipped for proper response, their actions may result in unnecessary expense, damage, or loss of life.

When notified of a transportation accident, facility managers should be prepared to provide assistance as quickly as possible. When providing advice and information about a product, it is helpful to be aware that responders may have already consulted the DOT Emergency Response Guidebook and/or have received information from CHEMTREC. It is necessary to be familiar with this information in advance and be prepared to explain any apparent discrepancies between it and that which you provide. If possible, shippers should be prepared to send one or more representatives to the scene of the accident to advise or help to carry out repair, containment and recovery activities. When advising by telephone, it is best to talk directly with responders at the scene. Communication through dispatchers or other third parties are likely to become garbled or confused and are, at best, time consuming.

Protective actions at transportation accidents will often include the closing of highways, rails or other shipping lanes along with evacuation of threatened areas. All parties involved in making the decision to carry out these actions must be aware of the risks involved and consider whether or not they exceed the risks associated with the chemical product. If you feel that the protective actions contemplated are not advisable you must be prepared to present your arguments clearly and without giving the appearance of being concerned with costs to your company, or public relations. Also be prepared to accede to protective actions that may seem overly conservative in the interest of maintaining a cooperative relationship with the emergency response community.

It is also helpful to be aware that emergency responders will often take the position that it is safest to off-load bulk containers such as cargo tanks and tank cars before they are uprighted or moved. If this is not possible or practical, you must be prepared to explain why clearly. Again, the confidence of emergency responders will be lost if your argument appears too self-serving or to take the hazards of the product too lightly. If possible during planning for highway incidents involving cargo tanks, it is very helpful to locate competent wrecker services along the route. Many wrecker services are not properly equipped and trained to deal with cargo tanks. Also, in many communities, police call for different wrecker services in rotation in order to distribute business fairly. It may be very difficult to override this system unless arrangements are made in advance.

The carrier is financially responsible for clean-up and other recovery activities. Again, emergency responders should not be expected to conduct clean-up. To avoid long-term problems, it is best to make sure a competent contractor is used for clean-up as civil liability for environmental problems is often extended to anyone who is even remotely associated and has the ability to pay.

Conclusion

Accident prevention is the best and most cost effective means of limiting loss from the release of chemical products. When accidents do happen, the effectiveness of the response will depend on the effectiveness of the planning and preparation process. Experience has shown that if planning, training and exercising for emergencies have no effect other than to establish a personal relationship between responders from various agencies and private sector personnel, much benefit will be derived. It is not unusual for public emergency responders to consider private sector personnel their adversaries and this attitude is difficult to overcome in the urgent atmosphere of an emergency. It is amazing how much better the coordination and cooperation in an emergency will be when the players have had a chance to work together under less stressful circumstances.

The facility manager has two important tasks during an emergency; coordinating the efforts of his personnel with those of other responders, and providing information. Obtaining, providing and utilizing information concerning the location and scope of the accident, the identity and characteristics of the chemical product and the availability and applicability of resources in a timely, clear and concise manner is a difficult and extremely important job. It requires planning, preparation and not a little diplomacy. The public is largely unaware of the tremendous benefits provided by the chemical industry and of its exemplary safety record. Accidents, though infrequent, are highly visible and industry representatives must be prepared when they happen to demonstrate that their primary concern is for the safety of the public.

FACILITY ENVIRONMENTAL AUDITS

Paul E. Morris, Jr.
Texas A&M University

INTRODUCTION

Evaluations, surveys, assessments, appraisals, and reviews are all terms used by different organizations to describe environmental auditing. An environmental audit is a management tool for systematically evaluating compliance with the numerous environmental requirements that face industry today. It is a formal and organized means of inventorying and reporting environmental assets and liabilities at individual facilities and, ultimately, company-wide. Auditing is also used in a variety of special situations to accomplish specific objectives. These situations include:

- considering acquisitions, mergers or divestitures
- selecting or continuing to use hazardous waste contractors
- providing RCRA required liability insurance information
- the insurance industry
- meeting SEC "material" disclosure requirements
- providing cost/benefit or risk assessment information needed for management decisions

Auditing is a critical part of a comprehensive environmental management system intended to verify that other components of the system are being implemented and are adequate. Where omissions or inadequacies exist in the system, auditing should illuminate these shortcomings and bring them to management's attention.

Environmental auditing is an activity which has received a good deal of attention for several years from both industry and regulatory agencies, particularly EPA. Hundreds of corporations engaged in a variety of industries across the country and internationally have established environmental auditing programs. Some programs were established only after serious environmental costs were incurred or courts ordered them. The great majority of companies established auditing programs voluntarily in order to preclude problems and because management viewed it as a sound and necessary business practice. With the increased attention to and regulation of hazardous materials handling and disposal, no other corporate activity has a greater need for environmental auditing.

EPA's Auditing Policy

After years of discussing different approaches to environmental auditing, (including the possible use of incentives such as decreased inspection frequencies for companies conducting audits), EPA issued a final Environmental Auditing Policy Statement in the Federal Register, July 9, 1986. This policy encourages both private and public organizations to use environmental auditing practices. It also states Agency policy on specific auditing issues. EPA believes that routine Agency requests for audit reports could inhibit auditing and, therefore, will not routinely request audit reports. The authority to seek reports will be exercised on a case-by-case basis where the Agency determines it necessary to accomplish a statutory mission or where a report is material to a criminal investigation. It is expected that such cases would be limited. Audit reports would not be allowed to shield information which would otherwise be reportable or accessible to EPA. In general, EPA promises no special incentives to encourage environmental auditing other than to restate EPA policy to take into account, on a case-by-case basis, the honest and genuine efforts of regulated entities to avoid and correct environmental problems (see Environmental Considerations in Real Estate Transactions). A properly designed and implemented environmental auditing program should fall within this definition.

Elements of An Audit Program

Included in the appendix to the EPA Auditing Policy Statement are seven elements of an effective audit program. While other publications on environment auditing may vary slightly in describing the principles of an audit program, the elements listed by EPA include those that most successful programs have in common and which many authors on the subject agree upon.

I.   "Explicit top management support for environmental auditing and commitment to follow up on audit findings." Top management support is imperative and the single most important element. Uncovering and documenting environmental deficiencies is ineffective if there is not a sincere top level commitment to correct them.

II.   "An environmental auditing function independent of audited activities." While self evaluation solely by line production or operating personnel can be a valuable exercise, it does not fit within the principle of impartiality called for in auditing.

III.   "Adequate team staffing and auditor training." There are successful auditing programs using both full-time and part-time auditors. Regardless of the type or mix used, auditors should be experienced in environmental regulations, pollution control technologies, facility operations, and auditing practices. While finding an individual with experience in all of these areas is almost impossible, significant experience in at least one area should be required when selecting auditors. The majority of auditors in established programs come from an engineering or science background and have more than five years of experience. Training should be provided in areas where there is a lack of experience. Attitudes, personality, and the ability to meet and establish a working relationship with new people are also important considerations when selecting auditors. Auditors should participate in continuing training and education in both technical disciplines and auditing practices.

IV.   "Explicit audit program objectives, scope, resources, and frequencies."

V.   "A process which collects, analyzes, interprets and documents information sufficient to achieve audit objectives." Auditing should be a systematic process designed to collect information which is sufficient, reliable, relevant, and useful. Audit protocols and checklists should be developed which ensure such information is obtained and documented.

VI.   "A process which includes specific procedures to promptly prepare candid, clear, and appropriate written reports on audit findings, corrective actions, and schedules for implementation." Audit procedures which prescribe and explain the reporting process should be in place. These procedures should include guidance on determining type or level of findings and the tracking and follow-up of findings.

VII. "A process which includes quality assurance procedures to assure the accuracy and thoroughness of environmental audits." Quality assurance can be accomplished by periodic independent reviews of the auditing program by internal or external evaluators, or both.

Conducting A Facility Environmental Audit

The following sequence of activities is representative of audit programs in United States industry today.

Preparation

Scheduling -- This includes not only the date for arriving at the facility but the number of days to be spent onsite and the activities or topics to be covered. Scheduling is normally done jointly with team selection since availability of needed auditors is a key issue. Scheduling consideration should be given to facility operations and activities, such as planned maintenance outages.

Audit Team Selection -- Lead auditor and team members with appropriate experience and expertise are selected. Outside expertise from consultants may be needed.

Notification of Facility -- Audit procedures normally prescribe who is to be notified (plant managers, division director, etc.) and the lead time for notification. This notification would typically contain audit date, audit subjects and scope, names of lead auditor and team members, number of days onsite, and information or instructions on any special assistance needed during the audit. The audit notification may include a request for information such as plant layout, storage capacities, process information, or copies of permits. A pre-audit questionnaire to be filled out by facility management may be used to obtain this information. An alternative could be to schedule a pre-audit meeting with facility representatives.

Determine Scope and Responsibilities -- Identify laws and regulations which cover activities to be audited and define limits or bounds of the audit. Assign specific areas of responsibility to individual audit team members.

Detailed Preparation -- Individual auditors prepare by identifying and reviewing audit criteria for their specific areas of responsibility. This would include:

- Federal, State, and local laws and regulations
- Applicable corporate policies
- Facility procedures
- Environmental permits and applications -- NPDES, air emissions, landfill, 404, TSDF, etc.
- Facility compliance files and reports
- Correspondence with regulators
- Previous audit reports

Appropriate protocols or checklists are then selected or developed for use during the audit. Any special needs, such as sampling apparatus, should be determined. Individual auditors develop onsite agendas and coordinate with each other and the lead auditor. The quality of this preparation often determines the overall quality of the audit and report.

Onsite

Entrance Meeting -- Audit team and facility management meet. Scope, objectives, and methods of the audit are restated and briefly explained. Facility personnel update the audit team on the current status of the facility, processes not in operation, safety and security policies, etc. Individual contacts and agendas are established.

Records Review -- This includes such items as facility files, manifests, monitor logs, sample collection and analysis records, operations and maintenance logs, all relevant procedures, and inspection records.

Inspection of Facilities and Observation of Operations -- This includes such items as laboratories, wastewater collection and treatment systems, product and waste storage, incinerators, precipitators, scrubbers, baghouses, monitors, landfills, chemical treatment processes, and injection wells. Facilities are evaluated not only in regard to their compliance with specific regulatory requirements but also in light of accepted engineering practices and common sense. Audits should identify ineffective and inefficient practices as well as regulatory noncompliances.

Interview Responsible Personnel -- Auditors are normally onsite a few days and can observe activities occurring only during this brief snapshot in time. Records review and inspection of facilities assist in giving a more complete picture. Interviewing responsible personnel, from unit operators through plant managers, is probably the most valuable method of gaining a complete picture of all types of activities under a variety of conditions. Part of an auditor's training should include interviewing techniques.

Documentation -- The completion of protocols or checklists and the maintenance of work papers by each auditor should provide a complete record of what was covered during the audit and what was found or observed.

Organize Findings and Concerns -- Prior to the exit meeting, time should be allowed for each auditor and the team as a whole to organize their work papers and concerns.

Exit Meeting -- The audit team summarizes for facility management what was covered, what was found, and what they can expect in the final audit report. This meeting also allows facility management the opportunity to correct any misconceptions or errors of fact. The exit meeting should be relatively brief and should not be allowed to become a forum for prolonged arguments over differences in judgment.

Report Preparation

Resolve Outstanding Issues -- There are sometimes issues, such as plant reports not being immediately available, or the precise requirements of a specific regulation under unique conditions, which must be resolved after leaving the plant site. This should be done promptly.

Prepare Draft Report -- Individual auditors draft their portions of the audit report and submit them to the lead auditor who reviews them and compiles the report. As a minimum, audit reports should contain the following: purpose and scope of audit operations observed and facilities inspected, audit team members, plant personnel contacted, time period under review, criteria audited against (laws, regulations, policies, procedures, etc.), findings or noncompliances which include description of the problem, specific regulatory references and recommendations, and any general observations (either positive or negative) judged significant enough to be covered in the report.

Draft Report Review -- Audit procedures normally prescribe the review process used by the particular organization. In some cases, audit review is done solely within a corporate or division staff. In other cases the audited organization is given the opportunity to review and comment on or correct errors in the draft audit. In most cases the corporate legal staff is involved in the review.

Report Issued -- The report is issued according to audit program procedures. Normally, distribution is limited and includes facility manager, division director, senior V.P., general counsel and CEO. Protecting the confidentiality of the report is an extremely important issue and needs to be addressed with legal counsel prior to conducting any audits.

Audit Follow-up

Response to Report -- Facility management is normally required to respond to audit findings within a prescribed time limit. The response should explain corrective actions taken or planned and, where not finalized, a schedule for completion.

Tracking and Closing Audit Findings -- Most audit program procedures include detailed instructions on tracking and closing audit findings. Responsibility for these activities depends on where in the organization the auditing program is located. Possibilities include independent audit staff, corporate or division environmental staff, or legal staff.

CONCLUSION

Environmental auditing is a well established and widely used practice in American industry today. The benefits that can be expected from environmental auditing include the obvious ones of providing top management with valuable information by assessing and documenting compliance status of facilities, and assisting in compliance by identifying and tracking deficiencies. In addition, auditing can elevate environmental consciousness throughout the company, assist in management accountability, contribute to information transfer between facilities resulting in better compliance and cost savings, be used in management development, and help in creating goodwill with regulators and the public. No industrial activity has a greater need for environmental auditing than the handling and disposal of hazardous materials.

WASTE MINIMIZATION

John H. Frick, Ph.D., CHMM
Defense Logistics Agency

INTRODUCTION

Our environmental protection efforts in this country have emphasized the control and cleanup of pollution caused by hazardous materials after they no longer serve a useful purpose and are considered hazardous waste. Today, greater emphasis is being placed on waste reduction at the source as well as other waste minimizing efforts.

The concept of waste minimization was incorporated into the 1984 amendment of the Resource Conservation and Recovery Act (RCRA) to add a specific statement of congressional policy. This policy states: "The Congress hereby declares it to be the national policy of the Unites States that, wherever feasible, the generation of hazardous waste is to be reduced or eliminated as expeditiously as possible. Waste nevertheless generated should be treated, stored, or disposed of so as to minimize the present and future threat to human health and the environment."

The need to minimize the volume and toxicity of all hazardous waste has been made clear and explicit. Recycling pollutants contained in effluents, emissions, and waste or other pollution streams is only one way of implementing this national policy.

Congress implemented its waste minimization policy in a relatively limited manner. First, it required EPA to submit a report to Congress by October 1, 1986, recommending any legislative changes that are feasible and desirable. Second, they added to RCRA three limited waste reduction provisions. As a result, new legislation was not recommended; leaving the three provisions of RCRA, the national policy statement, and the inherent economic benefits to become the only key elements in the current implementing authority for this concept.

REGULATIONS

The three regulatory provisions of RCRA are as follows:

1. Section 3002(a)(6) of HSWA requires, as part of any generator's biennial report to EPA, that the generator describe the efforts undertaken during the year to reduce in volume and toxicity of waste generated. He is also required to report changes in volume and toxicity of waste actually achieved during the year in question in comparison with previous years.

2. Section 3002(b) of HSWA requires generators to certify on their waste manifests (mandated under Section 3002(a)) that they have in place a program to reduce the volume or quantity and toxicity of such waste to the degree determined by the generator to be economically practicable.

3. Section 3005(h) of HSWA requires the same certification in relation to any new permit issued for treatment, storage, or disposal of hazardous waste.

These requirements are intended to increase the awareness of generators and facility owners and operators of the importance of minimizing hazardous wastes and to serve as the basis for more specific and farther reaching developments. Each generator must determine whether any particular waste minimization approach that might apply to a process is economically practicable.

Definitions

Waste Minimization

EPA presented, in their 1986 report to Congress, a working definition for the term "waste minimization" focusing on primarily two types of

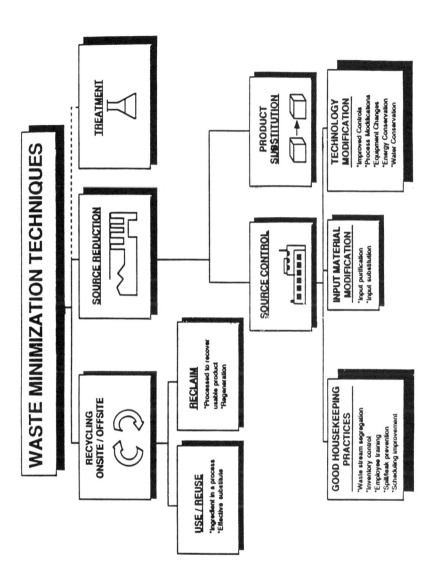

Figure 1: Waste Minimization Techniques from EPA's Report to Congress on Waste Minimization

activities: (1) source reduction; and (2) recycling (as defined in the "Definition of Solid Waste Final Rulemaking," January 1985). These definitions are as follows:

Source Reduction

Source reduction is the reduction or elimination of waste generation at the source, usually within a process. Source reduction measures can include some types of treatment processes, but they also include process modifications, feedstock substitutions, or improvements in feedstock purity, various housekeeping and management practices, increases in the efficiency of machinery, and even recycling within a process. Source reduction implies any action that reduces the amount of waste exiting from a process.

Recycling

Recycling is the use or reuse of a waste as an effective substitute for a commercial product, or as an ingredient or feedstock in an industrial process. It also refers to the reclamation of useful constituent fractions within a waste material or removal of contaminants from a waste to allow it to be reused. As used in the report, recycling implies use, reuse, or reclamation of a waste either onsite or offsite after it is generated by a particular process.

Waste Minimization

Waste minimization is the reduction, to the extent feasible, of hazardous waste that is generated or subsequently treated, stored, or disposed. It includes any source reduction or recycling activity undertaken by a generator that results in either (1) the reduction of total volume or quantity of hazardous waste, or (2) the reduction of toxicity of hazardous waste, or both, so long as the reduction is consistent with the goal of minimizing present and future threats to human health and the environment.

Figure 1 illustrates the waste minimization techniques referred to in EPA's definitions.

The Congressional Office of Technology Assessment (OTA) published a report, "Serious Reduction of Hazardous Wastes," in September 1986. The report stated the following:

> *Waste Reduction.* There is no common definition of waste reduction. There are few or no data on the extent of industrial waste reduction. Waste reduction is usually measured incorrectly. And, the information that the government collects on waste generation is not useful. Waste reduction might or might not include waste treatment. If waste reduction is defined to include waste treatment, companies will naturally pay more attention to treatment, which is a familiar activity, than to the reduction of waste.

> *Waste reduction.* In-plant practices that reduce, avoid, or eliminate the generation of hazardous waste, to reduce risks to health and environment. Actions taken away from the waste generating activity, including waste recycling or treatment of wastes after they are generated, are not considered waste reduction. Also, an action that merely concentrated the hazardous content of a waste to reduce waste volume or dilutes it to reduce degree of hazard is not considered waste reduction. This definition is meant to be consistent with the goal of preventing the generation of waste at its source rather than controlling, treating, or managing waste after its generation.

Waste Minimization Assessment

The idea underlying the promotion of waste minimization is that it makes far more sense not to produce waste rather than develop extensive treatment schemes to ensure that waste is managed in an environmentally sound manner. The initial step to accomplishing this end is to conduct a waste minimization assessment. This assessment is a systematically planned procedure with the objective of identifying ways to reduce or eliminate waste. The assessment consists of a careful review of a plant's operations and waste streams, and the selection of specific areas to assess. After a specific waste stream or area is identified as the focus, a number of options with the potential to minimize waste are developed and screened. Third, the technical and economic feasibility of the selected options are evaluated. Finally, the most promising options are selected for implementation.

Waste Minimization Incentives

There are several reasons for minimizing waste generations. Some are mandatory (i.e., regulatory) and others are non-mandatory (i.e., economic, liability, public image, and environmental concern).

Regulatory Requirements:

- Biennial reporting on the status of the waste minimization program (section 3002(a)).
- Certification of a waste minimization program on the Manifest (section 3002(b)).
- Certification of a waste minimization program in relation to TSD facility permitting (section 3005).

Economic Incentives:

- Increasing land disposal costs and land disposal bans.
- More costly treatment technology.
- Reduction in raw material and manufacturing costs.
- Reduced operating costs.

Liability Incentives:

- Potential reduction in generator liability for environmental problems at both onsite and offsite treatment, storage, and disposal facilities.
- Potential reduction in liability for worker safety.

Public Image and Environmental Concern:

- Energy conservation.
- Improved image in the community and from employees.
- Concern for improving the environment and the employee workplace.

Often times waste minimization incentives are associated with the reduction of risk to the health and safety of the operational personnel and to the environment. This is a favorable response where operational personnel are only peripherally involved (such as storage and handling of packaged products) and where the treatment, storage, and disposal facilities (TSDF's) are properly managed, maintained, and inspected.

Organizations need to recognize the possible benefits to be gained from waste minimization efforts even if it is considered a long-term ideal rather than an immediate goal. Most companies will embrace the concept but do not vigorously implement standard procedures. Because of this, a good mix of incentives and waste management controls are needed to encourage an acceptable level of participation.

The Environmental Protection Agency has published a document entitled, "Waste Minimization Benefits Manual" which discusses in detail the cost/benefit analyses of the waste minimization options. This manual was developed to assist plant managers in evaluating the "true" cost of current hazardous materials management against source waste minimization alternatives; i.e., primarily source reduction and recycling. Until these true costs, which are oftentimes underestimated by orders of magnitude, are correctly understood, more hazardous waste will be produced and managed than need be, thus imposing additional costs on the generator.

Waste Minimization Practices

Waste minimization strategies have focused largely on refinements in the manufacturing process such as process modifications and product reformation. These efforts have been mostly voluntary and many companies that have become involved have realized success in significant cost savings. Some businesses have improved the marketability of their products through the implementation of an internal waste minimization program. This has improved their competitive status with other businesses.

Many companies have initiated good housekeeping and storage management practices as part of their hazardous waste minimization plans, but the fundamental programs of some companies remain unchanged. The following are practices that can be incorporated into a waste minimization plan:

Inventory Control and Accounting Methods

Improvements in inventory control and accounting methods and the reduction of onhand quantities of potentially dangerous chemicals are effective management tools to reduce the amount of hazardous waste generated from spills, expired shelf-life, and excess quantities.

Waste Segregation

When hazardous waste is generated, proper handling and segregation are necessary to maximize the reclamation potential of the waste material. Simple plans designating specific areas for segregation of potentially valuable chemicals from unserviceable chemical wastes will enable a company to achieve lower quantities of hazardous wastes for disposal, lower disposal costs, and increased waste recycling.

Employee Training and Motivation

An employee training program can ensure that every person storing or handling hazardous material is aware of the potential of a hazardous material becoming hazardous waste. Many have initiated such training and awareness programs to keep employees informed of waste reduction advances and goals; and, some have established reward programs for employees who provide suggestions leading to successful waste reduction.

Material Handling Improvements

Improvements in the operation of material handling equipment can help minimize the waste generated at a facility. The best practice is minimizing unnecessary movement of hazardous material. When hazardous materials are handled, the proper equipment for safe movement should be used. Use of equipment not suited for the task can lead to damage and loss of product. For example, the rated capacity for a piece of equipment should never be exceeded. Overloading power equipment can create dangerous situations with the potential of generating hazardous waste through spills.

Involvement by All Employees

Waste reduction must be accepted as the responsibility of all workers and managers involved in production rather than just those who are responsible for pollution control and compliance.

Transfer of Knowledge

Waste reduction techniques learned in one part of the organization or company might have utility in another part. Isolated successful methods should be reviewed and considered for implementation as standard practices.

Spill Control and Good Housekeeping

When an audit is used to minimize generation of hazardous waste, identification of all waste sources is extremely important. Waste source identification and quantification may require an extensive onsite inspection. Once the waste sources are identified, the next step is to identify waste reduction methods. Methods for waste reduction must be evaluated for effectiveness, extent of current use, future application potential, and cost.

After all the waste sources and waste reduction methods are identified, discussed, and evaluated, a document outlining and explaining implementation options must be prepared and presented. The objective is to stimulate alternative reduction methods rather than to select from prepared options.

Information Exchange

Many avail themselves of the services of waste information and waste materials exchanges. The waste information exchange is, in effect, a clearinghouse for information. When a generator is faced with the problem of disposing of a particular waste, consideration of such factors as the cost of raw materials and waste management may prompt the solicitation of the services of a waste information exchange and, in turn, a waste material exchange for the actual removal and disposition of the waste. Participation in a waste exchange program as part of waste minimization provides an automated information system that can be accessed for the purpose of obtaining or exchanging successful waste minimization practices used throughout the country.

SUMMARY

Current pollution controls do little more than move waste around from one medium to another (i.e., air, land, and water). Also, many wastes are not yet regulated. Therefore a comprehensive, management approach to waste is essential. By reducing the generation of waste, industry can use materials more effectively and achieve improved protection to health and the environment. Waste reduction at the source is an economically sensible approach whereby industry can lower waste management and regulatory compliance costs, liabilities, and risks. Waste minimization efforts cannot eliminate all wastes, but it can help to lower costs to operators as regulations continue to expand. Congress is currently considering several options for future strategy as provided by the Office of Technology Assessment in their publication entitled, "Serious Reduction of Hazardous Waste for Pollution Prevention and Industrial Efficiency," September 1986.

HAZARDOUS WASTE REDUCTION, MINIMIZATION, AND TREATMENT GUIDELINES FOR TECHNOLOGY SELECTION

Jeffrey P. Perl, Ph.D., CHMM
Chicago Chem Consultants Corporation

INTRODUCTION

Until recently, only two options, bury or burn, were available to those responsible for the remediation of hazardous waste spills or end of pipe accumulations. Waste reduction/minimization, while spoken of often, was little understood or practiced. The Hazardous and Solid Waste Amendments (HSWA) to RCRA of 1984 (refer to the chapter on waste minimization and RCRA) set in motion the Land Disposal Restrictions. In order to monitor compliance and performance, Congress directed EPA to gather *Waste Minimization* data from generators. Also implicit in the land bans were treatment standards. In some instances, such as Superfund remedial action, the use of incineration can be implemented without the need for public approval. In other instances, however, public disapproval of incineration has forced remediators to look to other remedial action technologies.

The hazardous materials manager, therefore, is faced with new technological challenges:

1. The application of new, safe, environmentally effective technologies to the remediation of spills or end of pipe accumulations, and

2.   The identification and implementation of hazardous waste reduction and minimization activities to reduce or prevent hazardous waste generation and exposure to the work-force.

In this chapter, we shall develop a checklist approach to the selection of treatment and or minimization technology. These two have been lumped together because the equipment used to remediate or minimize waste is really chosen from a common pool of technology. The overall approach differs in each case hence each will be treated separately in the pages to follow.

HAZARDOUS WASTE TREATMENT TECHNOLOGY

Treatment Definition: The application of chemical or physical means to reduce or eliminate toxicity or hazardous characteristics.

Treatment process selection checklist

The regulatory aspects of spill or end of pipe remediation are often so involved that little up-front attention is paid to the remediation method to be used. Often overlooked is the fact that in most cases, a permit to treat will have to be issued. The success in obtaining the permit will revolve around the ability of the author to present a *complete* remediation plan. The hazardous materials manager (HMM) must, therefore, begin the treatment selection process at the same time as any on-going regulatory review.

The plan must demonstrate the ability of the approach to provide a safe, environmentally effective remediation. It must not have potential to cause more damage, i.e., transference from the medium of contamination, e.g., soil to the air or water. Care must be taken to contain the spill. For example, the remediation of underground storage tank leaks can, if improperly managed, cause the contamination to spread outside the zone of initial contamination. Contaminants removed from the ground must not be allowed to enter the surrounding air or water (above prescribed treatment levels). Care must be taken to ensure that remediation workers are not exposed to toxic levels of materials (see the chapter on personal protective equipment). This is done through development of a health and safety plan.

We will now examine four checklist items shown in Table 1.

Table 1
Technology Selection Checklist

1. Define Scope

2. Screen Alternatives

3. Evaluate Selected Technologies

4. Develop Final Design and Approach

Step 1. - Define the Scope

The purpose of this first step is to determine the extent and type of contamination. The work effort here revolves around sampling and analysis and various other considerations which together help set the stage for the project size, duration, and cost. Table 2 describes these steps in checklist form.

Type of Study -- The type of investigation to be undertaken can vary widely from RI/FS for Superfund cleanups costing an average of $1,000,000 to simple wipe tests or surface soil samples costing several hundred dollars. Differing levels of attention are prescribed by the regulations governing the cleanup. Off-site versus on-site remediation may be decided upon at this early stage in some instances such as those where the public safety may not be adequately protected.

Physical Dimensions -- This will actually have to be determined along with the analytical study. The area of contamination and depth will have to be known or estimated before choosing a technology. The total gallons, cubic yards, tons, etc., may be the deciding factor as some technologies may have insufficient processing rates, may not work below certain depths or may have other limitations or benefits dependent on the quantity of material to be processed. This goes for waste minimization as well.

Proximity to Groundwater -- Many states have regulations which kick in based on this parameter. Cleanup standards may vary with proximity to ground water. Remediation of subsurface contamination requires positive control of the contamination "plume" to prevent significant off-site migration. The method of achieving this, such as water injection or reinjection is as important as the removal technology, e.g., air stripping, UV peroxide oxidative destruction, etc.

Proximity to Significant Breathing Air Source -- Air pollution controls will vary from site to site and will depend on the proximity to community living space. In some instances, if the project is in a non-attainment zone as prescribed by the Clean Air Act, permits for technologies with significant air emissions, e.g., incinerators, may be difficult or impossible to obtain. This will help narrow the choice to approaches which minimize such emissions. Note, however, that the emissions from a properly operated hazardous waste incinerator consist almost entirely of carbon dioxide and water, and, to a much lesser extent, carbon monoxide, oxides of nitrogen, unburnt hydrocarbons and sulfur dioxide. These are all common emission gases for combustion devices of any type, particularly oil fired furnaces, and while not hazardous substances, can contribute to smog and other greenhouse effects.

Table 2
Checklist for Defining Scope of Cleanup or Waste Reduction

1. Type of Study
    - RI/FS
    - On-site
    - Off-Site

2. Physical Dimensions
    - Area
    - Depth

3. Air, Ground, or Water?
    (A) Air
        - Cubic Feet per Minute
        - Volume of Confined Space
    (B) Ground
        - Cubic Yards

- Tons
- Area
- Depth
(C) Water
  - Gallons
  - Gal/Min
(D) Proximity of Ground to Water
(E) Proximity of Air to Water or Ground

Analytical

An important part of the determination of scope, is the analytical data that is gathered. Here it is important to stress that two types of data may be needed. The first, of course, is the standard EPA compliance data. This is developed by sampling and analyzing by method as described in USEPA SW-846. The second type of data is that required to evaluate alternative technologies, namely, performance data.

The difference between the two can be found in their individual purposes. Data obtained by method is nothing more than that. The methods have been developed to account for a number of errors or inconsistencies which can arise in sampling. The numbers are then compliance oriented. A good example can be found in the method for the determination of fats, oils and greases (FOG) in water. The common EPA accepted gravimetric method loses, i.e., does not identify light to medium volatility components. The infra-red technique (FOG-IR), however, picks up light components which, while not regulated, can be an important factor in the technology chosen. Another important consideration is the length of time required to obtain data. The gravimetric technique can take 2-5 days or more depending on activity in the lab employed while the FOG-IR can be performed in the field in less than an hour. In some cases, methods testing labs actually report "less than" limits which are useless for comparing technologies.

In contrast to the methods type tests, performance data is used to determine absolute concentration or values of target contaminant levels. The accuracy of such techniques need not be greater than +/- 15%. The analyses may be performed using methods unacceptable to EPA from a regulatory standpoint, but perfectly usable, often faster ones for the selection of remediation technologies. The destruction and removal efficiency (DRE) will be determined from lab analytical data. These requirements may be based on methods testing.

Table 3 below shows the analytical checklist. Be careful when choosing a lab. Many labs are incapable of performing non-standard tests and are generally unaccustomed to doing the R&D type testing which is required to support treatability studies.

Table 3
Analytical Checklist

DETERMINE PRINCIPAL HAZARDOUS CONSTITUENTS

1. Organics, such as benzene, methylene chloride, PCBs

2. Inorganics, such as lead, cadmium, or both of these

3. Solids, such as soils, sludges, and particulates

4. Liquids, such as transformer liquid

5. Gases, such as hydrogen cyanide, ammonia

6. Combinations of these

The analytical data combined with the physical extent of contamination will provide a volume and concentration of material to be treated. This is typically stated in cubic yards, gallons or converted to weight, e.g., tons or pounds. In the case of end of pipe treatment, however, a stream is typically flowing with a contaminant concentration.

The first case is typified by a given number of cubic yards of soil contaminated at a certain concentration. The treatment technology selected will have a processing rate specified by the manufacturer in quantity of material per unit time, e.g., cubic yards/day, tons per day etc. In the case of end of pipe treatment, the technology will be called upon to treat a given volume of material per unit time, e.g., gallons per minute, or pounds per hour.

The length of time required to complete the remediation may be determined by dividing the volume of material to be treated by the treatment equipment processing rate. This number should be divided again by the efficiency factor for the equipment. Mobilization, setup, and shakedown time of the equipment must also be considered.

In the case of continuous flow end of pipe treatment, there is no end to the process hence the emphasis on waste minimization/reduction and recycling.

Step 2. Screen alternatives
Once the extent of contamination, analytical and other scope items has been determined, it is time to start the weeding out process. When organizing your own collection of technologies, it may be useful to separate them into categories which enhance your ability to select and reject. Some categories of contaminated media could include:

    soils
    liquids
    gases
    multiple media

Technology approach categories could include:
    organic destruction or fixation
    inorganic destruction or fixation
    both
    recycle
    experimental - not DRE tested (innovative)
    proven DRE tested

With such an organization, you first eliminate technologies which are entirely inappropriate such as on-site incinerators for water streams, soils technologies for gas treatment, etc. Once the easy eliminations are made the next step will require an examination of the technical feasibility of each remaining approach.

Table 4
Alternative Technology Screening Checklist

1. Select from Universe of Treatment Technologies

   • Federal and Local EPA Studies,
   • SITES Program (Superfund Innovative Technology Evaluations), and
   • General Literature, based on Scope of Work

2. Examine Technical Feasibility

3. Environmental Effectiveness

4. Safety of Operation

5. Performance History

6. Equipment Reliability Factor

7. Rough Cost Estimates

Before beginning the selection process let's review the basic categories of treatment technologies from which you will screen alternatives.

There are basically two types of technologies: Physical and Chemical.

Physical processes, such as distillation and others listed below, serve to separate and concentrate components. These processes cannot destroy or detoxify a hazardous substance but can often render a very large contaminated stream non-hazardous.

Example: The use of activated carbon to remove benzene from drinking water is a common example of such a physical process. Once adsorbed onto the carbon, the benzene can be recovered and either reused or sent for chemical treatment if necessary, while the treated water might be reused in a process or discharged into a water source such as a stream or a sewer system for further treatment. In the former case, a National

Pollution Discharge and Elimination Permit (NPDES) will be required; the latter case will require meeting the Publicly Owned Treatment Works (POTW) discharge requirements (refer to the chapter on Clean Water Act).

In chemical treatment, the hazardous constituent is itself destroyed or detoxified. Examples include incineration, chemical dechlorination of Poly-chlorinated Biphenyls (PCBs), and biological techniques (sometimes grouped into their own category of Biotechnology, or biochemical).

The use of hydrogen peroxide, ozone, catalysis or biological degradation on the above mentioned benzene contaminated drinking water stream constitutes a chemical treatment which generally, but not always, results in total destruction of the hazardous material, rendering it useless for recycle or reuse. The proper use of ozone, for example, would convert benzene into carbon dioxide and water, a non-hazardous but useless form.

Table 5
TREATMENT TECHNOLOGY SELECTION

Two Generic Categories of Treatment Technologies:
Physical and Chemical

A. PHYSICAL
1. Unit Operations
   • Involving No Chemical Change
   • Separation Processes
2. Separate Organics from Inorganics
3. Separate Organics from Other Organics
4. Volume Reduction
   • De-watering
   • Paint Solvent Stripping/Recycling
5. Distillation
6. Filtration
7. Extraction
8. Centrifugation
9. Soil Washing
10. Soil Roasting

B.   CHEMICAL
      1.   Rapid - Oxidation - Incineration
      2.   Slow to Fast - Chemical Reaction
      3.   Slow - Biological

Table 6
Choice of Technology

PHYSICAL UNIT OPERATIONS TO SEPARATE AND
CONCENTRATE
NO DESTRUCTION OR DETOXIFICATION

1.   CENTRIFUGATION - Produces organic, inorganic and solids
2.   SOLVENT DISTILLATION - Uses heat to separate organics
      or inorganics
3.   SOLIDS FILTRATION
4.   CARBON ADSORPTION
5.   GAS ABSORPTION

Table 7
Chemical Operations Used to Destroy or Detoxify

1.   Incineration is Best Known and Widely Used
2.   Chemical Reaction Can Detoxify Without Destroying, e.g. PCB-
      specific Dechlorination
3.   Biological - Bugs Metabolize Waste, e.g. Gasoline/Oily Wastes
4.   Catalytic Destruction
      • Vapor
      • Liquid Phase

Table 8
Hybrid Technologies

      •   Carbon Adsorption with Catalytic Combustion
      •   Peroxide Enhanced Ultraviolet Chemical Destruction
      •   Carbon Adsorption with Biotreatment Destruction
      •   Air Stripping with Organic Recovery Condenser

Step 3 - Evaluation of selected alternative technologies

After screening potential candidate alternatives, the selection process can begin. Table 9 shows the steps involved.

Generally, two to three alternatives are selected for evaluation. This is necessary for a number of reasons:

- Difficult to choose between two or more of the possibilities
- Uncertainty of permitting favored technology
- Contractual Evaluation Requirements

As mentioned earlier, permitting must be considered from the start of the process whether it be treatment or minimization. Many factors will weigh in some decision time and for this reason it is best to have several options available along with a clear winner.

At this point in the decision making process, it may be necessary to test the technology on a waste sample. A treatability study is highly recommended as it helps in the following ways:

- Demonstrate Destruction and Removal Efficiency (DRE) For Permit
- Identify Potential Operational Troubles With Technology
- Quantify Actual Treatment Processing Rates
- Determine Long Term Costs
- Identify Health and Safety Aspects of Technology

These tests are best performed by you or agents representing your organization to provide an overall objective analysis of the results obtained. Remember, cleanups or hazardous waste minimization programs can have lifetimes ranging from a few months, to several years, to forever. A carefully performed treatability study can keep you from getting locked-in to a technology which, while being environmentally effective, may not provide the least cost or highest degree of safety to those operating the equipment.

Finally, if the project scope warrants it, you may wish to go to a field test of the final chosen technology. This may be an agency prerequisite requirement for obtaining your permit.

Table 9
Select Alternatives Carefully

1. Generally Select 2-3 Alternatives Which May Work
2. Perform Treatability Study
    *   Small Bench Tests
    *   Vendor Performs Best if You Perform
3. Select Final Cleanup Technology
    *   On-Site Small Scale Demonstration
    *   Vendor Pilot Demonstration

Step 4. Final design and approach

The final step involves development of a design and approach. Data gathered in the preceding steps will be used to size and cost equipment. Before the contract is let to obtain the required equipment, you may wish to consider leasing or renting as opposed to purchasing. Many vendors are now providing equipment for lease which includes maintenance, servicing and, in some instances, operation of the equipment. This option is generally more expensive on paper but should be considered by generators if you consider the cost of training your personnel and their lost time, not to mention your company's lack of experience in remediation work.

Performance agreements, service contracts, availability of backup spare parts and required utilities are also to be determined at this time. Of particular importance is the equipment reliability factor, also referred to as up-time or stream-time. A reliability factor of 0.5 means the equipment is operational only 50% of the time, thereby doubling the total remediation time. Reliability factors of 0.8 to 0.9 are common depending upon the technology. Unusual or one of a kind parts may mean significant downtime while waiting for the replacement part to arrive. The complexity of the equipment may require highly skilled maintenance personnel in support roles. All of these will factor into the selection.

A strict set of laboratory protocols will have to be developed along with a health and safety plan. The lab protocols will describe to the regulatory agency how you plan to monitor the treatment effectiveness and guarantee the required DRE.

The health and safety plan must be drawn up to describe the manner in which those operating the equipment are to be protected as well as dealing with emergencies.

Often overlooked are the unique challenges of equipment startup, operation and shutdown (particularly under emergency conditions). These are specialized functions that must be dealt with up front. Too often, expensive equipment is broken, run out of specification, or its operators exposed to unnecessary hazards due to inexperience in these areas. A good equipment vendor will offer these services, particularly startup, as a part of the purchase price or for a nominal fee.

Table 10
Final Design And Approach

- Sizing Equipment
- Costing Equipment
- Mobilization/Demobilization
- Lease/Purchase
- Health and Safety Plans
- Purchasing/Contracting
- Lab Analytical Protocols
- On-going Process Monitoring Systems
- Performance Agreements
- Service Contracts
- Availability of Back-up Parts or Equipment
- Equipment Startup
- Equipment Operation
- Operator Training
- Utilities

Table 11
Treatability Study

LAB TEST TO DETERMINE THE ABILITY OF A GIVEN TECHNOLOGY TO REDUCE OR ELIMINATE A TARGET HAZARDOUS CONSTITUENT(S)

1. Usually Performed with Real Samples (Can be Performed with Surrogates)
2. Establish Equipment Size
3. Number of Stages Required
4. Residence Time
5. Destruction and Removal Efficiency (DRE)
6. Determine Costs
   - Equipment Construction and Assembly
   - Operating
7. Determine any Unusual Operating Conditions or Requirements
   - Soil Crushing
   - Pre-Filtration of Liquids
   - Conditioning, e.g. Permanganate Treatment of Water for Iron

WASTE MINIMIZATION

In the preceding pages, we have developed a process for selecting a waste treatment technology. The approach for waste minimization is similar in that the pieces of technology, distillation columns, reactor vessels, etc, applied are alike. A working definition as well as regulatory guidelines for waste minimization has been developed in a separate chapter.

In waste minimization/reduction, the goal is to reduce or eliminate the quantity or toxicity of a stream leaving a generator's facility, or being treated at a TSDF. The definitions have been outlined in the chapter on Waste Minimization.

Ranked highest in the area of effectiveness is process equipment or feed stock change. These involve, respectively, changing the way the chemical process actually occurs or changing the chemicals used to create the finished products.

Next in the hierarchy is on-site recycling, followed by off-site recycling. Keep in mind, however, that one goal is to reduce the amount of waste entering the hazardous waste treatment, storage and disposal system. The other is to minimize hazardous materials exposure to the work-force.

Table 12
Common Waste Reduction Technologies

   A.   Process Changes
      1.   Add on Solvent Recycle Loop (Hard Piped)
      2.   Add on Extraction Recycle Loop (Hard Piped)
      3.   Add Stages to Existing Equipment to Reduce Waste
   B.   Feedstock Changes
      1.   Chrome III for Chrome VI
      2.   Water-based Paints in Place of Solvent-based

WASTE TREATMENT AND MINIMIZATION EXAMPLES

Example: Hazardous Waste Minimization
A plant has a waste stream containing benzene. Currently about 500,000 gallons per year of 10% benzene, 90% oil is being shipped off-site for incineration. Determine a suitable waste minimization option.

In this case, we are dealing with end of pipe treatment which the facility would like to prevent. The simplest solution in this case would involve distillation of the oil/benzene stream. This would produce a light benzene fraction overhead and a heavy oil fraction in the bottom. Depending on the concentration of benzene in the bottom, further processing for removal could be accomplished by steam or air stripping. The resultant streams produced would include benzene for recycle within the plant or elsewhere, oil low enough in benzene to be de-listed (de-classified as hazardous), and air or water streams with low ppm concentrations of benzene. The air stream could be subjected to vapor phase carbon adsorption or catalytic destruction. The water stream in this case could be reused in the recycle system without removal of trace benzene.

Waste Treatment Example

Problem: A three million gallon above-ground fuel oil storage tank two-thirds full of oil, water and dirt contaminated with PCB and lead metal.

Step one determines the scope: samples were obtained from the oil layer, water layer and dirt layer. Results are shown in the accompanying table.

Incineration and stabilization/landfilling involved the treatment of a large quantity of water and was actually more expensive than processes which emphasize volume reduction. A lab treatability study demonstrated the ability of the emulsions to be separated by on-site continuous centrifugation. This produces three streams: oil free water, dirt, and oil. The oil stream (approximately 200,000 gallons) containing PCB was sent for incineration. This stream actually benefitted the incineration process as it was used as prime blending stock for other inorganic streams. The water stream (approximately 1.7 million gallons) was sent through a carbon bed and discharged into a nearby river under the facilities NPDES permit. A small quantity (approximately 50,000 gallon equivalent) of solids containing PCB and lead metal was sent for stabilization. This provided a volume reduction of over 80%.

Table 13
Treatment Technology Selection Example

PROBLEM: 2 MILLION GALLONS OF OIL WATER MIXTURE
PCB CONTAMINATED

STEP ONE: Define Scope
    20 % Oil
    75 % Water
    5 % Solids
    (A) Oil Phase Analysis
        PCB Contamination = 1000 PPM
        Lead   =   10 PPM

    (B) Water Phase Analysis
        PCB   LESS THAN 10 PPM
        Lead   50 PPM

    (C) Solids Analysis
        PCB   <5 PPM
        Lead   100 PPM

STEP TWO: SCREEN ALTERNATIVES

(A) INCINERATION - while feasible, it does not make sense to incinerate large volumes of water.

(B) LANDFILLING - Stabilization of large quantities of liquid would lead to a tremendous volume increase in waste disposed.

(C) OTHER ALTERNATIVE TECHNOLOGIES

STEP THREE: Evaluate Selected Alternatives

Centrifuge and Separate Water/Oil/Solids

OPTION 1:   Burn Oil
Carbon Adsorption on Water
Stabilize Solids
Phase Separate (Decant)
Filter Water

OPTION 2:   Filter Dirt
Burn Oil
Stabilize Solids

SUB-OPTION: CHEMICAL DECHLORINATION OF OIL - Ruled out due to high residual water content.

STEP FOUR: Final Design and Approach

- Option 1 Chosen
- Total Costs Determined (Approximately $2,600,000 in 1988 dollars)
- Job Estimate Made
- Equipment Purchased or Leased

REFERENCES

An In-Plant Approach to Hazardous Materials Management, Jeff Perl, Chemical Process Magazine, March 1989

Handbook on Hazardous Materials Management - Tom Carson and Doye Cox, 1990

Standard Handbook of Environmental Engineering, Robert A. Corbitt, 1990

Standard Handbook of Hazardous Waste Treatment and Disposal, Harry Freeman, 1989

Treatability Studies - A Valuable Cleanup Selection Tool, Jeff Perl, Chemical Process Magazine, June 1990

"Hazardous Waste Treatment and Minimization Guidelines for Technology Selection," Jeff Perl, *HazMat World Magazine*, October, 1991.

SUPERFUND SETTLEMENT

TO BE OR NOT TO BE A PRP PARTICIPANT: THAT IS THE QUESTION

Philip J. Schworer, Esq.,

and

Karen Dean, Paralegal
Dinsmore and Shohl

INTRODUCTION

In 1980, the United States Congress enacted the Comprehensive Environmental Response, Compensation, and Liability Act (CERCLA), which authorized the U.S. Environmental Protection Agency (EPA) to clean up hazardous waste sites considered a threat to human health or to the environment. In order to clean up these sites, Congress allotted CERCLA $1.6 billion, which would come from a Federal Trust fund financed by taxes on petroleum, chemical feed stocks, imported chemical derivatives, and a new "environmental tax" on corporations. It is this Federal trust fund that has given CERCLA the nickname "Superfund." CERCLA has since been revitalized by The Superfund Amendments and Reauthorization Act of 1986 (SARA) and reauthorized at $8.5 billion.

Congress insured the maintenance of the $8.5 billion "Superfund" by providing that certain "persons" be responsible for response costs:

The term "person" was defined to embrace:

(1)   the owner or operator of the site;
(2)   any person who owned or operated the site at the time hazardous substances were disposed there;
(3)   any person (generator) who arranged to have his own waste taken to the site for disposal or treatment; and
(4)   any person who transported waste for disposal or treatment to a site he selected.

These "persons" are referred to in Superfund actions as "Potentially Responsible Parties" (PRP).

In addition to defining potentially responsible parties, Section 107 established five criteria which must be met in order to recover response costs from PRPs. First, the expenses incurred must be "response costs" for money spent to respond to contamination. Second, defendants in Superfund cases must fall within the definition of "persons." Third, it must be proven that the response was to a "release" or "threatened release." Fourth, the substances that were released must be defined as "hazardous substances." Finally, it must be established that the hazardous substances were released or threatened to be released from a "facility."

The following is a brief overview of the Superfund litigation process which should aid you in evaluating your company's liability for response costs at a Superfund site and, if liable, how to keep those costs at a minimum.

National Priorities List

Whenever a waste site poses a threat to human health or the environment, the site will be placed on the National Priorities List (NPL). Sites which qualify for placement on the NPL have been determined by EPA to require remedial measures. The remediation will be either short-term removal programs to abate an immediate threat, or long-term studies and construction remediation which will ultimately make the site "permanently safe." If it is determined that a site poses no immediate threat but requires certain measures in order to be "permanently safe," EPA will initiate a remedial investigation/feasibility study (RI/FS), and select a remedy made public through a record of decision (ROD).

RI/FS

The remedial investigation and feasibility study (RI/FS) is two studies typically performed concurrently. The conditions at the site are characterized in the RI. The RI identifies the source and extent of contamination, the pathways of possible mitigation or releases to the environment, and the potential for human or other environmental harm. Based upon the RI information, the FS identifies a series of specific engineering or construction alternatives for cleaning up the site. For each major alternative prescribed, there will be a detailed analysis of the costs, effects, engineering feasibility, and environmental impact.

Once the RI/FS is complete, EPA will select the option which provides the most cost effective protection to human health and the environment. Historically EPA's emphasis has been on the protection factor, NOT cost. Thus, the option selected by EPA will likely be the most costly. Once selected, EPA issues a proposed ROD in which it announces and explains the selected remediation options.

Information-Gathering, Property Access Authority

As the initial RI/FS evaluation of the site is performed, EPA will simultaneously begin development of a list of PRPs. The list will include information on the type and volume of waste it has preliminarily attributed to each PRP. It is this allocation that often determines the percentage of cleanup cost each PRP will ultimately be assessed.

In order for the EPA to obtain records and other information needed to investigate the Superfund site and to assemble the list described above, information gathering and property access provisions were included in CERCLA and significantly expanded by SARA. Using what has become known as a 104(e) letter, EPA requires the targeted PRP to submit all documents and information related to its involvement in the site. Additionally, financial information relating to the PRP's ability to pay is often sought by EPA.

PRPs that have been named as the owner/operator of the site should be aware that mechanisms exist for EPA to require site access for construction or evaluation purposes. The EPA can also condemn the property to facilitate cleanup.

Further strengthening the government's authority for information gathering, SARA limited the rights of owner/operator to withhold information such as monitoring data related to disposal activities and information about the physical properties and health effects of hazardous substances. Finally, PRPs who choose to not comply with information or property access requests can be assessed a penalty of $25,000 per day.

Notification Letters

PRPs will be issued a notice letter which signifies that EPA believes the PRP may be liable for the cleanup. EPA will inform the PRP that it has the opportunity -- along with other PRPs -- to develop and fund its own remedial proposal before EPA funds the cleanup and commences a cost recovery action. Typically, the PRP has 60 days to undertake or denounce its own RI/FS or response action. If negotiations ensue, EPA may not commence the RI/FS for 60 days. However, EPA may, within that 60 day period, begin other studies and may respond to a significant threat to public health or the environment.

PRP GROUP

Generally, EPA will not negotiate with individual PRPs. Instead the focus is on groups of PRPs representing a "substantial portion" of the responsibility for the site cleanup. Therefore, it is essential that communications be established among all PRPs intending to negotiate with EPA. This is usually accomplished through the formation of a PRP group.

The PRP group invariably forms a Steering Committee which then develops an Agreement setting forth the background of EPA's notification of the PRPs regarding potential liability for the site, funding arrangements, officers, and provisions for withdrawal. In addition to preparing this agreement, the Steering Committee will also act as the primary liaison between the PRPs and the EPA.

An Allocation Committee for the PRP group will then develop a scheme for sharing costs associated with negotiations (i.e., legal and technical fees, administrative expenses and cleanup).

A Technical Committee will also be organized to serve as the Group's Primary negotiator, analyzer and advisor regarding the technical aspects of the RI/FS and the remediation method proposed in the ROD. This Committee will review the results of EPA's media sampling and monitoring results to ensure that the amount and type of contamination at the site correlates with the Agency's estimates, and will ensure that the planned remediation is truly necessary. The Committee will also oversee negotiations pertaining to the proposed remediation method. Technical expertise will aid the Committee in reviewing prior remediation methods used at other Superfund sites with similar contamination characteristics. Thus, the Technical Committee can advise if the proposed remediation method is excessive, both technically and financially, or if the remediation method is suitable for the type of contamination found at the site.

SUPERFUND LITIGATION

Once the PRP group is formed, the RI/FS has been conducted, and ROD issued, the group determines whether they will accept the remediation method proposed by the EPA; negotiate with EPA about the remediation method; or do nothing and await litigation.

Since EPA's proposed remediation plans are often perceived by most PRP groups as being "overzealous" "over expensive" and usually "overkill" in most instances the plan is not accepted without some sort of challenge.

However, litigation is not the route which most PRPs take because of the opportunities for settlement and the high cost of litigation. Additionally, as in all administrative actions, the cards will be stacked against the private sector because the government prevails unless its actions are shown to be arbitrary and capricious. Additionally, in CERCLA actions liability is:

(1)   retroactive, including acts or omissions occurring well before the date of CERCLA enactment;

(2) strict; it is irrelevant that the generator selected a licensed hauler to take waste to a licensed landfill, that all legal requirements at the time were fully met, or that a party used all due care;

(3) joint and several; one party out of many may be held liable for more than his/her "share" and may, in fact, be held liable for the entire site cleanup. Therefore, the most viable alternative is for the group to negotiate a settlement with EPA.

PRP Group Settlement

Before reviewing the settlement process, it should be pointed out that CERCLA did not provide guidelines for private party agreements. However, SARA not only addressed settlement procedures for Superfund sites, but strongly recommended them.

PRPs able to settle a Superfund action will enter into an agreement with the United States Government in the form of a "consent decree." This consent decree is the final product of months of negotiations regarding the extent and method of remediation that will take place at the site. Most consent decrees include provisions for:

(1) COMMITMENT BY THE PARTIES TO PERFORM THE REMEDIAL ACTION -- All parties are legally bound to meet the terms and conditions of the consent decree;

(2) PERIODIC REVIEW TO ASSURE PROTECTION OF HUMAN HEALTH AND ENVIRONMENT -- U.S. EPA will periodically review the remediation action to determine whether the remedy is adequately protecting human health and the environment.

(3) TECHNICAL IMPRACTICALITY PROTECTION -- Protects settling defendants from meeting performance goals which are impossible from an engineering standpoint;

(4) QUALITY ASSURANCE -- A plan submitted by defendants to assure quality of remediation;

(5) REPORTING REQUIREMENTS -- Contractor will prepare and provide U.S. EPA with monthly progress reports;

(6) REMEDIAL PROJECT MANAGERS/PROJECT COORDINATOR -- Observes and monitors progress at cleanup;

(7) FORCE MAJEURE -- Protects settling defendants from penalties for missed deadlines which are out of their control;

(8) DISPUTE RESOLUTION -- Guidelines for settling disagreements, either formally or informally;

(9) RETENTION AND AVAILABILITY OF INFORMATION -- Settling defendants shall provide EPA with all documentation relating to the provisions of the consent decree. These documents shall be retained for a specific time period;

(10) REIMBURSEMENT -- Settling defendants shall reimburse the United States for response costs incurred by the United States prior to entering into the consent decree;

(11) STIPULATED PENALTY -- Defendant's liability for missed deadlines;

(12) COVENANT NOT TO SUE -- Relieves settling defendants from future liability;

(13) DE MINIMIS BUYOUT -- Provisions for small contributors to "buy out" of future liability;

(14) OTHER CLAIMS -- Prevents settling defendants from suing U.S. EPA;

(15) LITIGATION AGAINST NON-SETTLERS -- Provision for the United States to recover response costs from non-settling PRPs;

(16) PUBLIC PARTICIPATION -- Availability of consent decree for public viewing and comments;

(17) COMMUNITY RELATIONS -- Availability of the RI/FS to the public;

(18) USE OF CONSENT DECREE -- Guidelines for using consent decree in judicial and administrative proceedings; and

(19) EFFECTIVE AND TERMINATION DATES -- Allows settling defendants to withdraw from consent decree if revisions to ROD differ significantly from RAP.

Four of these provisions, force majeure, covenant not to sue, de minimis buyout, and litigation against non-settlers, are of particular concern to most PRPs and are addressed in more detail below.

In all consent decrees, the United States Government will establish deadlines by which the decree requirements must be met. For example, there might be a six month limitation for initiation of cleanup. Additionally, the consent decree will invariably contain stipulated penalties for each day a deadline is not met. To protect against excessive penalties for missed deadlines, the PRP group should require that a "force majeure" clause be included. A force majeure is any event arising from causes beyond the reasonable control of settling defendants which delays or prevents the performance of any obligation required by the consent decree, ranging from an Act of God to the unavailability of a particular piece of equipment, and a "force majeure" clause will allow the PRPs to miss a deadline without the imposition of stipulated penalties. Consent decrees also typically provide that the EPA can make a final settlement with those PRPs who are considered "de minimis." De minimis PRPs are those "persons" who have contributed a small amount of waste to the site -- sometimes less than 1% of the total waste in volume. If a PRP qualifies as de minimis party, they will be allowed to settle, as soon as EPA determines the cost of the entire remediation. To settle, the PRPs will pay EPA more than their volumetric share in return for release from the extensive transaction costs and future liability. It was the belief of Congress when SARA was passed that de minimis contributors should be able to "buy out" of a Superfund site, because the cost of relieving these PRPs from future liability would be significantly outweighed by the benefit in immediately generating cleanup funds.

Two other concepts provided for in SARA to entice PRPs to enter into settlements with EPA are covenants not to sue and protection from being sued from non-settling PRPs. A major source of controversy under CERCLA is that settling PRPs remained liable for future claims brought by the U.S. Government in the event that additional liability arose out of the remedial action -- for example, if the remedy unexpectedly failed. In an attempt to eliminate this concern, Section 122 of SARA authorizes the inclusion of the "covenant not to sue" in settlement agreements whereby the United States promises not to sue settling parties for additional cleanup costs. However, there are exceptions to this covenant:

(1) Failure to perform the work in accordance with the law or failure to meet the requirements of the decree;
(2) Liability arising from the off-site disposal of wastes taken from the site;
(3) Claims arising out of any private party action;
(4) Any costs incurred by either the Federal or State government in responding to a release or substantial threat of release at a site, resulting from a settling defendant's failure to perform the work;

(5)   Any damages incurred by plaintiffs for the same reasons noted in (4) above; and,

(6)   Costs incurred by the Government in responding to conditions at or from the site that may present an imminent and substantial endangerment to the public health, welfare, or the environment.

The consent decree should also contain a provision to protect the settling PRPs from potential suits brought by other, non-settling responsible parties. To illustrate, a dispute might arise between two major responsible parties, where one party enters into a settlement agreement with EPA and agrees to pay 80% of the cleanup costs of the site, with EPA picking up the other 20%. When EPA later sues the non-settling party to recover that 20%, the non-settling party under traditional civil procedure could sue the settling party contribution, claiming that the settling party was responsible for more more than the 80% of the cleanup costs, and therefore must contribute to the 20% that EPA is attempting to recover from the non-settling party. Under SARA, however, settling defendants who enter into an administrative or judicial settlement agreement cannot be assessed additional liability from non-settling parties who claim that the settling parties did not pay their "fair share" of the cleanup costs. Thus, it is imperative that the consent decree protect settling defendants from third party claims.

CONCLUSION

The National Priority List currently consists of approximately 1,170 sites, and the Government Accounting Office has predicted the existence of at least 452,380 additional sites. This dramatic increase in the number of sites, coupled with increasingly more expensive and technically complicated cleanups, will ultimately result in EPA further strengthening their pursuit of PRPs for financing. As this trend progresses, companies which could be considered a PRP should be prepared to negotiate Superfund settlements if they are going to keep their liability for response costs at a minimum. Acceptable contamination levels, waste allocation and remediation methods and costs are all variables which can be negotiated during the settlement process. Negotiating these settlements is no easy task since EPA is zealously guarding the requirement that cleanups be "permanent." In closing, the best medicine for a generator to stay clear of Superfund is a keen awareness of the technical and legal requirements during all aspects of handling hazardous waste, including disposal. Involvement in a Superfund settlement is truly "damage control."

ENVIRONMENTAL CONSIDERATIONS IN REAL ESTATE TRANSACTIONS

C. Douglas Goins, Jr., JD, CHMM
Martin Marietta Energy Systems

INTRODUCTION

In 1980, very few people involved in real estate transactions paid any attention to environmental concerns when purchasing or selling real estate. Since then, the impact of environmental statutes and regulations at both the federal and state level have become so significant that every commercial real estate transaction should involve a consideration of these factors by sellers, buyers and lenders. The possible presence of air pollution, water pollution hazardous wastes and substance regulated by occupational safety and health agencies, underground storage tanks or a myriad of other pitfalls, significantly affects the worth of the property. Those involved in real estate transactions should be aware that environmental concerns are important and that they can and should be analyzed at an early stage in the transaction.

This chapter is intended only as a brief overview of the law pertaining to environmental considerations in real estate transactions. You should seek to apply these principles only with the assistance of legal counsel familiar with environmental laws.

Liability

In 1980, in response to such environmental catastrophes as Love Canal, Congress passed the Comprehensive Environmental Response

Compensation and Liability Act (CERCLA), often referred to as Superfund. CERCLA was designed as a comprehensive program which authorized the government to clean up hazardous waste sites and to undertake emergency response actions with regard to releases or threatened releases of hazardous substances in the environment. To finance this effort, Congress appropriated 1.6 billion dollars. In 1986, the Superfund was re-authorized and funded with an additional 8.5 billion dollars under the Superfund Amendment and Reauthorization Act of 1986, often referred to as SARA.

The statute provides three ways to achieve the goals of the legislation. First, Section 104 of CERCLA provided the Environmental Protection Agency (EPA) with the authority to respond to hazardous substance releases to help clean up hazardous chemical disasters. Second, Section 221 of CERCLA established the Hazardous Substance Response Trust Fund, known as Superfund, which is intended to finance response actions where it could not find a liable party, the liable party does not perform a cleanup, or the liable party cannot pay the cost of the cleanup and compensation. Third, CERCLA established a strong liability scheme that insured that those responsible for releases of hazardous substances will be held strictly liable for costs of response and damage to natural resources.

CERCLA contemplates two types of cleanup actions: removal actions and remedial actions. Removal actions are emergency-type responses to immediate threats to the public health or environment. Generally, they are short-term actions that can be undertaken by responsible parties or by the EPA using Superfund monies. Remedial responses are actions intended to provide a permanent solution in an abandoned or uncontrolled hazardous waste site. They are usually longer term and more expensive than removals. EPA can perform a remedial response only if the site is on the National Priorities List.

The CERCLA statute provides for two alternative mechanisms for hazardous waste clean up and reimbursement. First, the EPA can order potentially responsible parties to undertake remedial measures to clean up contaminated properties. Second, the EPA can take remedial actions on its own initiative and sue for recovery of its expenses from potentially responsible parties (PRPs). This legislation was designed to replenish the

Superfund through the EPA's recovery from liable parties of the clean up costs it incurred.

Three key factors make the scope of this legislation very sweeping:

1. The statute is applied retroactively to require payment for the present clean up of wastes that were disposed of long ago and whose disposal may have been lawful at the time.
2. The statute imposes strict liability which means no showing of fault is required.
3. The statute imposes joint and several liability which means any responsible party can be either fully or only partially liable for cleanup costs regardless of fault, and regardless of their contribution to the problem.

Therefore, sellers and purchasers of land and/or ongoing business concerns should be aware of this far-reaching statute and its potentially devastating impact on an owner or purchaser of property.

Who Is Liable?

The Superfund statute imposes liability on four basic categories of persons:

1. Current owners and operators of a facility.
2. Persons who owned or operated a facility at the time of disposal of any hazardous substance.
3. Persons who arranged for disposal or treatment of hazardous substances which they owned or possessed.
4. Persons who accept or accepted hazardous substances for transport to treatment or disposal facilities selected by them.

A seller or purchaser engaged in real estate transactions is basically concerned about whether he is a current or past owner or operator of the facility upon which hazardous substances were disposed.

The term "hazardous substances" is defined very broadly and would encompass many materials that contain very small amounts of substances EPA has declared to be hazardous under CERCLA or other environmental statutes. Once a potentially responsible party (PRP) has been identified, the liability provisions provide for civil actions to be maintained for release or threatened release of hazardous substances from hazardous waste facilities into the environment. EPA does this in two basic ways: cost recovery actions under CERCLA, Section 107(a), and injunctive relief actions seeking abatement or site cleanup under CERCLA, Section 106(a) and its companion statute, the Resource Conservation and Recovery Act (RCRA), Section 7000(3)(a). Under CERCLA, Section 106(a) and RCRA, Section 7000(3)(a), EPA can obtain injunctive relief upon establishing an imminent and substantial endangerment to the public health or welfare, or to the environment.

The term "imminent and substantial endangerment" has been interpreted very broadly in favor of the government. Federal court decisions have equated "endangerment" with "potential harm" and though the harm caused by contamination may be years in being realized, the danger is imminent if the *risk* of harm is imminent. B.F. Goodrich v. Murtha, 697 F. Supp. 89, 19ELR 20357 (D. Conn. 1988).

Every court to consider the issue has concluded that CERCLA imposes strict liability upon PRPs. *United States v. Ottati and Goss, Inc.*, 630 F. Sup. 1361 (D.N.H. 1985). The Second Circuit decided an owner was liable under strict liability regardless of fault or negligence. *New York v. Shore Realty Corporation*, 759 F. 2d 1032 (2d Cir. 1985). In addition to strict liability, courts have held that CERCLA can be applied to disposal practices that occurred prior to its passage in December 1980. In *United States v. Northeastern Pharmaceutical and Chemical Company, Inc.*, 810 F. 2d 726 (8th Cir. 1987), the 8th Circuit held that retroactive applications of CERCLA to impose liability upon responsible parties for areas contaminated and acts committed before the effective date of the statute do not violate due process.

In order to establish liability, the United States has to prove the following:

1. The site is a hazardous waste facility;
2. Release or threat of release of hazardous substances from the site has occurred;
3. The release or threat of release has caused the United States to incur response costs; and

4. The defendant is one of the persons designated as the party liable for costs, i.e., present owner or operators, past owners or operators, generators, or transporters.

To owners and operators, CERCLA places liability upon present site owners and operators, even though they have not disposed of hazardous wastes on the site during ownership tenure. *New York v. Shore Realty Corporation,* 759 F. 2d 1032 (2d Cir. 1985). The statutory term owner/operator has even been judicially construed to include both the landlord and tenant of a hazardous waste facility. An NBC television news broadcast stated that the EPA had gone so far as to declare the Drug Enforcement Agency as an operator of a toxic waste facility within the meaning of CERCLA after they seized hazardous waste from illegal methamphetamine factories.

This statute is all encompassing and the meaning is apparent -- attack the deep pocket in order to clean up the environment.

Defenses

There are several defenses under CERCLA, Section 107(b) (42 U.S.C. 9607(b)). These defenses are (1) act of God; (2) act of war; (3) act of omission of a third party; and (4) any combination of the above. Section 107(b) requires that a defendant prove that the release or threat of release of a hazardous substance and the damage resulting therefrom were caused solely by the acts referred to in the items 1 through 4 above. Therefore, if any act or omission of a third party which falls within the scope of 107(b)(3) is only a partial cause of release or threat of a release or the defendant's actions are also a partial cause, then the defendant is liable under CERCLA.

The defense that is most available, and the one we are concerned with, is the one referred to as that of an "innocent purchaser." Amendments to CERCLA: SARA, provide an innocent purchaser defense as a statutory defense. Under 42 U.S.C. 9601 (35)(A), the purchaser has a defense to liability if the property was acquired without knowledge or reason to know of the contamination. To demonstrate "no reason to know," according to 42 U.S.C. 9601 (35)(B), a purchaser:

. . . Must have undertaken at the time of acquisition, all appropriate inquiry into the previous ownership and uses of the property consistent with good commercial or customary practice in an effort to minimize liability. For purposes of the preceding sentence, the court shall take into account any specialized knowledge or experience on the part of the purchaser, the relationship of the purchase price to the value of the property if uncontaminated, commonly known or reasonably ascertainable information about the property, the obviousness or the presence of contamination at the property and the ability to detect such contamination by appropriate inspection.

Thus, in order to establish the "innocent purchaser" defense under 42 U.S.C. 9601(35)(A), the defendant must show by a preponderance of the evidence that the defendant acquired the property after the disposal or placement of hazardous substance in or at the facility, and the defendant must show one or more of the following circumstances:

1. At the time the defendant acquired the facility, the defendant did not know, and did not have reason to know, that any hazardous substances which are the subject of the release or threatened release were disposed of on, in, or at the facility;
2. The defendant is a government entity which acquired the facility by escheat or through any other involuntary transfer or acquisition, or through the exercise of imminent domain authority by purchase or condemnation; or
3. The defendant acquired the facility by inheritance or bequest. 42 U.S.C. 9601 (35)(A).

It seems that, as a minimum, the purchaser must, in order to avoid liability:

1. Inquire into the current and previous ownership and uses of the property;
2. Inquire into the environmental compliance record of all prior property owners, including review of all available public or government records concerning compliance; and
3. Conduct either itself or through a representative, an actual environmental inspection of the property.

Section 101 (35)(c) of CERCLA states that if a person obtained actual knowledge of release or threatened release of a hazardous substance at a facility which it owned and then subsequently transferred ownership of the property to another person without disclosing that knowledge, then the non-disclosing seller is treated as liable under Section 107. That defendant will not be permitted to raise the defense of act or omission of a third party under Section 107(b)(3), or that of an innocent purchaser.

Thus, it would seem that hear no evil, see no evil, speak no evil, will not relieve one of liability if hazardous waste is found on property sold, owned or purchased by the individual. In essence, if you own property on which hazardous substances are found to be disposed, you will be required to prove that you had no part in the disposal of those hazardous wastes nor did you have any knowledge or reason to know they were present. You will also be required to show that, prior to the purchase, you conducted a reasonable inquiry consistent with your relative commercial sophistication.

Lender Liability

Besides purchasers of real estate, there is one other class of potentially responsible parties that has to be discussed before discussion of how to protect oneself in dealing in real estate transactions. Specifically, lenders must be aware of their potential liability.

CERCLA excluded from its definition of "owner or operator" of a hazardous waste facility any person who, without participating in the management of a facility, holds security interest. 42 U.S.C. 9601 (20)(A). The term "owner" was not intended to include certain persons possessing indicia of ownership, such as a financial institution, who, without participating in the management or operation of such facility, held title in order to secure a loan or in connection with a lease financing arrangement under the appropriate banking laws, rules or regulations.

Problems arise when the lender becomes involved in the management of the property, as may happen in a workout situation, at which point the lender may become an "operator" within the meaning of the statute. Problems also occur when, as a result of a default, the lending institution forecloses on the property and takes possession. In the case of *United*

States v. Maryland Bank and Trust, 632 F. Supp. 973 (D. Md. 1986), the court found the mortgager liable under CERCLA as an owner. In that case, the court concluded that while the lender was not liable as an owner under CERCLA so long as it simply held its mortgage, it would subsequently become an owner by virtue of taking title through foreclosure and holding such title thereafter for four years. It noted:

> Lenders, however, already have the means to protect themselves by making prudent loans. Financial institutions are in a position to investigate and discover potential problems of under-secured properties. For many lending institutions, such research is routine. CERCLA will not absolve them from responsibility for their mistakes in judgement.

The courts have been divided as to the potential liability of creditors who do not foreclose on their debts nor engage in the debtors' day-to-day operations, but do seek to protect their interests. In *United States v. Fleet Factors* 901 F2d 1550 (11th Cir. 1990) the court determined that participation to influence the debtor's treatment and disposal of hazardous waste could create liability under CERCLA. However, in *re Bergsoe Metal Corp.*, 910 F2d 668 (9th Cir. 1990) that court held that there must be some actual management of the facility by the secured creditor before liability may be incurred. Several pieces of legislation have been offered to resolve the creditor's dilemma and the EPA has proposed a policy to delineate who will be liable but the parameters of lender liability remain unclear. It is certain that if a lender forecloses on a mortgage and takes possession of the property or evidences any indicia of control over the property, then it could conceivably be held liable as an owner or operator of the property. As such owner or operator, the lender would likely be liable for clean up costs should the EPA or the state determine that clean up or remedial action is necessary.

State Legislation

Purchasers or lenders must also be concerned not only with CERCLA of the EPA but also with state legislation such as those that govern the environment in the state of Tennessee. State statutes cover solid waste disposal, T.C.A. 68-31-101, *et. seq.*, hazardous waste management, T.C.A. 68-46-101, *et. seq.*, and underground storage tanks, T.C.A. 68-

53-1011, *et. seq.* Other environmental concerns are found in the Water and Sewage Act, T.C.A. 68-13-101, *et. seq.*, which includes the Safe Drinking Water Act and the Water Environmental Health Act. The Air Pollution Control Act is found at T.C.A. 68-33-101, *et. seq.*

It is important to note at this point that the Tennessee Hazardous Waste Management Act, T.C.A. 68-46-101, *et. seq.* provides that after July 1, 1988, any inactive or active cleanup site must be registered in the county where the property lies. When the site is eventually cleaned up or contained, an additional notice must be registered indicating that the site is now cleaned up, contained, or inactive. The purpose of the statute is to notify potential buyers of a hazardous waste site, and therefore to eventually preclude the sale of the property to anyone without knowledge, either actual or constructive, that the site is, in fact, a hazardous waste site. There are currently 280 of these sites in Tennessee. This requirement is not peculiar to Tennessee and you should check your state statutes.

Prior to January, 1989, Tennessee was one of the few states that had termed the "Superlien." This lien, when filed against the property by the State for the amount of the State's costs received in cleaning up a site, would have had priority over all other liens, including both prior and subsequent liens, filed against the property, in order to insure that clean up costs and the costs of remediation were paid by the owner. The "Superlien" has now been repealed, and any lien filed by the state to recover its cleanup and remediation costs is subordinate to pre-existing liens. Of course, given the question of lender liability, the presence of such a post-filed lien should give the lender pause before it chooses to foreclose.

A case out of Knox County, *Tennessee v. Foot Mineral Co., et. al.,* 12 TAM 47-28, evidences which way the environmental ball is rolling in the state of Tennessee as well as other states. In that case, Knox County became the owner of some property that was a hazardous waste site by virtue of the fact that the Dickerson Company, a successor in title of Foot Mineral, had executed a loan agreement with a promissory note to the County, secured by a Deed of Trust on the same property. After the Dickerson Company defaulted on the note and filed for bankruptcy in U.S.

Bankruptcy Court, the Bankruptcy Court ordered the Dickerson Company to convey all its right, title, and interest in the site to the County. It complied with that order, executed and delivered a warranty deed conveying the site to the County. The County contended that under the Tennessee Governmental Tort Liability Act, T.C.A. 29-20-101, *et. seq.*, it was immune from the provisions of the Hazardous Waste Management Act. The court did not accept that argument nor did it accept Knox County's contentions that it was not an owner-operator and that it had not fully accepted the deed because it did not register it in Knox County. The court determined that Knox County was an owner-operator within the meaning of the statute and determined that it was, in fact, one of the responsible parties.

Other Regulatory Concerns

Other regulatory concerns that a purchaser should consider prior to purchasing a property are listed below. These concerns are merely listed for identification, so any purchaser should seek legal advice in connection with their application to specific transactions.

1. *Environmental Permits.* Both state and federal regulations require permits for the discharge or generation of hazardous wastes in the form of air or water pollutants or other types of environmental pollutants. If permits are current, then the property has added value. If, however, they have been allowed to lapse, the cost of reapplying for the permits should be factored into the cost of the purchase because often it is more difficult to obtain a new permit for a particular operation than it would be to acquire the old one due to regulatory requirements becoming more stringent over time.

2. *Underground Storage Tanks.* Federal and state regulations governing the storage of materials in underground tanks will have a significant impact upon property transactions. It is important for a seller to disclose and for a buyer to learn about the existence of underground storage tanks on the property in advance of purchase and sale. The current condition of those tanks and the types of substances in those tanks must be disclosed. The existence of underground tanks should be a signal to the purchaser that an environmental audit should be

conducted to examine, among other things, tank integrity and possible releases.

3. *Toxic Substances Control Act.* The Toxic Substances Control Act (TSCA) regulates the clean-up of Polychloral Biphenyls (PCB's), a substance that is difficult to clean up and dispose of, and is present in many manufacturing sites. A substance used in transformers and machinery for years before it was regulated, it should be a point of focus at all industrial sites.

4. *Potential Pollutants.* Much of the environmental analysis of real estate transactions focuses on the outdoor environment regulated by EPA. For purchase of existing structures, actual or potential indoor air pollution is also a concern.

The presence of radon gas, asbestos fibers and lead paint, can lead to worker's compensation claims and claims by employees, among other contaminants, or personal injury claims by others who visit the facility. Currently, EPA has regulations that require removal of asbestos insulation from schools. EPA does not have similar requirements for commercial manufacturing facilities. However, EPA has issued a guidance document with suggestions for discovery and action to correct problems with old asbestos.

The Federal Occupational Safety and Health Administration (OSHA) currently has regulations which specifically govern the exposure of employees to asbestos (29 CFR 1910.1001). If there is the suspicion that asbestos fibers are present at the facility about to be purchased, testing by an industrial hygiene consultant can disclose the level of any asbestos fibers present in the facility. If that level indicates that the OSHA regulation is applicable, the expense of complying with the regulations and the possibility of claims of injury due to exposure should be factored into the purchase consideration.

EPA has recently suggested that every home be tested for radon. EPA has developed the guidance of radon. Usually, these actions have a goal of increasing the air exchange rate in the building or sealing cracks in lower levels of the building, so that the radon gas does not seep from the soil into the structure. Although EPA has concentrated on home owners, these concerns apply equally to business facilities.

In addition, OSHA has a number of regulations governing occupational exposure to various types of chemicals within the work environment. If an existing manufacturing facility is to be acquired, a review of the manufacturing process and the raw materials used will enable the purchaser and the seller to make an intelligent evaluation of the chemicals that might be present. OSHA requires that for many chemicals a material safety data sheet (MSDS) be maintained. The MSDS should be reviewed by your consultant prior to purchase.

How to Protect Yourself, Your Client, and Your Wallet

Environmental Assessment

Generally, as indicated earlier, to show one as an innocent purchaser and demonstrate that purchaser had no reason to know about any contamination to the property, the purchaser must have undertaken, at the time of acquisition, all appropriate inquiry into the previous ownership and leases of the property consistent with good commercial or customary practice in an effort to minimize liability. This inquiry has become known as the "due diligence assessment."

Initially, a review of the previous ownership and real estate to identify those who may have used, stored, handled, treated, or disposed of hazardous materials on the site is appropriate. A check of local, state and federal records to determine whether real estate is listed as an actual or suspected site of hazardous waste materials release should also be done. Records should be checked of any improper usage, any spill incidents or any underground storage tanks that may be present. Records should be checked to determine whether or not underground storage tanks comply with state and federal requirements concerning registration, and a determination should be made as to what stage the "upgrading" has attained.

A physical inspection of the property for the presence of any indicators such as pits, ponds, lagoons, or surface or subsurface disposal sites should be done. Unusual absence of vegetation, discolored soils, and dead or distressed vegetation are also indicators of contamination. If there are such indicators, soil and subsurface groundwater sampling with onsite qualitative screening of samples for contaminants, usually followed by quantitative analysis of samples in a laboratory, should be performed. Some type of geophysical testing to determine the presence of underground storage tanks or buried drums may also be indicated by a surface inspection.

Usually, the first two, that is, the review of the history of the previous ownership and a check of the local state and federal records would constitute a Phase I assessment. If this check reveals an actual or potential risk, then the second phase, involving the physical tests, should be conducted.

An environmental assessment is usually a good way to protect the buyer, in some cases, the seller, and in almost all cases, the lender in real estate transactions.

It is important for the parties involved in the transaction to determine what they hope to accomplish by the environmental assessment before hiring a consultant. It is also important to determine, as best they can, the scope of the assessment so that the scope will be clear to the consultant prior to the initiation of the environmental assessment. The type of assessment conducted by a consultant for a lender may be different in degree from what might be conducted by the buyer of the real estate or the seller of the real estate. Information is the important tool and the question becomes who has access to the information gleaned by the consultant?

Assuming that you need an environmental assessment, the scope of that assessment will depend on whether you are the buyer, the seller, or the lender. Usually, the assessment is done by the buyer looking to determine what risks there are in the actual purchase of this property. On occasion, a lender may require that the potential borrower have an environmental assessment conducted. This raises an interesting question on both counts. Who gets the report and who does the environmental consultant work for?

In the best of all possible worlds, the environmental consultant would be neutral, working for the good of all mankind. Many of them believe that they do. Unfortunately, in the reality of real estate transactions, full disclosure and widest possible dissemination would not be the norm when dealing with environmental assessment. The parties must first determine the scope of any environment assessment. Usually, the purchaser should consult his attorney to determine the initial scope of any environmental assessment, whether one is required or needed, and whether the attorney has any recommendations as to consultants.

In order to protect the information, the attorney should actually contract with an environmental consultant, perhaps after several bids and proposals from various consultants. Part of the parameters of the contract would be that a report would be initially drafted for the attorney and then, after some modification by the attorney, would be forwarded to the client. This does not preclude all three getting together to discuss various aspects of the report or any problems on the property, nor does it preclude the expert or consultant talking to the owner about some problems. It does, however, provide the opportunity for a subsequent assertion of an attorney-client privilege or an attorney work-product privilege to keep information from either an environmental protection agency or other entity during the course of a subsequent action concerning what may have been found on the land. This approach may also prevent competitors or potential bidders for the real estate from getting the advantage of information gathered as a result of this environmental assessment.

A secrecy agreement should also be signed by the consultant to provide additional assurances of protection, not only for the client, but also for the consultant.

The consultant's initial report should be directed to the attorney who should insure that certain things are in the report and certain things are not. Once the attorney has made his/her comments and sent them back to the consultant, the consultant will prepare a final report and send it back to the attorney. The attorney will then prepare a cover letter which amounts to a report written by the attorney. This cover letter could highlight portions of the consultant's report, explain the law, deal with any matters not addressed by the consultant, give a description of the limitations of the environmental review, and if appropriate, make recommendations of steps that might be taken to reduce the client's environmental risks in the transaction. Attorneys should work closely with consultants to ensure that the work of the consultant does not include interpretations or application of law.

The whole purpose of the environmental assessment and the cooperation between attorney and consultant is to provide the client, be it the purchaser or the lender, with the greatest amount of usable information and the best possible course of action, along with any alternatives.

Using the team concept, a good environmental assessment will provide the client with the experience and technical expertise of the consultant, the legal expertise and experience of a lawyer, combined to provide the client with various choices from which it can make the right decision. This decision may be to go on to additional testing under the Phase II concept, or to terminate the deal based on information gleaned in the initial phase of the assessment.

Protective Contract Clauses

Probably as a result of a plethora of lawsuits involving third party claims premised on environmental problems, as well as the Superfund, it has become extremely difficult, if not impossible, to obtain insurance, especially for manufacturing facilities. Insurance premiums have skyrocketed or insurance is simply unavailable. Although normally older insurance policies will try to indicate that they do not cover environmental damage, it is best to make the claim.

1. *Warranties* -- Purchasers of real estate have sought to protect themselves through warranties, representations and indemnifications from the seller. Sellers would prefer to sell the property on an *as is* basis. The warranty in the sales agreement that the property has never been used for any handling, treatment, storage, or disposal of hazardous waste is a good protection for the purchaser. However, it is unrealistic to expect that type of warranty on a manufacturing facility or in any type of property.

   Assuming you cannot get that type of warranty, it is important to pursue other warranties about the condition of the property or prior activities on it. The seller may not have complete knowledge of what has occurred on the property prior to his ownership, so the buyer should seek certification from the seller detailing the seller's knowledge and the seller's representations. It is important to obtain a warranty or certification that the seller's documents and records are accurate and complete to the best of the seller's knowledge.

The purchaser and developer should seek to get a representation or warranty by the seller that there have been no releases or threatened releases of hazardous materials, waste, substances, pollutants, or contaminants in and upon or under the real estate, not to the seller's knowledge, have there been any such releases with respect to adjacent or neighboring properties, through soil or groundwater migration which could have come to be located on or under the real estate. This warranty should be combined with an indemnity against all loss, liability, damage and expense, including expert and attorney fees on account of such representations and warranties proving to be inaccurate.

There should also be an understanding that the purchaser's obligations to acquire real estate are conditional upon site assessment not revealing the presence of a release of hazardous materials, pollutants, contaminants, or of any undisclosed condition, such as underground storage tanks, which may create future liability problems. There should also be an agreement as to which party is to pay for the costs of the site assessment and an agreement that the purchaser or its agent will have a right of access to the real estate to conduct such inspection.

The purchaser should also require a full disclosure of all conditions relating to any known and existing environmental concerns and an appropriate allocation of the responsibility and liability. What this means is that if there is an on-going problem, or if there is minimal contamination, the purchaser should make sure that responsibility is fixed at the point at which he purchases the property.

The purchaser should obtain warranties and representations that there are no outstanding notices of violations of enforcement actions and that there is no reason for the seller to believe that there are private environmental claims against the property. The purchaser should also seek a warranty that the seller has provided all required notification to environmental agencies.

The buyer will want to insure that the sales agreement provides that environmental warranties survive any environmental site investigation by the buyer and also survive the closing of the transaction. The buyer should insist on the removal of all hazardous waste before it takes possession of the facility. The buyer should also attempt to obtain the seller's agreement that it will remove all wastes, not just hazardous wastes, from the site before the buyer takes possession.

2. *Indemnification* -- Many sales agreements involving property with potential environmental contamination include an indemnification or hold harmless provision. This provision states that if environmental contamination problems are found, the seller agrees to reimburse the buyer for its costs, such as environmental compliance cost, including remedial action and/or damage to third parties. The seller must negotiate this clause very carefully because an open ended agreement could subject the seller to substantial liability over a long period of time.

It is important to recognize that seller and buyer cannot, by agreement, change their liability to the government under Superfund. Liability to the government at the time of disposal or liability as a past owner, or liability as a generator or transporter, cannot be contracted away. The government will still sue the parties liable under the statute, but indemnification for that liability or any other liabilities may shift the financial obligation among those responsible under the act. However, the indemnification provision is only as good as the solvency of the party giving it.

An additional question will be whether the indemnification would cover only the contamination caused by the immediate seller or will it also include previous owners? This, of course, would depend on the site itself. A purchaser or a seller owning a 100 year old manufacturing plant would not want to take on the indemnification requirements that might entail. A way to limit this particular problem would be to put a ceiling on the amount in dollars of claims the purchaser can make, either a flat ceiling or a staggered structure.

A time period could be another way of limiting the indemnification requirement. Any combination of time limit and monetary cap could be negotiated by the parties.

Another consideration is whether the indemnification covers all remedial acts or just those required by laws or regulations existing at the time the transaction is closed. For example, after the sale of the property, the EPA might propose that a material that is currently unregulated that has been spilled or disposed of on the property, be classified as hazardous waste. No clean up action would be required now but the new owner may be liable if EPA brings stringent new regulations into play. As with warranties, the buyer will want to insure that the sales agreement provides that all indemnification provisions survive any environmental site investigation by the buyer and also survive the closing.

If the seller is forced to retain liability for onsite contamination, it should try to negotiate a release from this liability if the buyer causes the situation to become worse or causes the contamination to migrate off site. The seller should also try to negotiate conditions requiring the buyer to meet certain standards of handling hazardous substances. The seller may also want to contract for the right to inspect environmental records and the right to inspect the property after the sale in order to protect itself.

In essence, if the seller retains any liability, it should make every effort to have written into the contract certain notification requirements, including notification of any sampling or testing onsite with the opportunity to be present. Also, the seller should seek notification of any complaint against and compliance by the current owner with all environmental rules and regulations.

3.   *Lenders* -- In order to protect itself, lenders should get certain concessions from the borrower as conditions to closing the loan. First, they should require that the lender be provided with a hazardous materials site assessment confirming that there are no

hazardous materials or contamination of the real estate. The loan commitment and loan agreement should provide that the consultant preparing the assessment works for the bank and will provide the assessment directly to the bank, even if the borrower is required by the lender to pay the fees for the preparation of the assessment. Part of the agreement should be that the borrower agrees to comply with all applicable environmental rules and regulations, including those pertaining to hazardous materials. Second, the borrower should agree to provide lender with immediate notice of hazardous material release on mortgaged real estate property and to pursue diligently the completion of all appropriate and/or required remediation actions in the event of such releases. This might include a self-help option where the mortgage holder is permitted at its option to undertake all or part of the remedial action in the event of hazardous material release and to add expenditures it so incurs to the loan.

The lender should structure the loan agreement in order to require as much information be provided to the lender as possible and also requiring that the borrower maintain the property and protect the collateral from environmental damage while, at the same time, attempting to avoid the possibility of foreclosure or the appearance that it has taken too much of an active direction in the business being conducted on the property. The lender has to be careful that it does not cross the line thereby causing them to be considered an "operator" within the meaning of the Superfund statute.

CONCLUSION

There are conflicting views on how much environmental information should be gathered, how it should be gathered, and how it should be disseminated. The purchasers of property, particularly commercial real estate, holds a veritable plethora of horror stories and pitfalls. Before jumping into the "environmental morass" purchasers should carefully analyze the property they would like to purchase either by use of their own personnel, a consultant, their lawyer or any combination of the above. It is important that purchasers and lenders understand that there is a probability of some sort of environmental contamination on property that has had a long history of manufacturing.

Buyers and developers should consider the production by the lawyer of a "Property Purchase Assessment" or "Transaction Assessment." This would be a collection of legal, financial, and environmental concerns in a report for the buyer. The report would include reports by CPA's, environmental consultants, and a title search, all tied together with a legal review and a recommendation. This would provide protection for the environmental audit and will assist the buyer in having all of the important aspects of a transaction in one report.

The risk belongs to those who make the decision to buy or not to buy, and to lend or not to lend, but those who do can help themselves by gathering as much information as they possibly can about the subject properly. Upon the decision to purchase, the buyer should conduct an appropriate inquiry, negotiate strong warranties, and full indemnifications, in order to protect itself. The CERCLA has added new meaning to the phrase *Caveat Emptor*, "Let the buyer beware."

DUE DILIGENCE ASSESSMENTS

H.T. (Tom) Carson, P.E., CHMM
Signal Environmental Services, Inc.

INTRODUCTION

A due diligence assessment is an environmental assessment that is "an all appropriate inquiry into previous ownership and uses of the property consistent with good commercial or customary practice in an effort to minimize liability." It must take into account "all commonly known or reasonably ascertainable information about the property, the obviousness of the presence or likely presence of contamination of the property, and the ability to detect such contamination by appropriate inspection." This language, from the Comprehensive Environmental Response, Compensation, and Liability Act (PL-96-510) (Superfund), is what an environmental assessment is judged against to determine if it has been performed with "due diligence" and the defense for an innocent landowner.

Why conduct a due diligence assessment?

The due diligence assessment is a method of avoiding future liability. If the property is found to be contaminated to the extent public health or the environment is threatened, a cleanup will be required. The property owner may also be liable for any real or perceived problems caused by other people's exposure to toxic chemicals. If a good due diligence assessment is conducted, and contamination is found before purchase, the purchase can be stopped or the property value can be reduced to cover the cost of cleanup. If a competent and *thorough* due diligence assessment was performed and contamination was later found, the property owner has some protection under Superfund, but it is still likely to be an unpleasant and costly experience.

What constitutes a good due diligence assessment?

A good due diligence assessment *cost effectively* minimizes future liability. There are no absolute guarantees that even after a thorough due diligence assessment a hazardous materials problem will not be found on or under your property. This risk can be minimized by increasing the scope, and unfortunately for the property owner, the cost of the due diligence assessment. It is the environmental professional's job to help the potential property owner balance the risk versus costs. The best method is to implement a "tiered" or phased approach where relatively inexpensive tasks or analyses are performed first. Quite often, data is uncovered early in an assessment that would preclude purchase. If this occurs, the assessment is over. The phased approach may require more time but can usually be tailored to fit the property history. Constructing a commercial building on a former farm offers different risks than construction of the same building in an industrialized area.

What constitutes a phase I or minimum due diligence assessment?

Phase I covers all commonly known or reasonably ascertainable information regarding the property and the obviousness of the presence or likely presence of contamination of the property. This is accomplished by the following:

RECORDS OF PAST PROPERTY USE -- A deed search will provide the assessor records of past ownership and often, but not always, uses of the land. For example, if the land was owned by Acme Metal Stamping during the mid 1960s a good assessor should suspect the presence of solvents and PCBs. Metal stamping facilities use solvents to remove grease and PCBs were common hydraulic fluids in presses. A deed search is only the first piece of the puzzle. It can only determine who owned the property. The property may have been owned by Blue Sky Enterprises but leased by Creative Transformer Salvage.

INTERVIEWS -- Interviews with former owners, employees, and neighbors can be valuable in filling in information not accessible from deed searches. An interview may reveal that an old gully out back was filled with waste and covered or that Midnight Waste Haulers rented the property for three years.

NEIGHBORING PROPERTY USES -- The property being assessed may be clean but there could be several contaminated sites nearby that could contaminate the groundwater flowing under the property being assessed. Also, a company upstream of the site may have polluted the sediment in a creek that flows through or bounds the property. The sediment in the creek may require cleanup.

AVAILABLE ENVIRONMENTAL DATA -- Several government agencies perform environmental studies. Information from these studies can be very helpful in understanding environmental problems in an area. A good example is TVA and the Chattanooga Creek Basin. TVA has studied the area since 1935 and published several reports including an excellent report in 1937 which detailed the industries operating in the area and their waste problems. Files from state health departments, wildlife resource agencies, forestry departments, state geological surveys, the U.S. Geologic Survey, and the U.S. Environmental Protection Agency can be valuable sources.

AVAILABLE GEOLOGIC DATA -- The state regulatory agency maintains a list of known or suspected Superfund sites. They also have records of all sites since 1980 that list sites notified as generators, treaters, or disposers of hazardous waste. This is readily available data, but we are aware of at least two sites where the assessors did not request this information. One site is already investigating how to clean up the contamination not identified by a poorly performed assessment.

MAPS AND AERIAL PHOTOGRAPHY -- On many sites aerial photography exists so that a history of the land use changes can be reconstructed for a 50-60 year period. However, aerial photography is only as good as the interpreter. If aerial photography is used, it should only be interpreted by a trained cartographer or remote sensing expert. Aerial photographs should be purchased in stereo pairs or triplets.

SITE WALKOVER -- This stage of Phase I involves a knowledgeable assessor walking over the site looking for evidence of contamination such as oil contaminated soil, stressed vegetation, and changes in contours that might suggest filling. The site walkover demands an experienced assessor.

ACQUIRED DATA -- Limited sampling may be done in Phase I if the assessor suspects a major problem that would stop purchase. This limited sampling is usually in suspicious areas such as former materials storage areas, areas of stressed vegetation, or discolored or odorous soils or waters.

PHASE I REPORT -- The Phase I report summarizes the data, assesses the extent of risk based on this data, and makes recommendation on property purchase or to proceed with Phase II. The Phase I report and any internal documentation or correspondence relating to property purchase should be kept as long as a chance exists for becoming a Potentially Responsible Party (PRP). If the site is determined to be contaminated years from now, the purchaser or his estate may be named as PRP and forced to contribute toward cleanup. A good due diligence assessment could save big money.

What constitutes a Phase II assessment?

Phase II studies are performed when the Phase I assessment is inconclusive and there is enough risk and uncertainty to undergo the costs. Careful planning must go into a Phase II since the costs of sampling, analysis and drilling can become very expensive very fast. A Phase II assessment may include any of the following:

GEOPHYSICAL TESTING -- This testing can include a seismic test, ground penetrating radar, magnetics, and other tests. These are performed when there is some question on where to drill, on underground tanks, or if buried material is suspected. They are also sometimes used to assist in siting wells in "Karst" (weathered limestone) areas. These tests require sophisticated equipment and provide data that must be interpreted by a specialist.

GEOHYDROLOGIC STUDIES -- These studies include drilling and sampling wells to determining groundwater flow and contamination. The design and placement of wells is critical. Improperly constructed wells can result in data that is invalid and can introduce contamination into clean aquifers. In aquifers where the contaminant is floating on top of groundwater an improperly placed well screen can miss the contamination.

SAMPLING AND ANALYSIS -- Sampling and analysis may be the two areas most prone to problems. Improper sampling and preservation may add, or subtract contaminants. If equipment is not properly cleaned, contaminants may be introduced from the last job or from hole to hole. Sampling groundwater with the wrong pump can result in loss of certain volatile contaminants. Improper sample preservation can allow volatile contaminants to evaporate or other contaminants to precipitate or degrade.

The lab chosen for analysis should have good quality control procedures. Often duplicate samples are sent for quality control. On one site the duplicate sample results came back with one clean and one highly contaminated. An investigation revealed that both samples were highly contaminated, but the laboratory's computer had an error causing it to print false negative values. If this had been a single sample, a dirty site might have shown up clean.

We were once asked to evaluate the work of another assessor for a client. The assessor had run total lead on 50 samples and found most concentrations to be in the 20-30 ppm range with only 2 being over 100 ppm. Being inexperienced, the assessor requested a RCRA EP analysis on all 50 samples. The EP test involves a 20 to 1 dilution. Thus, only 2 of the 50 samples could possibly exceeded the 5 ppm RCRA EP criteria. The inexperienced assessor had requested about $5000 worth of unnecessary lab work.

PHASE II REPORT -- Data obtained under the Phase II assessment requires very experienced interpretation. What does 10 ppm of arsenic or 20 ppm of lead mean in the soil? (Probably nothing in certain native clays). What do traces of bis 2-ethyl-hexyl-pthalate mean in groundwater? (This is a common sampling and lab-introduced contaminant). The experienced assessor makes use of existing criteria for waste land uses, toxicity, and exposure information, regulatory guidance, potential for exposure, and many other factors in developing this assessment.

How do I select an environmental assessor?

It is not easy.   There are no education, training, or certification requirements for the title "environmental assessor."*   Some financial institutions are turning toward registered professional engineers to do the job.   However, not all P.E.s, or even P.E.s with environmental engineering backgrounds, are qualified.   The Hazardous Materials Manager Certification adds some credence to the assessors ability, but this program was designed to assess the applicant's ability to manage an industrial hazardous materials management program -- not to do environmental assessments.

In selecting your assessor, check the educational background and experience records carefully. If you want an engineer to do the work, make certain their training and experience is in a related field. In most states, any person using engineer as part of their title in public matters must be a Registered Professional Engineer. You may also want to check with the State Engineering Registration Board to validate their registration and make sure there are no outstanding complaints. Ask to see examples of other due diligence assessments and check with their clients about their overall satisfaction. If these are not available due to client confidentially ask the assessor to provide the number and types of environmental assessments he has performed and what his role was in each assessment.

Ask the assessor for references attesting to their technical expertise in areas necessary to do environmental assessments. Find out who will be doing your assessment and their qualifications. Insist that all work be performed by the experts identified. Some companies may have 1 or 2 people competent to do the assessments and use their credentials for all assessments. Your assessment may then be done by a recent hire with education in a minimally related field and with little or no experience and only limited supervision.

Assessor credentiality is becoming an important enough issue that EPA and some professional organizations are working to develop standards and

---

*California has a legal qualification, but it is weak.

tests. Until these standards are available and put into practice, the "Caveat Emptor" should be purchaser's credo.

These assessment forms are included as part of this paper. Completing these forms does not constitute a due diligence assessment. The author assumes no liability for the use or misuse of these forms.

Information Given to Client to Help with Sellers Information Form

What are hazardous materials and wastes?

This is a very complex question and will take a complicated answer. Basically, a hazardous material or waste is a material that poses a danger to human health or the environment. Many of these are evident to almost anyone -- gasoline, arsenic, asbestos, explosives, etc.

This short description will help you assist us in evaluating your property for sale. Truthful and accurate answers to these questions will expedite the assessment of your property and may minimize your future liability. The days of "Let the Buyer Beware" and "My Liability Ends at Sale" are largely over when it comes to hazardous waste and materials. If a hazardous waste problem is found on your former piece of property, you will likely become a potentially responsible party (PRP) and be partially or wholly liable for cleanup.

Characteristics of hazardous materials/waste.

- Flammable/Ignitable/Combustible -- This includes a wide range of chemicals and petroleum-based products that readily burn.
- Corrosives are acids, bases, and materials that rapidly attack metals.
- Reactives are materials that react with water to produce fire, explosions, or toxic gases. Explosives are also reactives.
- Toxic Characteristic Leaching Procedures (TCLP) -- These materials leach toxic constituents if land disposed. Materials containing mercury, lead, chromium, arsenic, selenium, cadmium, silver, barium, and certain solvents and pesticides may be TCLP Toxic. Examples may be paints, used oils, batteries, metal plating sludges, and some foundry sands.
- Wastes from certain processes or types of wastes. Examples are wood-treating wastes, metal cleaning wastes, certain dye wastes.
- Certain chemical products -- Listed by EPA in 40 CFR Part 261.

- Underground Tanks. If underground tanks have ever been onsite, they probably contained a hazardous material at some time. Under certain conditions a petroleum leak 50 years ago may require cleanup.
- Polychlorinated biphenyls (PCBs) -- these were used in transformers and capacitors, hydraulic fluids, cutting oils, and in numerous products.
- Radioactivity -- Processes resulting in radioactive contamination are rare, but should be noted if suspected.
- Asbestos had been used in fire resistant building products, insulation, brake pads, thermal insulation for steam lines, etc. Asbestos fibers in the air cause serious lung diseases.
- Radon is a decay product of uranium that is naturally occurring in some geologic formations. Building products, especially cinderblocks made from materials high in uranium, may release radon gas. Radon becomes a problem in airtight buildings where the levels accumulate.
- Urea formaldehyde -- was used in certain foam insulations and in plywood. Usually released from these building materials when relatively new.

SELLER'S INFORMATION FORM

The following information is needed to assist in assessing the environmental condition of the property. If more space is needed to answer a question than that provided, please attach supplemental pages.

1. Name and principal address of seller (owner):

_____

_____

_____

_____

2. Location of the property if different than the address provided above:

_____

_____

_____

3. The seller owned the property approximately _____ year(s).

4. During the seller's ownership of the property, the property has been used for:

_____

_____

_____

_____

5. Before the seller acquired the property, to the best of his/her knowledge the property was used for:

_____

_____

_____

_____

6. Please provide the names and addresses of previous owners of the property to the extent known:

_____

_____

_____

_____

7. Has the site been filled? ☐ yes ☐ no. If yes, where did the fill come from? _____

8. Do you know what constitutes a hazardous waste or material?

☐ yes ☐ no

If no, definitions are attached.

9. Have either solid or hazardous wastes been disposed of, used, stored, or otherwise located on the property?

☐ yes ☐ no

10. Have any hazardous substances been released, either intentionally or accidentally, on the property?

    ☐ yes ☐ no

11. If the answer to questions 7 or 8 is yes, please identify to the extent known, the kind of wastes/substances, their location or the location of the release on the property, and when they came to be located on or released to the property:

    _____

    _____

    _____

    _____

    _____

12. Have any activities been conducted on the property that required environmental permits?
    If so, please identify the activities and the permits:

    _____

    _____

    _____

    _____

    _____

13. Have any of the activities conducted on the property been investigated by an environmental agency or are they the subject of an ongoing investigation? If so, please identify those activities and the agency(ies):

_____

_____

_____

_____

14. Have any citations for violations of environmental requirements or permits been issued because of activities on the property? If so, please identify those activities and the violations:

_____

_____

_____

_____

15. Are there any underground tanks located on the property or have such tanks been located on the property in the past? If so, please identify the location or former location of such tanks, the age of the tanks, and what is stored in them.

_____

_____

_____

16. To the best of your knowledge, have there been any releases of hazardous substances or wastes on the property adjoining this property? If so, please state what you know about such releases:

_____

_____

_____

17. Has an environmental site assessment been prepared for this property by you or someone else? □ yes □ no. If the answer is yes please provide a copy of this assessment.

18. Are you aware of any environmental pollution or contamination of the air, soil, surface, water, or groundwater on or beneath the property? If so, please describe this:

_____

_____

_____

I HEREBY CERTIFY THAT I AM AUTHORIZED TO PROVIDE THE ABOVE INFORMATION EITHER AS THE OWNER OF THE PROPERTY OR ON BEHALF OF THE OWNER OF THE PROPERTY AND THAT THE ABOVE INFORMATION IS TRUE AND CORRECT TO THE BEST OF MY KNOWLEDGE AND BELIEF.

_____

SIGNATURE   Title (if acting for an entity)

_____

DATE   Witness

REAL ESTATE

TRANSFER

ENVIRONMENTAL REVIEW CHECKLIST

Client _____

Client Contact _____

Property Owner (seller) _____

Property Description _____

_____

_____

Special Notes _____

PREVIOUS OWNERS

_____ _____ _____

_____ _____ _____

_____ _____ _____

_____ _____ _____

_____ _____ _____

_____ _____ _____

_____ _____ _____

AERIAL PHOTOGRAPHY SURVEY

Photography Available

Photographic Analysis Attached

FIELD SURVEY

NATURAL FEATURES OBSERVED (Place checkmark beside all that apply)

Geologic Features   ☐ sink holes   ☐ excavations

☐ mining activities   ☐ soil stockpiles

☐ diversion ditches

Water Features   ☐ wells   ☐ streams

☐ wetlands   ☐ surface erosion

☐ ponds   ☐ evidence of flooding

Vegetation Features and Conditions:

Type _____

Maturity _____

Density _____

Condition _____

MANMADE FEATURES OBSERVED

(Place checkmarks beside all that apply)

☐ Landfills

☐ Waste Dump

☐ Supplies/Waste Materials
Storage Yards

☐ Settlement Basins
(catchment ponds)

☐ Wastewater Discharges

☐ Discarded wastes,
(e.g., drums, batteries,
electrical equipment)

☐ Manholes/Catch Basins/
Drains/Fills Pipes

☐ Oil Stains

☐ Fuel storage

☐ Solvent storage

☐ Asbestos

☐ Chemical Transfer Points
(paved or unpaved/spill
evidence)

☐ Air Discharge Points

☐ PCB Equipment/
(Electric/Hydraulic/
other)

☐ Adjacent Land Use
(industrial, landfill)

☐ Spills (discolored soil or
surface water/odors/ash or
blackened areas/"unnatural
soil")

Other abandoned liquids or solid wastes (describe)

_____

_____

_____

_____

Comments:

_____

_____

_____

_____

_____

Signature

ENGINEERING OR CHMM SEAL

GLOSSARY

Compiled by John Frick, Ph.D.,

and

Gene Burns

AA	Atomic absorption spectrophometry. Refers to the analytical method or apparatus used for metals analysis.
AAPCO	Association of American Pesticide Control Officials, Inc. This association consists of officials charged by law with active execution of the laws regulating sale of economic poisons, and of deputies designated by these officials employed by State, Territorial, dominion, or Federal agencies. The group objective is to promote uniform and effective legislation, definitions, rulings, and enforcement of laws relating to control of sale and distribution of economic poisons.
AAR	Association of American Railroads
Absorption	(a) Penetration of a substance into the body of another;
	(b) transformation into other forms suffered by radiant energy passing through a material substance.

455

ACGIH

American Conference of Governmental Industrial Hygienists: An organization of professional personnel in governmental agencies or educational institutions engaged in occupational safety and health programs. ACGIH develops and publishes recommended occupational exposure limits (see TLV) for hundreds of chemical substance and physical agents.

Acid

A hydrogen-containing compound that reacts with water to produce hydrogen cations. Acid chemicals are corrosive (see also pH).

Acute Effect

An adverse effect on human or animal, generally after a single significant exposure, with severe symptoms developing rapidly and coming quickly to a crisis (also see "chronic effect").

Acute Toxicity

The adverse (acute) effect resulting from a single dose of, or exposure to, a substance.

Adsorption

Attachment of the molecules of a gas or liquid to the surface of another substance. This procedure is often used for the removal of a hazardous substance from water or air with activated carbon.

Aerosols

Liquid droplets or solid particles dispersed in air, that are of fine enough particle size (0.01 to 100 microns) to remain so dispersed for a period of time.

AIHA

American Industrial Hygiene Association

Alcohol

A low reactive, highly flammable class of organic compounds containing at least one hydrocarbon group and at least one hydroxyl group (R-OH).

Alkali	Any substance that in water solution is bitter, more or less irritating, or caustic to the skin. Strong alkalies in solution are corrosive to the skin and mucous membranes (see also pH). Forms the OH anion.
Alkane	A straight-chain saturated hydrocarbon with the generic formula C_nH_{2n+2}.
Alkene	A straight-chain unsaturated hydrocarbon with the generic formula C_nH_{2n}.
Alkyne	A straight-chain unsaturated hydrocarbon, characterized by the presence of a triple bond and possessing the generic formula C_nH_{2n-2}.
Alpha particle (α)	A radioactive decay emanation of relatively low penetrating power, travelling only a few millimeters in air. An alpha particle is a double-charged helium ion, with a positive charge of 2 and a mass number of 4.
Anhydrous	Free from water.
Anorexia	Lack or loss of appetite for food.
ANSI	American National Standards Institute
Asbestos	Any material containing more than 1 percent asbestos in any form.
Asbestosis	Lung disease caused by asbestos exposure.
Asphyxiant	A vapor or gas which can cause unconsciousness or death by suffocation (lack

of oxygen). Most simple asphyxiants are harmful to the body only when they become so concentrated that they reduce oxygen in the air (normally about 21 percent) to dangerous levels (18 percent or lower). Asphyxiation is one of the principal potential hazards of working in confined spaces.

ASTM	American Society for Testing and Materials
Atrophy	Arrested development or wasting away of cells and tissue.
Auto-ignition Temperature	The minimum temperature at which the material will ignite without a spark or flame being present. Along with the flashpoint, auto-ignition temperature gives an indication of relative flammability.
BADCT	Best Available Demonstrated Control Technology applies only to new industrial sources of pollution. Pollution control is built into the entire facility.
Base	Any material that produces hydroxide ions when it is dissolved in water. Other properties include bitter taste, slippery feel in solutions, and the ability to react with acids to form salts.
BAT	Best Available Technology or most stringent type of control for existing discharges and applies to toxic pollutants as well as conventional and some nonconventional pollutants.

BCT

Best Conventional Technology for discharges of conventional pollutants; more stringent than BPT.

Becquerel (Bq)

The unit for measuring radioactivity, equivalent to one disintegration per second (dps). It is named after the French physicist Henri Becquerel (1838-1906), who discovered the radioactivity of uranium salts and the existence of gamma radiation. See also dps.

BEJ

Best Engineering Judgment or type of control for pollution sources for which EPA has not issued regulations.

Beta particle (β)

A fast-moving particle emitted by an atomic nucleus during radioactive decay. These particles may be either positively or negatively charged, and one MeV particle can travel 400 cm in air but only 0.5 cm in water.

BIF

Boiler and Industrial Furnace Laws -- A new set of EPA regulations, pertaining to the combustion of RCRA regulated materials in systems other than true incinerators, which includes boilers, rotary kilns, and industrial furnaces.

Bioassay

A term used to describe the techniques by which a toxic agent, such as an insecticide, is tested and measured for potency. The technique involves testing of the toxicant at different dosage levels of ability to cause a physiological response (often death) in a test organism (e.g., insect, rat). In bioassay, chemicals are not identified individually. Bioassay may be used to determine the rate of loss after application of an insecticide to crop or soil, as confirmation of chemical assays of residues, for detection of insecticides as a cause of honeybee losses, etc.

Biocide

A substance that, when absorbed by eating, drinking, or breathing, or otherwise consumed in relatively small quantities, causes illness or death, or even retardation of growth or shortening of life.

Biohazard area

Any area (a complete operating complex, a single facility, a room within a facility, etc.) in which work has been, or is being performed with bio-hazardous agents or materials.

Biological Half-Life

The time required for a given species, organ, or tissue to eliminate half of a substance which it takes in.

Biological
Hazardous Wastes

Any substance of human or animal origin, other than food wastes, which are to be disposed of and (infections) could harbor or transmit pathogenic organisms including, but not limited to, pathological specimens such as tissues, blood elements, excreta, secretions, and related substances. This category includes wastes from health care facilities and laboratories, and biological and chemical warfare agents. Wastes from hospitals would include malignant or benign tissues taken during autopsies, biopsies, or surgery; hypodermic needles; and bandaging materials. Although the production of biological warfare agents has been restricted and production of chemical agents has been restricted and production of chemical agents discontinued, some quantities still remain and must be disposed of. See Title 9 CFR Part 102 (licensed veterinary biological products), Title 21 CFR Part 601 (Licensing) or Title 42 CFR Part 72.

Biological Magnification The concentration of certain substances up a food chain. A very important mechanism in concentrating pesticides and heavy metals in organisms such as fish.

Biological Treatment A process by which hazardous waste is rendered non-hazardous or is reduced in volume by the action of microorganisms to degrade organic waste.

Biological Wastewater Treatment A type of wastewater treatment in which bacterial or biochemical action is intensified to oxidize the unstable organic matter present. Intermittent sand filters, contact beds, trickling filters, and activated sludge tanks are examples of the equipment used.

Blasting Agent A material designed for blasting that has been evaluated according to one of the tests described in Title 49 CFR 173.114a of the Department of Transportation and found to be so insensitive that there is little probability of accidental initiation of explosion or of transition from deflagration to detonation.

BLEVE Boiling Liquid Expanding Vapor Explosion. In addition to its technical meaning, this acronym has acquired a common usage definition that has come to stand for virtually any rupture of a tank of liquid or liquefied compressed gas and has been expanded to include all vapor explosions. The technical definition of BLEVE presents the hypothesis that rapid depressurization of a hot, saturated liquid may result in an explosion. The temperature of the hot liquid must be above the superheat limit temperature at 1 atmosphere, and the drop in tank pressure must be very rapid. This requires instantaneous homogeneous nucleation of the hot liquid. This phenomenon has NOT been observed as the cause of failure of a transportation container.

BMP	Best Management Practices
BOE	Bureau of Explosives. Association of American Railroads.
Boiling Point	The temperature at which a liquid changes to a vapor state at a given pressure usually expressed in degrees Fahrenheit at sea level. Flammable materials with low boiling points generally present special fire hazards.
BPT	Best Practicable Technology -- minimum acceptable level of treatment for existing plants.
Breathing Zone	Air sample, collected in the breathing area
Sample	(around the nose) of a worker to assess his exposure to airborne contaminants.
°C	Degrees Centigrade (Celsius)
"C" or Ceiling	The maximum allowable human exposure limit for an airborne substance, not to be exceeded even momentarily (see also "PEL" and "TLV").
CAA	Clean Air Act

Canister	(Air purifying) A container filled with sorbents and catalysts that remove gases and vapors from air drawn through the unit. The canister may also contain an aerosol (particulate) filter to remove solid or liquid particles.
Capacitor	A device for accumulating and holding a charge of electricity and consisting of conducting surfaces separated by a dielectric.
Carcinogen	A substance capable of causing cancer.
cc	Cubic Centimeter: A volume measurement in the metric system equal in capacity to one milliliter (ml). One quart is about 946 cubic centimeters.
CDC	Center for Disease Control
Centigrade (Celsius)	The internationally used scale for measuring temperature, in which 100° is the boiling point of water at sea level (1 atmosphere), and 0° is the freezing point.
CEQ	Council on Environmental Quality
CERCLA	Comprehensive Environmental Response, Compensation and Liability Act (1980) (Superfund)
CFC/chloro-flourocarbons	Used as a propellent in aerosol cans. CFC poses no hazards in the workplace, but is a large contributor to ozone depletion. This substance remains stable until it reaches the ozone layer, where it breaks down ozone molecules.

CFR	Code of Federal Regulations
CGA	Compressed Gas Association
CGNRC	Coast Guard National Response Center
Chemical-Resistant	Materials that inhibit or protect against Materialspenetration chemicals.
CHEMTREC	Chemical Transportation Emergency Center, operated by the Chemical Manufacturing Association (CMA).
CHRIS	Chemical Hazards Response Information System published by the United States Coast Guard.
Chronic Effect	Adverse effects resulting from repeated doses of, or exposures to, a substance over a relatively prolonged period of time.
CMA	Chemical Manufacturers Association
Combustible Liquid Class II (NFPA Usage)	Class II liquids include those with flashpoints points at or above 100°F (37.8°C), and below 140°F (93.3°C), the total volume of which make up 99 percent or more of the total volume of the mixture. Class IIIB liquids include those with flashpoints at or above 200°F (93.3°C) (Title 29 CFR 1910.106).
Combustible Liquid (DOT Usage)	Flashpoint 100°F to 200°F.
Combustion	The chemical combination of oxygen with another element or compound, induced by high temperature and resulting in the formation

of one or more new compounds; this process is often called burning.

Compressed Gas

Material packaged in a cylinder, tank, or aerosol under pressure exceeding 50 psi at 70°F or other pressure parameters identified by DOT.

Concentration

The relative amount of a substance when combined or mixed with other substances. Examples: 2 ppm hydrogen sulfide in air or a 50 percent caustic solution.

Consignee

The addressee to whom the item is shipped.

Container

Any portable device in which a material is stored, transported, disposed of, or otherwise handled [see Title 40 CFR 260.10(a)(9)].

Container,
Intermodel ISO

An article of transport equipment that meets the standards of the International Organization for Standardization (ISO) designed to facilitate and optimize the carriage of goods by one or more modes of transportation without intermediate handling of the contents and equipped with features permitting ready handling and transfer from one mode to another. Containers may be fully enclosed with one or more doors, open top, tank, refrigerated, open rack, gondola, flatrack, and other designs. Included in this definition are modules or arrays that can be coupled to form an integral unit regardless of intention to move singly or in multiplex configuration.

Containerization

The use of transport containers [container express (CONEX), military-owned demountable containers (MILVAN), commercially or Government-owned (or leased) shipping containers (SEAVAN), and roll on/roll off (RORO) trailers] to unitize cargo for transportation, supply, and storage. Containerization aids carriage of goods by one or more modes of transportation without the need for intermediate handling of the contents, and incorporates supply, security, packaging, storage, and transportation into the distribution system from source to user.

Corrosion

An electrochemical change in a metal surface, caused by reaction of the metal with one or more substances with which it is in contact for long periods. Corrosion usually has a harmful effect on the metal.

Corrosive Acid

A liquid or solid, excluding poisons, that causes visible destruction or irreversible alterations in human skin tissue at the site of contact, or has a severe corrosion rate on steel. Liquids show a pH of 6.0 or less. See Title 49 CFR 173.240.

Corrosive Alkaline

A liquid or solid, excluding poisons, that causes invisible destruction or irrevocable alteration in human skin tissue at the site of contact; or has a severe corrosion rate on steel. Liquids show a pH of 8.0 or above. See Title 49 CFR 173.240.

CPR

Cardiopulmonary resuscitation

CPSA

Consumer Produce Safety Act, Title 16 CFR 1500 series.

CPSC

Consumer Products Safety Commission

CWA	Clean Water Act
Cyanosis	Blue appearance of the skin, especially on the face and extremities, indicating a lack of sufficient oxygen in the arterial blood.
Dangerous When Wet	A label required for certain materials being shipped under US DOT, ICAO, and IMO regulations. Any of this labeled material that is in contact with water or moisture may produce flammable gases. In some cases, these gases are liable to spontaneously combust.
DCM	Dangerous Cargo Manifest (see Title 49 CFR 176.30).
Dermal Toxicity	Adverse effects resulting from skin exposure to a substance.
Dermatitis	Inflammation of the skin from any cause. There are two general types of skin reaction: primary irritation dermatitis and sensitization dermatitis (see irritant and sensitizer).
Desiccant	A substance such as silica gel that removes moisture (water vapor) from the air and is used to maintain a dry atmosphere in containers of food or chemical packaging.
Dioxin	The compound 2,3,7,8-tetrachlorodibenzo-p-dioxin, a member of the family of chlorinated dioxins. It is a carcinogen, a teratogen, and a mutagen, and was present in the defoliant Agent Orange used in the Vietnam War. [Note: Recent studies suggest dioxins may not be as dangerous as initial studies suggest.]

Disposal Drum

A non-professional reference to a drum used to overpack damaged or leaking containers of hazardous materials for shipment; the proper shipping name is Salvage Drum as cited in Title 49 CFR 173.3.

Distribution System

A complex of facilities, equipment, methods patterns, supply and procedures designed to receive, store, maintain, distribute, and control the flow of items from one point to another.

DOC

Department of Commerce

DOD

Department of Defense

DOE

Department of Energy

DOJ

Department of Justice

DOL

Department of Labor

DOS

Department of State

Dose

The amount of energy or substance absorbed in a unit volume or an organ or individual. Dose rate is the dose delivered per unit of time (see also Roentgen, RAD, REM).

DOT

Department of Transportation

dps

Disintegrations Per Second -- a unit of measure relating to the breakdown of a radioactive material.

Dust

Solid particles generated by handling, crushing, grinding, rapid impact, detonation, and decapitation of organic or inorganic materials, such as rock, ore, metal, coal wood, and grain. Dusts do not tend to flocculate except under electrostatic forces; they do not diffuse in air but settle under the influence of gravity.

Dyspnea

Shortness of breath, difficult or labored breathing.

Ecology

A branch of science concerned with interrelationship of organisms and their environments; the totality or pattern of relations between organisms and their environment.

Economic Poison

As defined in the Federal Insecticide, Fungicide, and Rodenticide Act (FIFRA), an economic poison is "any substance or mixture of substances intended for preventing, destroying, repelling, or mitigating any insects, rodents, nematodes, fungi, or weeds, or any other forms of life declared to be pests . . . any substance intended for use as a plant regulator, defoliant, or desiccant." As so defined, economic poisons are known generally as pesticides.

Edema

A swelling of body tissues as a result of fluid retention.

Effluent Guidelines

(CWA) Minimum, technology-based levels of pollution reduction that point sources must attain.

Effluent Limitations

(CWA) Specific control requirements directed at a specific discharge site.

Electromagnetic
Radiation

Electromagnetic radiation consists of X-rays and gamma rays and is the most dangerous type of radiation. The wavelengths are very short and, therefore, the energy is very great.

This type of radiation is also dangerous because a one MeV gamma ray can travel 7 m in air and 10 cm in water. Lead is frequently used as shielding material.

Empty Packaging

As related to Title 49 CFR:

1. The description on the shipping paper for a package containing the residue of a hazardous material may include the words "RESIDUE: Last Contained Material" in association with the basic description of the hazardous material last contained in the packaging.

2. For a tank car containing the residue (as defined in Title 49 CFR 171.8) of a hazardous material, the requirements of Title 49 CFR 172.203(e) and 174.25(c) apply.

3. If a packaging, including a tank car, contains a residue that is a hazardous substance, the description on the shipping packages must be with the phrase "RESIDUE: Last Contained" and the letters "RQ" must be entered on the shipping paper either before or after the description.

EPA

United States Environmental Protection Agency

Epidemiology

The science that deals with the study of disease in a general population. Determination of the incidence (rate of occurrence) and distribution of a particular disease (as by age, sex, or occupation) may provide information about the cause of the disease.

Etiological Agent

A viable microorganism or its toxin, which causes or may cause human disease; limited to the agents identified in Title 42 CFR Part 72.

Etiology

The study of the causes of disease.

Evaporation Rate

The rate at which a particular material will vaporize (evaporate) when compared with the rate of vaporization of a known material. The evaporation rate can be useful in evaluating the health and fire hazards of a material. The known material is usually normal butyl acetate (NBUAC or n-BuAc), with a vaporization rate designated as 1.0. Vaporization rates of other solvents or materials have three classifications:

1. FAST evaporating if greater than 3.0. Examples: Methyl ethyl ketone (MEK) = 3.8, acetone = 5.6, hexane = 8.3.

2. MEDIUM evaporating if 0.8 to 3.0. Examples: 190 proof (95 percent) ethyl alcohol = 1.4, WM&P naptha = 1.4, MIBK = 1.6.

3. SLOW evaporating if less than 0.8. Examples: xylene = 0.6, isobutyl alcohol = 0.6, normal butyl alcohol = 0.4, water = 0.3, mineral spirits = 0.1.

Exotoxin

A toxin produced and delivered by a microorganism into the surrounding medium.

Explosion-proof Equipment

Apparatus enclosed in a case capable of withstanding an explosion of a specified gas or vapor that may occur and of preventing the ignition of a specified gas or vapor surrounding the enclosure by sparks, flash, or explosion of the gas or vapor within, and that operates at an external temperature such that a surrounding flammable atmosphere will not be ignited.

Explosive, Class A

Any of nine types of explosives as defined in Title CFR 173.53, and listed in Title 49 CFR 172.101. Any chemical compound, mixture, or device having the primary or common purpose to function by detonation (i.e., with substantial instantaneous release of gas and heat, unless such compound, mixture, or device is otherwise classified for storage or transportation).

Explosive, Class B

Explosives that, in general, function by rapid combustion rather than detonation and include some explosive devices such as special fireworks, flash powders, some pyrotechnic signal devices, and solid or liquid propellant explosives including some smokeless powders. These explosives are listed and defined in Title 49 CFR 172.010 and Title 49 CFR 173.88 of the Department of Transportation, respectively.

Explosive, Class C

Certain types of manufactured articles that contain Class A or Class B explosives, or both, as components but in restricted quantities; and certain types of fireworks. These explosives are listed and defined in Title 49 CFR 172.101 and Title 49 CFR 173.100 of the Department of Transportation, respectively.

Explosive Limits

Some items have a minimum and maximum concentration in air which can be detonated by spark, shock, fire, etc. The lowest concentration is known as the lower explosive limit (LEL). The highest concentration is known as the upper explosive limit (UEL).

Exposure   Subjection of a person to a toxic substance or harmful physical agent in the course of employment through any route of entry (e.g., inhalation, ingestion, skin contact, or absorption); includes past exposure and potential (e.g., accidental or possible) exposure, but does not include situations where the employer can demonstrate that the toxic substance or harmful physical agent is not used, handled, stored, generated, or present in the workplace in any manner different from typical nonoccupational situations. An exposure to a substance or agent may or may not be an actual health hazard to the worker. An industrial hygienist evaluates exposures and determines if permissible exposure levels are exceeded.

Extraction   The removal of soluble components from a solid or liquid mixture by means of an appropriate solvent.

°F   Degrees in Fahrenheit

Fahrenheit   The scale of temperature in which 212° is the boiling point of water at 760 mm Hg and 32° is the freezing point.

FFDCA   Federal Food, Drug, and Cosmetic Act

FHSLA   Federal Hazardous Substances Labeling Act

Fibrosis   A disease resultant from the inhalation of fibers.

FIFRA   Federal Insecticide, Fungicide, and Rodenticide Act (see Title 40 CFR).

Flammable Limits	Flammable liquids produce (by evaporation) a minimum and maximum concentration of flammable gases in air that will support combustion. The lowest concentration is known as the lower flammable limit (LFL). The highest concentration is known as the upper flammable limit (UFL).
Flammable Liquid Class IA (OSHA Usage)	Any liquid having a flashpoint below 73°F (22.8°C) and having a boiling point below 100°F (37.8°C) except any mixture having components with flashpoints of 100°F (37.8°C) or higher, the total of which comprise 99 percent or more of the total volume of the mixture (Title 29 CFR 1910.106).
Flammable Liquid Class IB (OSHA Usage)	Any liquid having a flashpoint at or below 73°F (22.8°C) and having a boiling point at or above 100°F (37.8°C) or higher, the total of which make up 99 percent or more of the total volume of the mixture (Title 29 CFR 1910.106).
Flammable Liquid Class IC (OSHA Usage)	Any liquid having a flashpoint at or above 73°F (22.8°C) and having a boiling point below 100°F (37.8°C), except any mixture having components with flashpoints of 100°F (37.8°C) or higher, the total of which make up 99 percent or more of the total volume of the mixture (Title 29 CFR 1910.106).
Flammable Liquid (DOT Usage)	Any liquid with a flashpoint less than 100°F.
Flammable Solid (DOT Usage)	Any solid material, other than one classed as an explosive, that under conditions normally subject to storage is liable to cause fire through friction or retained heat from manufacturing

or processing; or that can be ignited readily, and when ignited burns so vigorously and persistently as to create a serious storage hazard. Flammable solids, excluding Dangerous When Wet, are further defined in Title 49 CFR 173.150.

Flashpoint

The lowest temperature at which a liquid gives off enough vapor to form an ignitable mixture with air and produce a flame when a source of ignition is present. Two tests are used -- open cup and closed cup.

Force Majeure

An action beyond the control of a contractor which delays a project (e.g., bad weather, vendor bankruptcy).

FP or fl. pt.

Flashpoint

Friable

Capable of being pulverized with hand pressure as relates to asbestos (Title 29 CFR 1910).

ft^3

Cubic Feet. Volumetric measurement calculated by multiplying length by width by depth, all in feet, of an item or space.

Full Protective
Clothing

Such units are typically recommended where high chemical gas, vapor, or fume concentrations in air may have a corrosive effect on exposed skin, and/or where the chemical in air may be readily absorbed through the skin to produce toxic effects. These suits are impervious to chemicals, offer full body protection, and include self-contained breathing apparatus (SCBA).

Fully Encapsulated
Suits

Full chemical protective suits that are impervious to chemicals, offer full body protection from chemicals and their vapor/fumes, and are to be used with self-contained breathing apparatus (SCBA).

Fume

Gas-like emanation containing minute solid particles arising from the heating of a solid body such as lead. This physical change is often accompanied by a chemical reaction, such as oxidation. Fumes flocculate and sometimes coalesce. Odorous gases and vapors should not be called fumes.

FWPCA

Federal Water Pollution Control Act (1972)

Gas

A state of matter in which the material has very low density and viscosity; can expand and contract greatly in response to changes in temperature and pressure; easily diffuses into other gases; readily and uniformly distributes itself throughout any container. A gas can be changed to the liquid or solid state by the combined effect of increased pressure and/or decreased temperature.

Gastr-, gastro

(Prefix) Pertaining to the stomach

GC/MS

Gas chromatography / mass spectrometry. Refers to both analytical method and apparatus used for organics analysis.

Genetic effects

Mutations or other changes which are produced by irradiation of the germ plasm.

g/kg

Grams per kilogram, an expression of dose used in oral and dermal toxicity testing to indicate the grams of substance dosed per kilogram of animal body weight (see also "kg").

Groundwater	Water that is located beneath the surface of the earth. It can be collected with wells, tunnels, or drainage galleries; it also flows naturally to the earth's surface via seeps or springs.
GSA	General Services Administration
HAP	Hierarchical Analytical Protocol. A procedure identified by the EPA to demonstrate the presence or absence of RCRA (Title 40 CFR) classes or Appendix VIII compounds in groundwater.
Hazard Assessment Risk Analysis	A process used to qualitatively or quantitatively assess risk factors to determine mitigating actions.
Hazard Class	A category of hazard associated with an HM/HW that has been determined capable of posing an unreasonable risk to health, safety, and property when transported (see Title 49 CFR 171.8). The hazard class used by the United States DOT and published in Title 49 CFR 172.101. The hazard classes used in the United States include Explosive (Class A, B, or C); Flammable Liquid; Flammable Solid; Corrosive Material; Oxidizer; Poison A; Poison B; Radioactive Material; Nonflammable Gas; ORM-A, -B, -C, -D, and -E; Etiological Agent; Irritating Material; Organic Peroxide; Combustible Liquid; Flammable Gas; and Blasting Agent.
Hazardous Air Pollutant	A pollutant to which no ambient quality standard is applicable and that may cause or contribute to an increase in mortality or in serious illness. For example, asbestos,

beryllium, and mercury have been declared hazardous air pollutants.

Hazardous Chemicals   Chemicals or materials used in the workplace that are regulated under the OSHA Hazard Communication Standard or the "right-to-know" regulations in Title 29 CFR 1910.1200.

Hazardous Material   In a broad sense, a hazardous material (HM) is any substance or mixture of substances having properties capable of producing adverse effects on the health and safety or the environment of a human being. Legal definitions are found in individual regulations.

Hazardous Substances   Chemicals, mixtures of chemicals, or materials subject to the regulations contained in Title 40 CFR. For transportation purposes, means a material, and its mixtures or solution, identified by the letter "E" in Title 49 CFR 172.010 when offered for transportation in one package, or in one transport vehicle if not packaged, and when the quantity of the material therein equals or exceeds the reportable quantity (RQ). For details, refer to Title 49 CFR 171.8 and Title 49 CFR 172.101.

Hazardous Waste   Any material listed as such in Title 40 CFR 261, Subpart D, or that possesses any of the hazard characteristics of corrosivity, ignitability, reactivity or toxicity as defined in Title 40 CFR 261, Subpart C, or that is contaminated by or mixed with any of the previously mentioned materials (see Title 40 CFR 261.3).

Hazardous Waste Generation	The act or process of producing hazardous waste.
Hazardous Waste Landfill	An excavated or engineered area on which hazardous waste is deposited and covered; proper protection of the environment from the materials to be deposited in such a landfill requires careful site selection, good design, proper operation, leachate collection and treatment, and thorough final closure.
Hazardous Waste Leachate	The liquid that has percolated through or drained from hazardous waste emplaced in or on the ground.
Hazardous Waste Management	Systematic control of the collection, source separation storage, transportation, processing, treatment, recovery, and disposal of hazardous wastes.
Hazardous Waste Manifest Uniform (EPA Usage)	The shipping document, originated and signed by the waste generator or his authorized representative, that contains the information required by Title 40 CFR 262, Subpart B.
Hazardous Waste Number	The number assigned to each hazardous waste listed by EPA and to each hazardous waste characteristic.
Hazardous Waste Site	A location where hazardous wastes are stored, treated, incinerated, or otherwise disposed of.
Hematology	Study of the blood and the blood-forming organs.
Hepatitis	Inflammation of the liver.

Herbicide	A chemical intended for killing plants or interrupting their normal growth. A weed, grass, or brush killer (also see pesticides).
HMTA	Hazardous Materials Transportation Act (1975)
HPLC	Also called LC. High performance liquid chromatography is used in organics analysis.
HSWA	Hazardous and Solid Waste Amendments of 1984
Hygroscopic	Descriptive of a substance that has the property of adsorbing moisture from the air, such as: silica gel, calcium chloride or zinc chloride.
Hypothermia	Condition of reduced body temperature.
IATA	International Air Transport Association
IC	Ion chromatography
ICAO	International Civil Aviation Organization
ICP	Inductively coupled (argon) plasma. Used with reference to both the analytical method and the apparatus.
Identification Number for EPA	The individual number assigned to each generator, transporter, and treatment, storage, or disposal facility by state or federal regulatory agencies.
IDLH	Immediately dangerous to life and health. An environmental condition which would immediately place a worker in jeopardy. Usually used to describe a condition existing where self-contained breathing apparatus must be used.

ID Number	Four-digit number preceded by UN or NA, assigned to hazardous materials and dangerous goods (see column 3a of the Hazardous Materials Table included in Title 49 CFR 172.101 and column 4 of Title 49 CFR 172.102. Note also the cross-reference list for number-to-name that follows the Hazardous Materials Table 102 as Appendix A).
Ignitable (EPA Usage)	A liquid with a flashpoint less than 140°F.
IMDG	International Maritime Dangerous Goods
IMDGC	International Maritime Dangerous Goods Codes
IMDG Designation	A hazardous material identifier published by the International Maritime Organization in their Dangerous Goods Code.
IMO	International Maritime Organization (formerly IMCO).
Impoundment	See Surface Impoundment.
Inactive Facility	The EPA designation for a treatment, storage, or disposal facility that has not accepted hazardous waste since November 19, 1980.
Inactive Portion	A portion of a hazardous waste management facility that has not operated since November 19, 1980, but is not yet a closed portion (no longer accepts waste to that area).
Incineration	An engineered process using controlled flame combustion to thermally degrade waste materials. Devices normally used for incineration include rotary kilns, fluidized

beds, and liquid injectors. Incineration is used particularly for the destruction of organic wastes with a high BTU value. The wastes are detoxified by oxidation, and if the heat produced is high enough, they can sustain their own combustion and will not require additional fuel. EPA's draft regulations specify a recommended temperature of 1000°C, with a residence time (the time the gases should stay in the combustion chamber) of 2 seconds.

Incompatible Waste

Waste unsuitable for co-mingling with another waste or material, where the co-mingling might result in the following:

1. Extreme heat or pressure generation.
2. Fire
3. Explosion or violent reaction.
4. Formation of substances that are shock sensitive, friction sensitive, or otherwise have the potential to react violently.
5. Formation of toxic dusts, mists, fumes, gases, or other chemicals.
6. Volatization of ignitable or toxic chemicals due to heat generation, in such a manner that the likelihood of contamination of groundwater or escape of the substances into the environment.

Industrial Wastes

Unwanted materials produced in or eliminated from an industrial operation. They may be categorized under a variety of headings, such as liquid wastes, sludge wastes, and solid wastes. Hazardous wastes contain substances that, in low concentrations, are dangerous to life (especially human) for reasons of toxicity, corrosiveness, mutagenicity, and flammability.

Infectious Waste	Waste that contains pathogens or consists of tissues, organs, body parts, blood, and body fluids that are removed during surgery or other procedures. See Title 42 CFR Part 72 (also see Biologically Hazardous Waste).
Infiltration	The flow of fluid into a substance through pores or small openings. The word is commonly used to denote the flow of water into soil material.
Ingestion	The process of taking substances into the body, as in food, drink, medicine, etc.
Inhalation	The breathing in of a substance in the form of gas, vapor, fume, mist, or dust.
Inhibitor	A chemical added to another substance to prevent an unwanted occurrence of chemical change.
Injection	The subsurface emplacement of a fluid or waste.
Injection Well	A well into which fluids are injected.
Inner Liner	A continuous layer or lining of material placed inside a tank or other container that protects the construction materials of the tank or container from the contents.
Inorganic Compounds	Chemical compounds that do not contain the element carbon.
Inorganic Matter	Chemical substances of mineral origin, not containing carbon to carbon bonding. Generally structured through ionic bonding.

Insecticide

A chemical product used to kill and control nuisance insect species (also see pesticide).

Institutional Waste

All solid waste emanating from institutions such as, but not limited to, hospitals, nursing homes, orphanages, schools, and universities.

Interim Authorization

The conditional permission from EPA that enables a state to operate its own hazardous waste management program.

Interim Status

A period of time, which began November 19, 1980, when hazardous waste storage and treatment facilities and hazardous waste transporters could continue to operate under a special set of regulations until the appropriate permit or license application is or was approved by EPA.

Intermunicipal Agency

An agency established by two or more municipalities with responsibility for planning or administration of solid waste.

IPY

Inches per year [as corrosion rate reference in Title 49 CFR 173.240(a)(2) and 173.500(b)(2)(i)].

Irritant

Any material, liquid or solid substance, that upon contact with fire or when exposed to air gives off dangerous or intensely irritating fumes, such as tear gas, but not including Poison Class A or B material. Materials named as irritants are presented in Title 49 CFR 173.38.

ISO

International Organization for Standardization

kg	Kilogram. A metric unit of weight, about 2.2 United States pounds.
Label (DOT)	Diamond, square, or rectangular-shaped attachment to a package that identifies the hazardous nature of a material (see Title 49 CFR Part 172, Subpart E).
Land Treatment Facility	A facility or part of a facility where hazardous waste is applied or incorporated into the soil surface; such facilities are disposal facilities if the waste will remain after closure.
Latent Period	The time which elapses between exposure and the first manifestation of damage.
LC_{50}	Lethal concentration$_{50}$, the concentration of a material which on the basis of laboratory tests is expected to kill 50 percent of a group of test animals when administered as a single exposure (usually 1 or 4 hours). Also, other LC values can be expressed (e.g., LC_{10} and LC_{20}).
LCLo	Lethal Concentration Low. The lowest concentration of a substance in air, other than LC_{50}, which has been reported to have caused death in human or animals. The reported concentrations may be entered for periods of exposure that are less than 24 hours (acute) or greater than 24 hours (subacute and chronic).
LD_{50}	Median Lethal Dose. The dose which is required to produce death in 50 percent of the exposed species. Death is usually reckoned as occurring within the first 30 days.

LD_{Lo}

Lethal Dose Low. The lowest dose of a substance introduced by any route, other than inhalation, over any given period of time in one or more divided portions and reported to have caused death in humans or animals.

Leak or Leaking

Any instance in which an article, container, or equipment has any hazardous material (e.g., PCB) on any part of its external surface or has released this substance to the surrounding environment.

LEL

Lower Explosive Limit. The lowest concentration of the material in air that can be detonated by spark, shock, fire, etc.

LFL

Lower Flammable Limit. The lowest concentration of the material in air that will support combustion from a spark or flame.

LUST

Leaking Underground Storage Tanks. (Now it is called UST, but it is still lust in our hearts.)

m^3

Cubic Meter or Stere. A metric measure of volume, about 35.5 cubic feet or 1.3 cubic yards.

Macroencapsulation

The isolation of a waste by embedding it in, or surrounding it with, a material that acts as a barrier to water or air (e.g., clay and plastic liners).

Magnetized Materials

Any material which, when packed for air transport, has magnetic field strength of 0.159 A/M or more at a distance 2.1 m from any point on the surface of the assembled package (see ICAO Technical Instructions).

Malaise	Vague feeling of bodily discomfort.
Manifest, Uniform Hazardous Waste	Shipping papers when properly prepared and distributed, provide a tracking system that consists of forms originating with the generator or shipper and following from the generator to disposal in a permitted TSDF.
Manometer	An instrument for measuring pressure that usually consists of a U-shaped tube containing a liquid, the surface of which in one end of the tube moves proportionally with pressure changes on the liquid in the other end. Also, a tube type of differential pressure gauge.
Marking	Applying the required descriptive name, instructions, cautions, weight, or specifications or combinations thereof on containers of HM/HW (see Title 49 CFR 171.8).
Material Safety Data Sheet (OSHA Usage)	See MSDS.
Melting Point	The temperature at which a material changes from a solid to a liquid.
MeV	Million electron-volts.
mg	Milligram. A metric unit of weight. There are 1,000 milligrams in one gram (g) or a substance.
mg/m^3	Milligrams Per Cubic Meter. A unit for measuring concentrations of dusts, gases or mists in air.
MHE	Material Handling Equipment

Microorganism	A living organism discretely invisible to the unaided eye. These organisms obtain nutrients from and discharge waste products (largely CO_2 or O_2) into the fluid in which they exist, thus serving to lower the nutrient level.
ml	Milliliter. A metric unit of volume, equal in volume to one cubic centimeter (cc), or about 1/16 of a cubic inch. There are 1,000 milliliters in one liter (l).
mm	Millimeters
Monolithic	Describing a structure that is without cracks or seams, self-supporting, and essentially homogeneous.
MSDS	Material Safety Data Sheet. An MSDS must be in English and include information regarding the specific identity of hazardous chemicals. Also includes information on health effects, first aid, chemical and physical properties, and emergency phone numbers.
MSHA	Mine Safety and Health Administration of the United States Department of Interior.
MTB	Materials Transportation Bureau (formerly of DOT); now the Research and Special Programs Administration (RSPA) of DOT.
Mutagen	A substance capable of causing genetic change.
NAAQS	National Ambient Air Quality Standards. CAA Section 109.

NA Number	North American identification number. When NA precedes a four-digit number, it indicates that this identification number is used in the United States and Canada to identify a hazardous material (HM) or a group of HMs in transportation.
Narcosis	Stupor or unconsciousness produced by chemical substances.
Necrosis	Destruction of body tissue.
NEPA	National Environmental Policy Act (1969)
NESHAPs	National Emission Standards for Hazardous Air Pollutants. CAA Section 112 also refers to chemicals regulated under this program.
Neutralization	The process by which acid or alkaline properties of a solution are altered by addition of certain reagents to bring the hydrogen and hydroxide concentrations to an equal value; sometimes referred to as pH 7, the value of pure water.
Neutralization Units	Surface impoundments that (1) are used to neutralize wastes considered hazardous solely because they exhibit the characteristic of corrosivity; (2) contain no other wastes; or (3) neutralize the corrosive wastes sufficiently rapidly so that no potential exists for migration of hazardous waste from the impoundment.
Neutralize	To make harmless anything contaminated with a chemical agent. More generally, to destroy the effectiveness.

NFPA — National Fire Protection Association. An international voluntary membership organization to promote and improve fire protection and prevention and establish safeguards against the loss of life and property by fire. Best known on the industrial scene for the maintenance of National Fire Codes, (i.e., 16 volumes of codes, standards, recommended practices, and manuals) and periodically updated by NFPA technical committees.

NIOSH — National Institute for Occupational Safety and Health of the Public Health Service, United States Department of Health and Human Services (DHHS). Federal agency which, among other activities, tests and certifies respiratory protective devices and air sampling detector tubes, recommends occupational exposure limits for various substances and assists OSHA and MSHA in occupational safety and health investigations and research.

Nonflammable Gas — Any material or mixture, in a cylinder or tank, other than poison gas, or flammable gas having in the container an absolute pressure exceeding 40 psi at 70°F, or having an absolute pressure exceeding 104 psi at 130°F (Title 49 CFR and CGA).

Nonpoint Sources (CWA Usage) — Ill-defined runoff that enters waterways. (More stringent future regulation is likely).

NOS or n.o.s. — Not otherwise specified (DOT Usage).

NPDES — National Pollutant Discharge Elimination System (Water quality usage).

NPTN

National Pesticide Telecommunications Network. A national pesticide poison control center restricted to use by health professionals. The network assists the health professional in diagnosing and managing pesticide poisoning. Services include product active ingredient identification, symptomatic review, toxicologic review, specific treatment recommendations, physician consultation, and referrals for laboratory analyses. These services are provided 24 hours a day.

NQT

Nonquenched and tempered.

NRC

(1) National Response Center (1-800-424-8802). (Title 40 CFR usage).

(2) Nonreusable container (see Title 49 CFR 173.28 and Title 49 CFR 178.8).

(3) Nuclear Regulatory Commission (10 CFR usage).

Nuisance

The class of wrongs that arise from the unreasonable, unwarranted, or unlawful use by a person of his own property, either real or personal, or from his own lawful personal conduct working an obstruction or injury to the right of another, or of the public and producing material annoyance, inconvenience, discomfort or hurt.

OBA

Oxygen Breathing Apparatus

OHMR

Office of Hazardous Materials Regulation (formerly within DOT's Materials Transportation Bureau). Now known as OHMT.

OHMT	Office of Hazardous Materials Transportation of the Research and Special Programs Administration of DOT.
Onsite	The same or geographically contiguous property that may be divided by public or private right-of-way, provided the entrance and exit between the properties is at a crossroads intersection, and that access is by crossing as opposed to going along the right-of-way. Noncontiguous properties owned by the same person but connected by a right-of-way that he controls and to which the public does not have access is also considered onsite property [Title 40 CFR 260.10(a)(48)].
Oral Toxicity	Adverse effects resulting from taking a substance into the body through the mouth.
Organic Peroxide	Any organic compound containing the bivalent O-O structure and that may be considered a derivative of hydrogen peroxide where one or more of the hydrogen atoms have been replaced by organic radicals.
ORM (A-E)	Other Regulated Materials. Several classes of ORM materials are recognized (i.e., ORM-A, ORM-B, ORM-C, ORM-D, and ORM-E).
OSC	Onscene Coordinator in emergency response actions.
OSHA	Occupational Safety and Health Administration of the United States Department of Labor. Federal (or State) agency with safety and health regulatory and enforcement authorities for most United States industry and business.

Outside Packaging	A packaging plus its contents (see Title 49 CFR 171.8).
OVA	Organic Vapor Analyzer
Overpack	Except when referenced to a packaging specified in Title 49 CFR Part 178, means an enclosure used by a single consignor to provide protection or convenience in handling of a package or to consolidate two or more packages. "Overpack" does not include a freight container.
Oxidizer	A chemical other than a blasting agent or explosive as defined in Title 29 CFR 1910.109(a), that initiates or promotes combustion in other materials thereby causing fire either of itself or through the release of oxygen or other gases.
Package	According to the United Nations definition, a complete product of the packaging operation, consisting of the packaging and its contents prepared for transport.
Packaging	The assembly of one or more containers and any other components necessary to assure compliance with minimum packaging requirements; includes containers (other than freight containers or overpacks), and multi-unit tank car tanks (Title 49 CFR 171.8), also restates the methods and materials used to protect items from deterioration or damage; this includes cleaning, drying, preserving, packaging, marking, and unitization.
Packing	Assembly of items into a unit, intermediate, or exterior pack with necessary blocking, bracing,

cushioning, weather-proofing, reinforcement and marking.

Pallets — A pallet is a low portable platform constructed of wood, plastic, or fiberboard, built to specified dimensions, on which supplies are loaded, transported, or stored in units.

Part A — Interim permit for TSDF of hazardous waste prior to 1981 (RCRA usage).

Part B — Final permit for TSDF (RCRA usage).

Pathogen — Any microorganism capable of causing disease.

PCB — Polychlorinated biphenyl (see Title 40 CFR 761.3).

PCB contaminated Electrical Equipment — Any electrical equipment, including transformers that contains at least 50 ppm less than 500 ppm PCB (Title 40 CFR 761.3).

PCB Item — An item containing PCBs at a concentration of 50 ppm or greater (Title 40 CFR 761.3). (The concentration requirement may vary by State).

PCB Transformer — Any transformer that contains 500 ppm PCB or greater (Title 40 CFR 761.3).

PCDF — Polychlorinated dibenzofurans: A class of toxic chemical compounds occurring as a thermal degradation product of PCBs.

PCP — (1) Abbreviation for pentachlorophenol (q.v.), a wood preservative used on military ammunition boxes and telephone poles.

(2) 1-(1-Phenylcylohexyl) piperidine or angel dust or HOG, an analgesic and anesthetic that may produce serious psychologic disturbances.

PEL

Permissible exposure limit. An exposure limit established by OSHA regulatory authority. May be a time weighted average (TWA) limit or a maximum concentration exposure limit (see also "skin").

PEP

Preventive Engineering Practices

Permeability

As applied to soil or subsoil, the degree to which the penetration of fluids, particularly water, is retarded.

Pesticide

Any liquid, solid, or gaseous material that demonstrates an oral LD_{50} of greater than 50 mg/kg but less than 5,000 mg/kg, or an inhalation LC_{50} of greater than 0.2 mg/L, but less than 20 mg/L, or a dermal LD_{50} of greater than 200 mg/kg but less than 20,000 mg/kg (Title 40 CFR 162).

PF

Protective Factor. Refers to the level of protection a respiratory protective device offers. The PF is the ratio of the contaminant concentration outside the respirator to that inside the respirator.

pH

pH is the symbol of hydrogen ion concentration. A pH of 7.0 is neutrality, higher values indicate alkalinity and lower values indicate acidity.

Phase I
(RCRA Usage)

The regulations issued in May 1980 include the identification and listing of hazardous waste, standards for generators and transporters of hazardous waste, standards for owners and operators of facilities that treat, store, or dispose of hazardous waste facility permits, and rules governing delegation of authority to the states.

Phase II
(RCRA Usage)

Technical requirements for permitting a hazardous facility. Sets specific standards for particular types of facilities to ensure the safe treatment, storage, and disposal of hazardous waste on a permanent basis by methods that will protect human health and the environment. Phase II standards enable facilities to move from "interim status" to final facility permits.

pK

The negative logarithm of the equilibrium constant, K, for reactions. This constant can be used to indicate the strength of an acid or a base.

Pneumonitis

Inflammation of the lungs characterized by an outpouring of fluid in the lungs. Pneumonia is the same condition, but involves greater quantities of fluid.

Pneumonoconiosis
Producing Dust

Dust which, when inhaled, deposited, and retained in the lungs, may produce signs, symptoms and findings of pulmonary disease.

Point Sources
(CWA Usage)

Well defined places at which pollutants enter waterways.

Poison Class A

Poisonous gases or liquids of such a nature that a very small amount of the gas, or vapor of the liquid, mixed with air is dangerous to life (Title 49 CFR 173.326).

Poison Class B	Demonstrates an oral LD_{50} of up to and including 50 mg/kg, or an inhalation LC_{50} of up to and including 2 mg/L, or a general LD_{50} of up to and including 200 mg/kg; or is either classed as a Poison Class B per Title 49 CFR 173.343, or qualifies as a Category I Pesticide per Title 40 CFR Part 162 excluding the corrosivity criteria.
Potentially Responsible Party (CERCLA)	A "person" who potentially contributed to a hazardous substance release or threatened release.
PPE	Personal Protective Equipment
ppm	Parts Per Million: A unit for measuring the concentration of a gas or vapor in air-parts (by volume) of the gas or vapor in a million parts of air. Usually used to express measurements of extremely low concentrations of unusually toxic gases or vapors. Also used to indicate the concentration of a particular substance in a liquid or solid.
Pre-manufacture Notification (PMN)	A major control mechanism exercised under the Toxic Substances Control Act to allow EPA to assess the safety of new chemicals before manufacture.
Pretreatment Standards (CWA Usage)	Specific industrial operation or pollutant removal requirements in order to discharge to to a municipal sewer.
PRP	Potentially Responsible Party
PSD	Prevention of Significant Deterioration (of air quality).

psi   Pounds Per Square Inch

psia   Pounds Per Square Inch Absolute

psig   Pounds Per Square Inch Gauge

Proper Shipping   The name of the hazardous material shown
Name   in Roman print (not italics) in Title 49 CFR
                             172.101 or 172.102 (when authorized).

Pulmonary   Pertaining to the lungs.

Pyrophoric   A chemical that will ignite spontaneously in air
                             at a temperature of 130°F (54.4°C) or below.

R   The symbol used to represent an organic group
                             in a chemical formula, e.g. CH_3, C_2H_5, C_6H_5,
                             etc.

RAD   A unit for measurement of radioactivity. One
                             RAD is the amount of radiation that results
                             in the absorption of 100 ergs of energy by 1
                             g of material.

Radioactive Material   A material that might or might not require the
                             issuance of a license, according to 10 CFR, to
                             persons who manufacture, produce, transfer,
                             receive, acquire, own, possess, or use by-
                             product materials.

RAM   Radioactive Material

RAM Licensed   Any radioactive material, the radionuclide of
Exempt   which is not subject to the licensing
                             requirement of Title 10 CFR.

RCRA   Resource Conservation and Recovery Act
                             (1976)

Recovery Drum	A nonprofessional reference to a drum used to overpack damaged or leaking hazardous materials (see disposal drum).
Relative Biological Effectiveness (RBE)	A measure of the relative effectiveness of absorbed doses of radiation.
REM	A measure of radiation dose meaning roentgen equivalent man. The dose in rems is calculated by multiplying the dose in rads by the relative biological effectiveness of the radiation considered.
Reportable Quantity (DOT and EPA Usage)	The quantity specified in column 2 of the Hazardous Materials Table in Title 49 CFR 172.101, for any material identified by the letter "g" in Column 1 (Title 49 CFR 171.8), or any material identified by EPA on Table 117.3, Reportable Quantities of Hazardous Substance in Title 40 CFR 302. The letter "E" in Column 1 (Title 49 CFR 172.101) identifies this material as a potential hazardous substance.
Residue	As related to Title 49 CFR 171.8, residue is the hazardous material remaining in a packaging after its contents have been emptied and before the packaging is refilled, or cleaned and purged of vapor to remove any potential hazard. Residue of a hazardous material, as applied to the contents of a tank car (other than DOT Specification 106 or 110 tank cars), is a quantity of material no greater than 3 percent of the car's marked volumetric capacity.
Respiratory System	Consists of (in descending order) the nose, mouth, nasal passages, nasal pharynx, pharynx, larynx, trachea, bronchi, bronchiolus, air sacs

	(alveoli) of the lungs, and muscles of respiration.
Risk Assessment	An investigation of the potential risk to human health or the environment posed by a specific action or substance. The assessment usually includes toxicity, concentration, form, mobility, and potential for exposure of the substance.
Roentgen	A measure of the charge produced as the rays pass through the air.
Roentgen Equivalent Man or REM	The product of the absorbed dose in rads multiplied by the RBE.
RQ	See Reportable Quantity
RSPA	Research and Special Programs Administration (of DOT).
SADT	Self-Accelerating Decomposition Temperature Test. A test which establishes the lowest temperature at which a peroxide, in its largest commercial package, will undergo self-accelerating decomposition.
Salvage Drum	A drum with a removable metal head used to transport damaged or leaking hazardous materials, containers, and their contents for repackaging or disposal (see Title 49 CFR 173.3). (Also referred to as disposal or recovery drum).
Saturation	1. Occurs when a solution contains the highest possible concentration of a solute at a given temperature.

2. The state in which all valence bonds of an atom (especially carbon) are attached to other atoms.

SCBA

Self-Contained Breathing Apparatus (see Full Protective Clothing and Fully Encapsulating Suits).

SDWA

Safe Drinking Water Act (1974)

Secondary Materials

Spent materials, sludges, by-products, scrap metal and commercial chemical products recycled in ways that differ from their normal use.

Sensitizer

A substance which on first exposure causes little or no reaction in man or test animals but which on repeated exposure may cause a marked response not necessarily limited to the contact site. Skin sensitization is the most common form of sensitization in the industrial setting although respiratory sensitization to a few chemicals is also known to occur.

Sievert (Sv)

A unit for measuring the amount of radiation that a biological system can absorb, defined as absorbed radiation dose times the quality factor of the radiation as compared to gamma-radiation. One Sievert is equal to 100 REM and will soon replace the REM. See also REM.

Significant New
Use Rule (SNUR)
(TSCA Usage)

Stipulation (applied as a criterion for manu-facture of a specific chemical) that EPA must be notified of significant new use of the chemical.

SIP

State Implementation Plan, CAA Section 110

"Skin"   A notation, sometimes used with PEL or TLV
                                    exposure data; indicates that the stated
                                    substance may be absorbed by the skin,
                                    mucous membranes and eyes -- either airborne
                                    or by direct contact -- and that this additional
                                    exposure must be considered part of the total
                                    exposure to avoid exceeding the PEL or TLV
                                    for that substance.

Sludges   High solids content suspensions, sludges, or
                                    residues usually resultant from treating air or
                                    waste water or other residues from pollution
                                    control operations.

Smoke   An air suspension (aerosol) or particles, often
                                    originating from combustion or sublimation.
                                    Carbon or soot particles less than 0.1 in size
                                    result from the incomplete combustion of
                                    carbonaceous materials such as coal or oil.
                                    Smoke generally contains droplets as well as
                                    dry particles.

Solubilty   The ability or tendency of one substance to
                                    blend uniformly with another substance.

SOP   Standard Operating Procedures

SPCC Plan   Spill Prevention, Control and
(OSHA Usage)   Countermeasures Plan

SPM   Spill Prevention Management

Spontaneously   Solids or liquids possessing the common
Combustible   property of being liable to spontaneously
(IMDG Code)   heat and ignite.

SRP   Spill Response Plan

SRT	Spill Response Team
STC	Single Tip Container (see Title 49 CFR 173.28 and Title 49 CFR 178.8).
STEL	Short term exposure limit; ACGIH terminology.
Storage	When used in connection with hazardous waste, means the containment of hazardous waste, either on a temporary basis or for a period of years, in such a manner as not to constitute disposal of such hazardous waste.
Storage Facility	Any facility used for the retention of HW prior to shipment or usage, except generator facilities (under Title 40 CFR) which is used to store wastes for less than 90 days, for subsequent transport.
Storage Tank	Any manufactured, nonportable, covered device used for containing pumpable hazardous wastes.
Strict Liability	The defendant may be liable even though he may have exercised reasonable care.
Surface Impoundment	Any natural depression or excavated and/or diked area built into or upon the land, which is fixed, uncovered, and lined with soil or a synthetic material, and is used for treating, storing, or disposing wastes. Examples include holding ponds and aeration ponds.
Synergism	Cooperative action of substances whose total effect is greater than the sum of their separate effects.

TCDD	Tetrachlorodibenzodioxin. A TCDD associated with the manufacturer of 2,4,5-T (Silvex) and occurring as a thermal degradation product of chlorinated benzenes.
Teratogen	A substance or agent which can result in malformations of a fetus.
Threshold (OSHA Usage)	The level where the first effects occur; also the point at which a person just begins to notice a tone (sound) is becoming audible.
TI	Transport Index. Applicable to radioactive materials. [See Title 49 CFR 173.403(bb)].
TLV	Threshold Limit Value. An exposure level under which most people can work consistently for 8 hours a day, (day after day) with no harmful effects. A table of these values and accompanying precautions is published annually by the American Conference of Governmental Industrial Hygienists (ACGIH).
Totally Enclosed Manner	Any manner of usage that will result in no exposure of human beings or the environment to any concentration of PCBs (TSCA Usage).
Toxicity	A relative property of a chemical agent that refers to a harmful effect on some biological mechanism and the condition under which this effect occurs.
Trade Secret	Any confidential formula, pattern, process, device, information or compilation of information (including chemical name or other unique chemical identifier) that, issued in an employer's business, that gives the employer an opportunity to obtain an advantage over competitors who do not know or use it.

TSCA	Toxic Substances Control Act (1976)
TSDF	Treatment, Storage, or Disposal Facility
TWA	Time Weighted Average Exposure. The concentration of a material to which an organism is exposed, averaged over the total exposure time -- generally the total workday (see also "TLV").
TWA-C	Time Weighted Average -- Ceiling Limit. The limit placed on fast acting substances that restricts all exposures to a level below the applicable "C" limit. All time weighted average concentrations and "peak" exposures must be less than this limit.
UEL	Upper Explosive Limit. The highest concentration of the material in air that can be detonated by spark, shock, fire, etc.
UFL	Upper Flammable Limit. The highest concentration of the material in air that will support combustion.
UL	Underwriters Laboratories, Inc.
UN Number	United Nations Identification Number. When UN precedes a four digit number, it indicates this identification number is used internationally to identify a hazardous material.
Unitization	Creating any combination of unit, intermediate or exterior packs of one or more line items of supply (not a single load) in such a manner that the load can be handled as a unit through the distribution system. Unitization (unitized loads-unit loads) encompasses consolidation in

in a container, placement on a pallet or load base or securely binding together.

Unit Pack

The first tie, wrap, or container applied to a single item or group of items which constitutes a complete or identifiable package. The unit pack should be overpacked for shipment unless the unit container is specifically designed to provide shipping protection.

Unsaturation

The state in which not all of the available valence bonds of an atom are satisfied, usually resulting in the formation of double or triple bonds. These compounds are less stable than saturated compounds.

UST

Underground Storage Tanks (see LUST).

Vapor

An air dispersion of molecules of a substance that is liquid or solid in its normal physical state, at standard temperature and pressure. Examples are water vapor and benzene vapor. Vapors of organic liquids are loosely called fumes; however, it is not technically appropriate to use the term "fume" for vapors of organic liquids.

Vapor Density

The ratio of the vapor weight of the commodity compared to that of air. Vapors will diffuse and mix with air due to natural air currents. In general, if the ratio is greater than 1, the vapors are heavier and may settle to the ground; if lower than 1, the vapors will rise.

Vapor Pressure

The pressure of the vapor in equilibrium with the liquid at the specified temperature. Higher values indicate higher volatility or evaporation rate.

INDEX